William Pickersgill
and the
Caledonian Railway
'956' Class Locomotives

An Objective Assessment

No. 956 with the 5 pm Glasgow Buchanan St to Aberdeen Pullman Tea and Dining Car Express, near Glenboig. The rear three coaches were to be detached at Perth and taken forward to Dundee.

Henry L. Salmon, CRA460225

No. 959 on the 12.30 Aberdeen to Glasgow
Pullman Service, south of Perth in 1922.
Henry L. Salmon, CRA460235

William Pickersgill

AND THE

Caledonian Railway '956' Class Locomotives

An Objective Assessment

Donald Peddie

Lightmoor Press & the Caledonian Railway Association

LM&SR No. 14802 at Polmadie, 5th June 1933. *CRA460173c*

LM&SR No. 14801 at Kingmoor, circa 1930. *CRA460164*

LM&SR No. 14801 at Balornock in the early 1930s prior to being refitted with derived motion for the centre cylinder in late 1931. *Author's collection*

CONTENTS

Foreword 7

CHAPTER 1   Introduction. 9

CHAPTER 2   The McIntosh Legacy 19

CHAPTER 3   William Pickersgill at St Rollox 27

CHAPTER 4   1914-1918 Wartime Conditions at St Rollox 39

CHAPTER 5   Post-War Developments at St Rollox 41

CHAPTER 6   Traffic Requirements for the '956' Class and the Design Process 47

CHAPTER 7   Locomotive Constraints, Power Requirements, Construction and Initial Trials 49

CHAPTER 8   The '956' Class Locomotives as Designed and Built 53

CHAPTER 9   Pickersgill and the St Rollox Drawing Office Staff 55

CHAPTER 10   Anecdotal Comments on '956' Class Performance. 59

CHAPTER 11   Rationale for a Rebuild. 63

CHAPTER 12   Locomotive Withdrawals and Use of Surviving Tenders 65

CHAPTER 13   Boiler Design 69

CHAPTER 14   Draughting, Grate and Ashpan Arrangements 83

CHAPTER 15   Cylinder Arrangements, Dimensions and Valve Gear 89

CHAPTER 16   Balancing and Mechanical Design 123

CHAPTER 17   Some Overall Conclusions. 131

APPENDICES   Caledonian Railway '956' Class Trials: Trials Data from 1921 and 1922. 135

          1: Glasgow to Perth Return Working, 9th August 1921 136

          2: Glasgow to Carlisle Return Working, 11th August 1921 145

          3: Polmadie to Kingmoor Return Working, 25th October 1922 155

Bibliography 165

Index 166

Published by LIGHTMOOR PRESS in conjunction with the CALEDONIAN RAILWAY ASSOCIATION
© Donald Peddie, Lightmoor Press and the Caledonian Railway Association 2016
Designed by Nigel Nicholson

British Library Cataloguing-in-Publication Data. A catalogue record for this book is available from the British Library

ISBN 9781 911038 05 4

LIGHTMOOR PRESS
Unit 144B, Lydney Trading Estate, Harbour Road, Lydney, Gloucestershire GL15 5EJ
www.lightmoor.co.uk
Lightmoor Press is an imprint of Black Dwarf Lightmoor Publications Ltd

Printed in Poland; www.lfbookservices.co.uk

CRA460171

LM&SR No. 14802 at Kingmoor in early livery.

FOREWORD

Being by nature an inquisitive engineer, I have always been reluctant to accept technical opinion which appeared unsupported by objective judgement. This approach, fostered throughout an engineering career, remains embedded in my psyche, is difficult to shake off, and surfaces occasionally in retirement. For example, after reading of the recurring and apparently random derailments of the Caledonian Railway '151' Class 2-4-2 tank engines, designed by George Brittain in 1880 for the Callendar & Oban line, I became interested in understanding why these locomotives regularly left the track. My membership of the Caledonian Railway Association (CRA) provided the route to the '151' Class general arrangement drawings, which at the time were undergoing conservation work through The Ballast Trust at Johnstone.

During these visits to The Ballast Trust, I had a number of interesting conversations on locomotive matters with Campbell Cornwell who was engaged in cataloguing the Montague Smith Collection of Scottish railway technical material, normally housed at the National Records of Scotland (NRS) in Edinburgh. At one point, and quite by chance, our discussions drifted to the Pickersgill '956' Class 3-cylinder locomotives built at St Rollox in 1921. I had read a little of the apparent poor performance of these majestic 4-6-0s, and my curiosity was aroused since drawings and test data related to them were within the material on which Campbell was then working.

My father, a keen Caledonian Railway enthusiast, recalled seeing one of these blue liveried '956' Class engines at Carlisle in 1923, so my interest was further stimulated. As related technical material for the class was to hand at Johnstone, and with Campbell's encouragement, it seemed natural that I should look into the reported difficulties, especially as one noted commentator had condemned the class in the most pejorative of terms. As I was later to discover, the CRA archive also contained a large amount of '956' Class data, including production drawings, so perhaps there was sufficient surviving technical material to support any objective assessment of these long forgotten engines.

What I could not have appreciated, when starting on this course over four years ago, was the compelling nature of the investigative work, the locations to which it would take me in the quest for data and the number of technical publications I was to read. Moreover, the exercise was reinforced through the uncovering of material which had not seen the light of day for over ninety years, and, as more material emerged, questions arose which could only be answered by further investigation, which uncovered more material, and so on. Indeed, I felt at times quite close to some of the major St Rollox personalities of the time, as I attempted to understand why they had taken particular courses of action.

This book, which is the result of these investigations, would not have been possible without the on-going support and encouragement of a number of people whom I have the pleasure to know now as friends. In Campbell Cornwell I have found a source of detailed knowledge of Caledonian Railway locomotives which is unsurpassed and whose perceptive challenging of my emerging conclusions has caused me significant and necessary reflection. Moreover, Jim MacIntosh, the CRA Chairman, who has put his personal archive of CR material and photographs at my disposal, has been a constant source of the most helpful advice and has guided my thinking in publication matters. I should also place on record my thanks to many CRA members for their continuing support.

To Phil Atkins, a former librarian at the NRM, York, I am indebted for his detailed knowledge of relevant sources at NRM and for his continuing interest. Additionally, I have been most fortunate in securing the assistance of Dr Ann Glen, who has made available various photographs of '956' Class engines under construction at St Rollox.

As my enthusiasm for the '956' Class investigation progressed, it was essential that my feet were kept firmly on the ground technically, and I am pleased to acknowledge the insightful observations and assistance given by both Joseph Cliffe and his brother John, the former having been a premium apprentice under Edward Thompson. I also wish to thank Angus McIntosh for his help in turning my somewhat untidy sketches into presentable diagrams, and to Julia Stephen of the Scottish Railway Preservation Society for providing access to the John G. Barr papers. To Stuart Rankin of the Glasgow & South Western Railway Association, my thanks are due for lending GA drawings of the G&SWR '128' Class 4-6-0s and other related material.

No acknowledgement of thanks for assistance with my quest for detail would be complete without a big thank you to Kiara King and staff at The Ballast Trust, and also to Claire Paterson and her colleagues at The University of Glasgow Archive Services, where the CRA archive is housed. Their cheerful enthusiasm in providing data and drawings to an enthusiastic non-archivist must, at times, have stretched their forbearance. To the NRS staff, at New Register House and elsewhere, I would also record my thanks for their assistance in providing numerous Caledonian Railway Co. records.

I would record my grateful thanks to NRS for access to their unique archive of material related to the Caledonian Railway '956' Class and for its copying in support of this publication. In similar fashion, I would place on record my sincere thanks to the National Railway Museum at York for permission to draw on and use images from their extensive collection, without whose inclusion this publication would be much the poorer.

In a publication of this type, one difficulty facing any author relates to the presentation of engineering drawings, many of which, in this case, are approaching or have passed their centenary. Inevitably, some are 'tired' from previous extensive usage, almost certainly have been rolled for storage and are at times creased, with the image suffering from diverse imperfections and varying degrees of impaired clarity. In presenting drawing material, I elected to photograph specific drawings in support of the text, in the recognition that, whilst a better result might have been available using rotary scanning, the display of original material, with faults, would add to the provenance of the whole. Moreover, photography would spare the material any further trauma.

Another potential problem relates to comparative technical assessments made between different classes of locomotive and ensuring that a consistent approach is used to the way in which particular parameters are derived and presented. This point applies particularly to boiler parameters and the calculation of tube and superheater surface areas. As far as is possible, I have ensured that when quoting from particular references, and setting out my own calculations, numerate comparisons are made on a consistent basis.

Significant use has been made of many data sources and these are noted at the end of respective chapters. Where a source is subsequently referred to again in the same chapter, the first reference number is repeated.

Any objective technical view on the '956' Class could not be undertaken without accounting for the prevailing conditions at St Rollox during Wm. Pickersgill's tenure and the legacy bequeathed to him by J.F. McIntosh. Additionally, the period of the First World War and its immediate aftermath were difficult times for all railway companies and their staffs, both in terms of inflationary pressures and the uncertainties of future corporate development in the face of compulsory amalgamation. Any opinions offered must take due account of these circumstances, which I trust I have addressed adequately.

Finally, to Neil Parkhouse, Nigel Nicholson and their colleagues at Black Dwarf Lightmoor, my thanks are due for their continuing encouragement and support as process translated to publication.

Whilst I have drawn some conclusions on the '956' Class design and performance, for which I alone am responsible, I leave it to readers to weigh up the position themselves, for which I hope I have provided sufficient technical detail and related references.

Blanefield
August 2015

Plate 1
William Pickersgill CBE (1861 to 1928), CR Locomotive Superintendent 1914 to 1923, when President of the ILocoE in 1920. Recognising Pickergill's humble beginnings, he undoubtedly had significant aptitude and made the most of the early opportunities presented to him through his training and development when with the GER. *IMechE*

CHAPTER 1
INTRODUCTION

WILLIAM PICKERSGILL

William Pickersgill succeeded John F. McIntosh as Locomotive Superintendent of the Caledonian Railway following the latter's retirement on the 28th May 1914.[1] McIntosh, who was born at Montrose in February 1846, and who, it has been suggested, had intimated his wish to retire around two years previously,[2] had spent the whole of his working life[3] with the Caledonian company and its constituents, taking up the reins at St Rollox in February 1895 on the death of John Lambie, having been deputy to Lambie since 1891. In the nineteen years of his having responsibility for all motive power provision, McIntosh and his staff had equipped the Caledonian company with a wide range of free-steaming, free-running locomotives, more than equal to the efficient handling of the company's expanding traffic.

Moreover, during McIntosh's tenure, major advances in steam locomotive technology had emerged, including the efficient use of superheating, McIntosh having successfully introduced it to the Caledonian company on a number of classes. Whilst initially having appointed McIntosh on a six month probationary basis, the Caledonian Board of Directors could have had no possible reason to regret their choice, a point emphasised by the increase in his annual salary to £1,750 in 1906.[3] In locomotive matters the Caledonian company's position was one of pre-eminence, with McIntosh designed engines being much respected both in the UK and Europe.

Graeme Miller,[4] who started his premium apprenticeship under McIntosh at St Rollox in 1911, referred to his chief as having a *'handsome appearance, befitting the position he held'*. Quite regularly, McIntosh would arrive by tramcar at St Rollox around 8.30 am to be met by William Urie, the Works Manager, and proceed on a tour of the shops before going to his office.[4] This practice kept each foreman on his toes, such that from the start of work each day, the foremen would, from their reviews of work-in-progress, be in a position to anticipate any questions arising during the chief's visit. Interestingly, William Urie also retired on the same day as McIntosh, the 28th May 1914,[1] his position being assumed immediately by Irvine Kempt junior.[5]

McIntosh seemingly had complete faith in his staff and, by virtue of his engaging style, this trust was much appreciated and reciprocated. Known the length and breadth of the line, McIntosh, who was seen as something of a flamboyant character, addressed his drivers by their christian names, and in modern parlance might have been referred to as *'one of the boys'*.[6] He was intimately connected throughout the working level of the railway, whether in the workshops or on the footplate.

By contrast, the appointment of Pickersgill in 1914 was in many respects an enigmatic choice for a variety of reasons. Paradoxically, though perhaps understandably, the Directors chose to make an external appointment, rather than from their own ranks, the latter approach having been so successful for the McIntosh era. Little is now known of the other candidates who may have been considered for the post, but one has to assume that the Board, no doubt having taken McIntosh's advice, discounted internal candidates such as John Barr and Irvine Kempt junior. Additionally, recognising that Thomas Weir,[3] the Chief Draughtsman, had been in post since 1897, the Board may have felt an external appointment was called for to further improve the breed, safe in the assurance that Weir's presence, and his intimate involvement in all major McIntosh locomotive developments, would provide a high degree of technical security

for the future. The Board may have decided that since locomotive engineering matters were becoming more technically complex, the age of 'the home spun scholar' was passing. So the choice fell upon Pickersgill, who is pictured in Plate 1, when President of the ILocoE in 1920. His duties at St Rollox commenced on the 1st May 1914[3] at a starting annual salary of £1,250,[3] some £500 per annum less than that paid to his predecessor.

FAMILY MATTERS

Very little has been written of Pickersgill's early years. He was born on 1st March 1861,[7] at Market Place, Monks Coppenhall, Nantwich, near Crewe, his father being John Gaukroger Pickersgill,[8] a railway engine fitter who was born at Burnsall, Yorkshire in 1817.[9] As a 42-year-old widower, John G. Pickersgill had married Pickersgill's mother, Mary Whittle, at Manchester in December 1859, the 1861 Census[9] return for the family, then living at Monks Coppenhall, recording the one month old William Pickersgill as resident there, together with several step-siblings.

Pickersgill's father, John G., died in February 1865, his mother then marrying William Duncanson in March 1875,[9] at St Philip's Manchester, the family thereafter moving south to West Ham, Essex. In the 1881[9] Census return for West Ham, William Duncanson, aged 44, was recorded in employment as *'Engine fitter at Works'*, his son William Duncanson (actually his step-son, William Pickersgill), aged 20, also being employed as *'Engine fitter at Works'*, the 'Works' referring to the GER works at Stratford. It would seem that subsequent to his mother's remarrying, Pickersgill adopted the surname Duncanson for some years, though not exclusively so, and indeed without consistency. His birth certificate, however, retained the surname Pickersgill.[9]

At the age of 15, in 1876, he joined the Great Eastern Railway as an apprentice at Stratford works and, by his own account,[10] he served seven years at Stratford, in what he described as *'doing his time'*, with some years spent in the machine shops, followed by time in both the fitting and erecting shops. Whilst at Stratford he was granted a Whitworth Scholarship, through which applicants who had started their engineering careers via the vocational route could undertake more academic studies, leading to appropriate qualification. These scholarships had been set up by Sir Joseph Whitworth in 1868 to encourage the advancement of mechanical engineering, one of the stipulations of the scheme being that applicants must have had several years' experience *'on the tools'*.

The Great Eastern company had a strong educational tradition, whereby Directors' Scholarships[11] were awarded annually to employees, thereby enabling their further education at the Great Eastern Mechanics Institute in West Ham, such facilities having been inaugurated in 1851; six GER Directors' Scholarships were awarded annually. Pickersgill secured his Whitworth Scholarship in 1882,[12] a fellow GER Whitworth Scholar that year[12] being Alfred J. Hill, who would become Chief Mechanical Engineer at Stratford in November 1912. In his application for membership of the IMechE,[7] in April 1923, Pickersgill listed his places of education as Public School and Academy, Crewe; Finsbury College, London; and Birbeck Institute, London.

On the award of his Whitworth Scholarship, he registered as a student at Birbeck College in session 1882/83,[8] his address at the time being given as 120 Caledonian Road, London, the scholarship[8] actually being awarded in the name of William Duncanson. In

1883, aged 22, Pickersgill[13] was appointed a locomotive inspector, being in charge of tests made on Holden oil-fired locomotives and compounding.[14] Thereafter he was appointed Chief Locomotive Inspector of the GER in 1890, then taking up the position of District Locomotive Superintendent at Norwich in 1891.[13] As regards family life, Pickersgill had married Mary Ann Hope at Stratford, Essex,[9,15] on the 6th July 1885, there being four children of the marriage: William (junior), born in Essex in 1887, Ellen, born in Essex in 1891, Edwin, born in Aberdeen in 1898 and Mary, also born in Aberdeen in 1904.

This strange continuing juxtaposition of surnames is well illustrated by the family's return for the 1891 Census,[9] in which, when living at Stratford, the entry notes *'William Duncanson, aged 30'*, employed as a *'Locomotive Inspector'*, his wife Mary Ann plus children William and Ellen also living there. Pickersgill's mother, also Mary Duncanson, died in April 1887,[9] suggesting that Pickersgill might have reverted to the surname on his birth certificate, but this reversion seemed only to have permanently crystalized in 1894,[13] when he joined the Great North of Scotland company. In July of that year[13] he succeeded James Johnston as Locomotive, Carriage & Wagon Superintendent of the GNSR, Pickersgill being recommended[8] for the post by William Dean, Locomotive Superintendent of the GWR, and James Holden, the latter having been Dean's chief assistant[16] at Swindon from 1878 until his appointment as Locomotive Superintendent of the GER in 1885.

The 1911 Census[15] for Inverurie records the Pickersgill family living at a house named 'Hopeville', which had *'12 rooms with more than one window'*, Pickersgill himself being noted as aged 50 and employed as a *'Mechanical Engineer, Railway Locomotive Works'*. His wife Mary Ann Pickersgill, aged 44, his mother-in-law Mary Ann Hope, aged 78, and three of his children, Ellen Elizabeth, aged 20, Edwin Gordon, aged 13, and Mary Alice, aged 7, are also recorded in the return for the property.

Rather late in his career, in April 1923, Pickersgill applied for membership of the IMechE.[7] The calibre and standing of the proposers and referees to his candidature, drawn from the most eminent industrialists and academics of the day, attest to the esteem in which he was held by his peers. The proposal was made by Sir Hugh Reid CBE, Chairman of the North British Locomotive Co. and seconded by Walter Dixon, Coalmaster and Ironmaster, Glasgow. The three referees were Professor W.E. Dalby FRS, Professor at The City & Guilds Institute, London; Professor A.L. Mallenby, Professor of Mechanical Engineering at The Royal Technical College, Glasgow; and Sir Henry Fowler KBE, deputy CME of the LM&SR, Derby. It would have been difficult to find a more august body of supporters and, indeed, Pickersgill's nomination for membership was duly approved.

INVERURIE

Unusually, the GNSR had no 0-6-0 tender locomotives and relied upon 4-4-0 tender engines to work both its passenger and freight traffic. In standardising the 4-4-0 as a mixed-traffic type[13] on the GNSR, Pickersgill adopted a driving wheel diameter of 6 ft 1 in., a dimension he would replicate at St Rollox in the Caledonian '60' and '956' Classes. On the GNSR, the Pickersgill 'T' Class 4-4-0 locomotives, twenty-six of which were built in two batches[17] between 1895 and 1898, were a development of an earlier Johnston design and proved to be both free-running and economical. One of the 'T' Class was timed at 79 mph by Rev W.J. Scott,[18] the class being remarkably long-lived, several of the original 1895 Neilson & Co. batch being withdrawn[19] as British Railways' property in the early 1950s.

Pickersgill developed the 'T' Class further, his next 4-4-0 design, the 'V' Class, appearing in 1899. Plate 2 shows 'V' Class engine No. 115, built by Neilson Reid & Co. in GNSR green livery at Inverurie. This locomotive ran in traffic for fifty-eight years, becoming BR

Plate 2
GNSR 4-4-0 'V' Class No. 115, was built by Neilson Reid & Co. in 1899 to Pickersgill's design. This locomotive, shown in green livery at Inverurie works, was withdrawn in March 1957 as BR No. 62264, the penultimate survivor of the L&NER designated 'D40' Class. One of Pickersgill's earlier 4-4-0 'T' Class engines was timed at 79 mph, locomotives of this class also being long-lived, with several of the original 1895 batch being withdrawn in the early 1950s.
NRM/LPC66623

Plate 3
In addition to providing new construction, Pickersgill rebuilt several older types, including GNSR No. 58. Supplied originally by Neilson & Co. in 1878 to William Cowan's design, the locomotive is shown as rebuilt in 1903. Renumbered 6858, it was withdrawn in May 1927 as the last member of the L&NER 'D45' Class.
NRM/LPC66611

No. 62264, prior to withdrawal in 1957 as the penultimate survivor of the L&NER 'D40' Class. In addition to providing new construction, Pickersgill also rebuilt several older types, one example being the '57' (later 'M') Class, which had originally been provided by Neilson & Co. under William Cowan's aegis in 1878. The rebuilt No. 58, shown in Plate 3, was withdrawn from traffic in 1927.

Just prior to Pickersgill joining the GNSR, that company's Board had investigated moving their locomotive works to a new site at Dyce or Inverurie,[20] the latter being chosen. At that time, the GNSR Locomotive Committee visited[20] various English company facilities, including Doncaster, Swindon and Stratford, with William Dean of the GWR and James Holden of the GER being invited to advise on the new buildings and machinery. Dean visited Aberdeen[20] in February 1894, at which time his sketch plans for the new works' facilities were approved. After Pickersgill's appointment as GNSR Locomotive Superintendent later that year, he collaborated with Dean.

In 1898, building of the new locomotive works started on a greenfield site at Inverurie,[13] which replaced the cramped and unsatisfactory facilities at Kittybrewster, in Aberdeen. These new facilities, opened in 1905, increased the population at Inverurie by some 1,500, the company building housing accommodation for over one hundred families.[13] As one might have expected in the comparatively small community at Inverurie, and with the new railway workshops being an important factor in the town and its economy, Pickersgill took an active part in local affairs, becoming *inter alia* a Baillie (a Scots Magistrate).[8]

St Rollox

By all accounts the selection of Pickersgill, was, *prima facie*, by no means a poor one, and no doubt he would have provided appropriate references. Whilst no papers have come to hand regarding these references, one might surmise that his former colleague and long standing acquaintance A.J. Hill, only recently appointed to the CME's role on the GER, would surely have attested to his technical abilities if asked. One point which possibly would not have escaped the Directors' considerations was Pickersgill's limited experience in the design and operation of superheated locomotives, though it could perhaps justifiably be claimed the

majority of Directors would have little knowledge of such matters themselves. St Rollox, naturally, could claim to be at the forefront of such emerging technology, having considerable experience of its successful application to several classes of Caledonian engines in the immediately preceding four years.

The Directors would of course have been aware of Pickersgill's considerable impact at Inverurie. As well as planning and implementing the move there, he had been responsible for the provision of thirty-nine new locomotives and the successful rebuilding of a further thirty.[20] Moreover, he had provided these engines, capable of efficiently working the company's traffic, within GNSR capital expenditure constraints and a load limitation of 16 tons per powered axle. A significant amount of standardisation had also been achieved.

Seen by Graeme Miller[4] as a *'dignified and scholarly figure'*, with a quiet personality, yet *'inclined to be a bit regimental'* and quite opposite in style to McIntosh, Pickersgill's more academically based education, plus his twenty years as Locomotive Superintendent at Inverurie, would have had appeal to the Caledonian Board in an age where a less empirical approach to locomotive engineering was gaining credence. To ensure a smooth handover to the incoming Locomotive Superintendent, it has been suggested that McIntosh remained at St Rollox for several months,[14] finally leaving Caledonian company service in mid-1914.

Concurrent with Pickersgill's appointment, John Barr,[3,21] who is pictured in Plate 4, was selected to fill the post of Assistant Locomotive Superintendent for running matters. Barr, whose father had been Caledonian company Divisional Civil Engineer for the northern area, based at Perth, had started his career at the Civil Engineer's office there in 1891. Shortly thereafter, he transferred to the mechanical engineer's department and completed a full apprenticeship in the workshops at Perth and St Rollox. Prior to his 1914 appointment, Barr had been locomotive foreman for both the Dundee and Aberdeen districts, followed by the post of Running Assistant, at St Rollox, to the Locomotive Superintendent. Through Barr's appointment, the running-side experience, which McIntosh possessed in depth, was given visibility at senior level in support of the new Locomotive Superintendent.

J.F. McEwan recalled that on the formation of the LM&SR company, Derby senior staff were studying the options for the new set-up and to whom certain senior appointments might be given. According to McEwan,[22] Pickersgill offered to retire *'if it would assist matters'*. It would seem that Derby wanted R.H. Whitelegg, the G&SWR Locomotive Superintendent and a former MR employee, who was younger than Pickersgill, to be appointed to the new company's Northern Division Mechanical Engineer post, based at Glasgow. As we now know, however, Derby was overruled and Pickersgill was appointed, at an annual salary of £3,500,[23] a position from which he retired early, on health grounds, in 1925. Pickersgill's latter years were spent at Bournemouth, where he died on the 2nd May 1928.[24] He is interred in Wimborne Cemetery, Poole, Dorset, a simple headstone, making no mention of his CBE, recording:

*'William Pickersgill,
born 1861, died 1928, aged 67'.*[8]

Barr's career also progressed with the formation of the LM&SR – he became Superintendent of Motive Power (Northern Division) at an annual salary of £1,500,[23] a position from which he retired in January 1939.

Kempt too prospered under the new ownership, being appointed LM&S Carriage & Wagon Superintendent (Scotland) at the same salary as Barr[23] and is pictured in Plate 5. From this position Kempt retired in May 1931,[25] he and his father having served the Caledonian and LM&S companies for a total of almost ninety years. His father, also Irvine Kempt, had entered the service of the Scottish North Eastern Railway at Aberdeen early in life and rose to become General Superintendent of the Caledonian company. Kempt junior had been intimately involved in the August 1895 railway races to the north, when, as a Locomotive Inspector, he had travelled from Carlisle on the footplate of the 8.00 pm Down Tourist train, London to Aberdeen, which established the record run of 540 miles in 512 minutes,[25] including stops.

On that record-breaking night of the 22nd August, Kempt rode on Drummond 4-4-0 No. 90, driven by Archie Crooks of Kingmoor from Carlisle to Perth, and on Lambie No. 17, driven by John Soutar from Perth to Aberdeen.[26] Driver Crooks, in running the Carlisle to Perth leg non-stop, had run himself so short of water in the process that having coupled off on arrival at Perth, he refused to move further and was towed to the shed.[26] When St Rollox realised that Crooks had brought his 207 ton train into Perth that morning with a tank that had been dry for the last fourteen miles,[27] the clear need for larger water capacity tenders had become apparent, this incident seemingly resulting in the introduction of bogie tenders with the '766' Class.

THE '956' CLASS – AN OBJECTIVE ASSESSMENT

The CR '956' Class has been the subject of many articles over the years, some expressing strongly held opinions as to the success, or otherwise, of the class and drawing attention to what were seen, in layman's terms, as particular faults and deficiencies. Such terms as *'poor steamers'* and *'crossed eccentric rods'* appear in many references to the class, and various respected authors have written of the locomotives and their individual performances in less than glowing terms, some quite pejoratively and perhaps without objective

Plate 4
John G. Barr, CR Assistant Locomotive Superintendent (Running) 1914-23, then LM&SR Northern Division Locomotive Superintendent 1923-39. Noted by O.S. Nock as one of the *'strongest powers behind the throne'* in the Pickersgill era, Barr was mentioned by E.S. Cox as one of the five principal architects of locomotive developments on the LM&SR in the 1923-32 period, alongside Sir Henry Fowler, George Hughes, James Anderson and Hewitt Beames.   ***LM&SR***

justification – O.S. Nock, for example, referring to the '956' Class as *'one of the most monumental flops of all time'*.[28] As might have been expected, advances in locomotive engineering sometimes led to 'teething troubles', and a measure of the strength and success of respective railway companies' technical departments was determined by the way in which these unexpected problems were analysed and resolved, plus the time taken to so do.

Historically, little in the way of '956' Class extant technical documentation has been readily available to assist any objective review – although, in the last few years, previously undiscovered or misplaced '956' Class data has come to hand. Moreover, and fortunately, in the period 1900 to 1920 much technical information on the generalities of steam locomotive design and development was published in textbooks and elsewhere. It is therefore possible, for the '956' Class, to broadly translate the outline train load and speed requirements which might have been set to Pickersgill by his traffic department (or *vice versa*) into a more definitive form, and then to compare the resulting design and performance with both previous CR practice and the contemporary approaches used by other railway companies.

Additionally, the work of Professor W.E. Dalby FRS[29] in the 1905 to 1915 period cannot be discounted. Dalby, a most distinguished scientist and engineer, was the acknowledged expert in many aspects of locomotive design, and was consulted regularly by major railway CMEs. Starting his career aged 14 in the Stratford works of the Great Eastern Railway, Dalby rose to be Professor of Civil & Mechanical Engineering at Imperial College, London. In 1913 he was elected a Fellow of the Royal Society. On matters of locomotive valve gear design, balancing and heat transfer, Dalby, through his many textbooks and other publications, contributed significantly to the foundations of the emerging analytical approach to locomotive engineering. For example, the excellent balancing of Gresley 3-cylinder locomotives on the GNR was based on Dalby's analytical work applied by Bulleid.[30] The fact that some railway companies were prepared to invest in Dalby's approach to design matters might be taken as, *de facto*, an indictment of short-sightedness on the part of those who did not.

From a different aspect, in the 1908 to 1918 period, the Pennsylvania Railroad Company (PRC) undertook significant locomotive testing work at their Altoona plant,[31] the company regularly publishing much data on boiler performance and related matters. Indeed, in a golden era from around 1910 to 1915, the PRC was considered by some as the first to quantify the benefits for superheat and the best means to obtain it.[32] These Altoona technical publications, which were devoured around the globe,[32] together with other US technical outputs from ALCO and Professors Goss[33] and Ludy[34] at Purdue University, were used by the more progressive UK railway CMEs as a guide in design matters, Churchward being a particularly well-known follower of US developments. Indeed, Pickersgill and his staff may have been followers of PRC detailed design practice, making use of it on the '956' Class.[35]

From this contemporary information and a limited amount of '956' Class design and performance data, together with first-hand accounts of actual locomotive operation, some objective conclusions can be offered as to where the St Rollox team were on the correct lines, where there might have been improvements, or where there appear to have been shortfalls. In addition to reviewing the original design, comment has also been made on the various modifications made or proposed to the small class of four engines, not all of the modifications being as successful as the St Rollox team might have anticipated or wished. Today, as one might expect, absolute numeric conclusions are often not possible, since much of the original detail and supporting calculations, if they existed, are no longer available. Imperial units are used throughout this publication for obvious reasons.

Of necessity, due to the number of valve gear variations made by St Rollox to individual members of the class, and the difficulty in determining what was actually fitted to each locomotive, when, and for how long, it has not been possible to be absolutely definitive on valve gear matters. However, from available information, including photographic evidence and recollections of former CR and LM&SR employees, a view on valve gear arrangements for each class member is set out. Needless to say, some questions on these valve gear arrangements remain unanswered.

Plate 6 shows an official Caledonian company photograph of No. 956 as originally built, whilst Figure 1 gives the general arrangement, in both elevation and plan,[36] for the class when entering service in August 1921. Figure 2 shows the weight diagram,[36] and Figure 3 a part sectioned front elevation through the smokebox.[36] A sectioned front elevation through the middle coupled axle is given as Figure 4,[36] whilst a section through the cab showing the boiler backhead arrangement is shown in Figure 5.[36] The four locomotives of the class entered traffic from June to August 1921, the actual dates being noted by Alan Dunbar[37] as: No. 956 on the 24th June, No. 957 on the 9th July, No. 958 on the 8th July, No. 959 on the 13th August.

Plate 5
Irvine Kempt (junior), CR Assistant Locomotive Superintendent (Works) 1914-23, then LM&SR Northern Division Carriage & Wagon Superintendent 1923-31. As a locomotive inspector, Kempt had been intimately involved in the 1895 railway races to the north and on the record-breaking night of the 22nd August, when 540 miles were covered in 512 minutes, including stops, he rode on Drummond No. 90, from Carlisle to Perth, and Lambie No. 17, from Perth to Aberdeen.
LM&SR

SOURCES OF INFORMATION

In accessing the remaining known technical information on the '956' Class, and searching for new data, much use has been made of material held in the archives of the Caledonian Railway Association, especially the Campbell Cornwell Collection,[38] plus material from the Jim MacIntosh Collection.[39] Additionally, the available trials data recorded for engine No. 956 in August 1921, when fitted with the original derived motion, and the trials data from October 1922, when No. 956 was fitted with a separate Stephenson's link motion for the centre cylinder, have been consulted. This '956' Class trials material is held in the Montague Smith Collection[40] housed in the National Records of Scotland (NRS), from which other records have also been accessed, not only for locomotive matters but also for general operation of the Caledonian Railway Company. The Alan Dunbar papers,[41] also held at the NRS, have proved a useful source of additional information, as have the J.F. McEwan papers[14] held at the William Patrick Library (East Dunbartonshire Council) in Kirkintilloch.

The National Railway Museum (NRM) at York retains indicator diagram data for engine No. 956, taken during the August 1921 trials,[42] this data complementing the logs prepared by the Caledonian company and held in the NRS.[40] The NRM and the NRS[43] also hold some details on subsequent '956' Class tender usage post the associated locomotive withdrawals. Additionally, the NRM holds the papers of the late A.J. Powell,[44] sometime assistant mechanical engineer under E.S. Cox during the design of the British Railways standard classes. Powell laid out some draft design calculations to demonstrate what might have been possible by way of a '956' Class rebuild, should the LM&SR authorities have embarked

Plate 6
The official CR photograph of No. 956 is dated June 1921, prior to trials running. The locomotive is in workshop grey.
NRM/SRX37

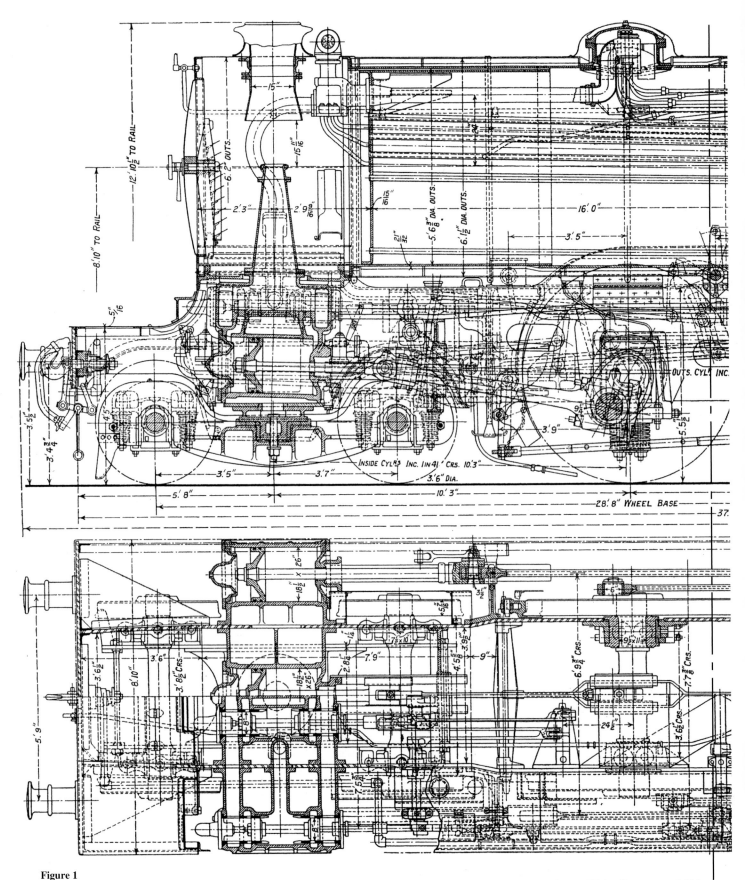

Figure 1

'956' Class. Sectioned General Arrangement, Elevation and Plan. The plan shows the locomotive built to the maximum CR loading gauge of 12 ft 10½ ins from rail level and the initial form of the derived motion. The main frames are cranked inwards some 3 ft 6 ins forward of the leading coupled axle, this being done to provide adequate clearance for valve motion and rear bogie wheels. The large boiler is of 5 ft 6 ins diameter having 16 ft between tubeplates.

The Railway Engineer, *October 1921*

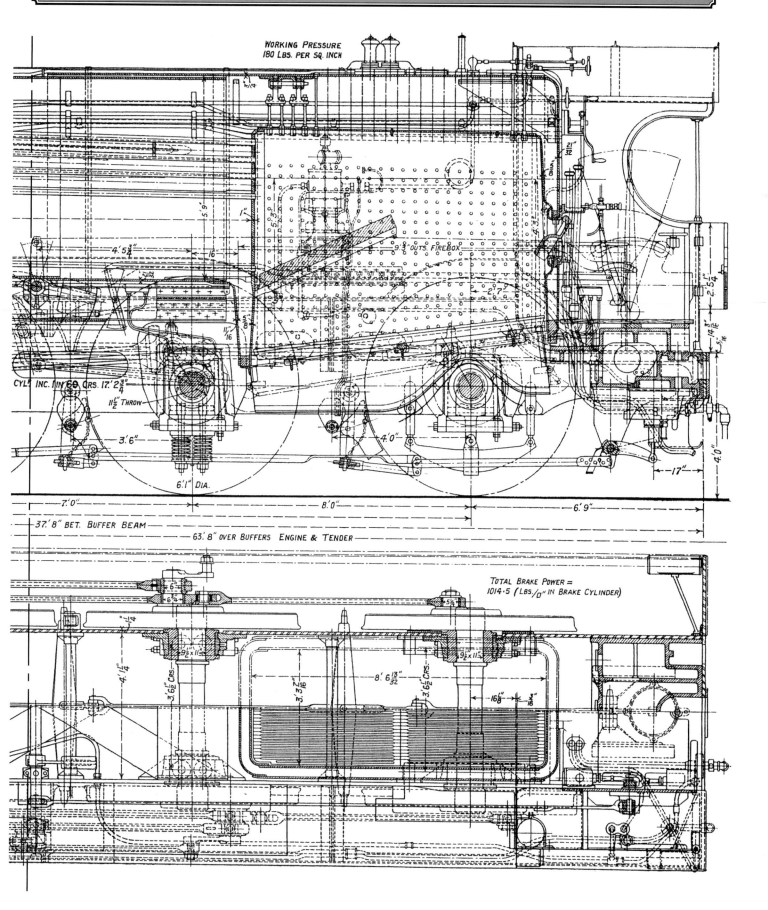

WORKING PRESSURE
180 LBS. PER SQ. INCH

9'.3" OUTS. FIREBOX

TOTAL BRAKE POWER =
1014·5 (LBS./☐" IN BRAKE CYLINDER)

37'.8" BET. BUFFER BEAM

63'.8" OVER BUFFERS ENGINE & TENDER

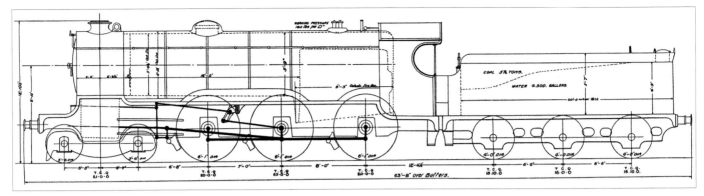

Figure 2
'956' Class. Weight Diagram, Engine and Tender. The anticipated engine weight at 81 tons would have been very near the company's permanent way maximum, the coupled axle static load of 20 tons being the Civil Engineer's limit. With 21 tons taken by the bogie, allied to an extended heavy front end with all cylinders being in-line, close attention should have been focused on the bogie side control springing to prevent 'nozing' at speed. Rough riding at the higher speeds may well have been a problem, the highest recorded speed for the class being 66 mph.   *The Railway Engineer, October 1921*

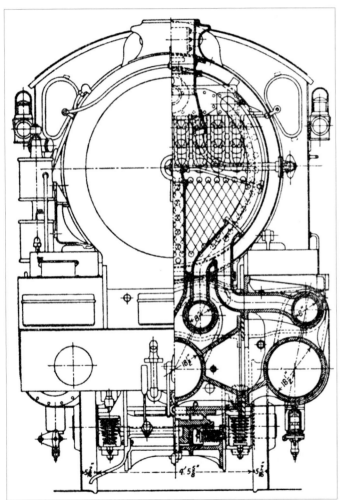

Figure 3
'956' Class. Sectioned Front Elevation through Smokebox. The arrangement for feeding the centre and left-hand cylinders with steam via one supply pipe from the superheater header is clearly illustrated. The pipe diameters selected for the right- and left-side steam feeds from the header were identical, but marginally undersize. The supplying of two cylinders from one such pipe would measurably constrain steam supply at the higher outputs, but perhaps this was never noticed since boiler output probably never rose to levels where the effect was appreciable.   *The Railway Engineer, October 1921*

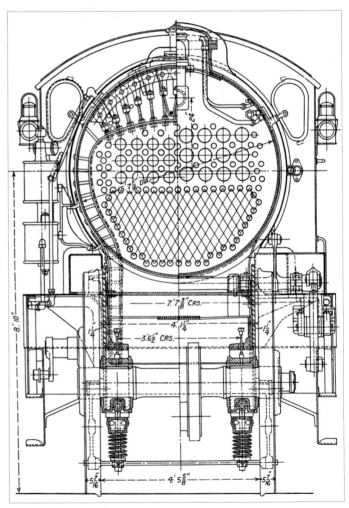

Figure 4
'956' Class. Sectioned Front Elevation through Centre Driving Axle. This view illustrates a cross section of the firebox in way of the sling stays, which attach it to the boiler barrel. Two rows of sling stays were provided between the boiler outer wrapper plate and the firebox crown sheet, screwed staying being used for the remainder. Staying arrangements for the water legs at the right-hand side are also shown. The curved firebox crown sheet is apparent, this arrangement, of questionable merit, being standard on larger Caledonian Railway locomotives. Its application on the '956' Class conveyed no appreciable benefit, imposed an artificial constraint on steam space volume and may have increased the probability of water carry-over and reduction in superheat.   *The Railway Engineer, October 1921*

on such a course. A section summarising Powell's outline proposals is included.

Considerable and invaluable assistance has been given to the author by Philip Atkins,[45] sometime NRM Librarian, who has made available his private papers on the '956' Class, especially original items of correspondence between himself and Caledonian company employees, such as Graeme Miller and Alan Dunbar, together with observations from David Newlands, James F. McEwan and others. The John G. Barr papers,[46] held by the Scottish Railway Preservation Society, have also proved a useful source of relevant material.

The author is also greatly indebted to Dr Ann Glen, whose father A.E. Glen was a St Rollox 'University Apprentice' in the 1919 to 1923 period, and who witnessed, at first hand, the '956' Class engines being built. During his St Rollox apprenticeship time, Ernest Glen carried a simple pocket camera and recorded build details of the class, having been given full permission to do so for any matters which were of interest to him. Dr Glen's agreement to the use of this material from her father's archive[47] has provided succeeding generations with a unique record of St Rollox work and, moreover, has attested to Ernest Glen's engineering perception in capturing details of what was, at that time, advanced locomotive engineering.

In reviewing drawing material for inclusion in this text, it quickly became apparent that dates allocated to specific drawing numbers in the St Rollox drawing register[48] often bore no relation to the dates annotated in the top right-hand corner of the identically numbered drawing sheets being examined by the author. This of course can be explained through drawing revisions and subsequent re-issue under the pre-existing or prime number. However, it becomes virtually impossible to check on individual re-issues since they are not annotated as such, other than by a date change. To find a consistent way of handling this enigma, when the majority of the re-issues may not be available, proved beyond the author's intellectual capacity. As a result, where dates are mentioned against a drawing number in the text, the author has usually selected the date from the drawing register,[48] unless there are compelling reasons to the contrary.

One example will illustrate the dilemma. Drawing No. 21020[49] is annotated in the drawing register as '2-6-0 Goods Engine', the register date being the 27th December 1920: the draughtsman is Alexander Linn. The actual drawing sheet examined by the author and numbered No. 21020 still records Mr Linn as the draughtsman, though it is now titled '2-6-0 Express Goods Engine' and is dated the 16th October 1923. No evidence of intermediate issues, or for that matter the original issue is mentioned on the October 1923 issue.

OBJECTIVITY

To sustain an objective view of the '956' Class design and performance, care has been taken to ensure that, as far as possible, comment and analyses is made against known technical criteria and opinion of the day, this applying particularly to boiler and valve gear matters. No attempt has been made to make an in-depth and definitive comparison of the '956' Class design and performance with contemporary locomotives produced by private builders or other railway companies, though comment is made on other designs of the period to illustrate particular points. To attempt an in-depth comparison with contemporary designs would be an onerous task and objectivity could well be lost through the selection of well-known designs of undoubted merit.

The author believes it is more appropriate to assess the '956' Class against known and available technology of the day, and to examine the design and performance against such criteria, resulting in a text which is complementary to, rather than competitive with, other specialised works which may have majored on comparative evaluation. Trials data for the '956' Class are included in the Appendices to this volume.

In any assessment of this nature, due account needs to be taken of the conditions prevailing at St Rollox during the 1914-18 war and in the immediate post-war period, since they undoubtedly influenced the '956' Class design process, construction programme and any subsequent efforts to modify the locomotives. As far as can be gleaned from available records, this has been done for both technical and financial influences.

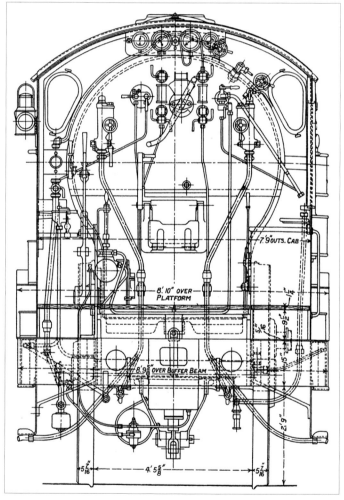

Figure 5
'956' Class. Elevation of Cab and Boiler Backhead. In this forward looking view, the main components for operating the locomotive are evident – two water gauges, two backhead mounted lifting injectors, the regulator and the reversing lever on the left-hand side, with its steam assisted servo. The usual gauges for boiler and steam chest pressure, vacuum and air pressure status plus carriage heating would have been provided. For clarity, not all pipework appears to be shown.
The Railway Engineer, *October 1921*

REFERENCES
1. Caledonian Railway, Extracts from Board Meeting Minutes, NRS, BR/CAL/5/13
2. Caledonian Railway, Officer's Pension Arrangements, NRS, BR/CAL/4/49
3. Caledonian Railway, Staff Emoluments 1900-1920, NRS, BR/CAL/15/14
4. Private Correspondence, Graeme Miller to CP Atkins, 1978
5. Caledonian Railway, Book of Miscellaneous Manuscript Notes on CR Officers, NRS, BR/CAL/4/81
6. Private Correspondence, A.G. Dunbar to C.P. Atkins, 1965
7. Wm. Pickersgill, Application for Membership of IMechE, April 1923
8. 'Pickersgill, A Relative View', Ralph Needham, in *The Caledonian Journal*, No. 5, 1988, pp. 11ff (Ralph Needham was Pickersgill's great-nephew)

9. Births, Deaths & Marriages Records, plus Census Records, England

10. William Pickersgill, ILocoE Presidential Address, 23rd September 1920

11. *Edward Thompson of the LNER*, Peter Grafton (Oakwood Press, 2007), p. 23

12. *Great Eastern Railway Magazine*, May 1920, p. 165

13. 'The New Locomotive Superintendent of the Caledonian Railway and his Work on the Great North of Scotland Railway', G.A. Sekon, in *Railway & Travel Monthly*, May 1914, pp. 385ff

14. J.F. McEwan papers, William Patrick Library, Kirkintilloch, ref. T25/1/29, etc

15. Registrar General for Scotland: Births, Deaths & Marriage Records, Inverurie District; 1911 Census Records, Inverurie

16. *Swindon Steam*, L.A. Summers (Amberley, 2013), pp. 57ff

17. *Great North of Scotland Railway Locomotives*, Hugh Gordon (Irwell Press Ltd, 2008), p. 44

18. *Great North of Scotland Railway Locomotives*, Hugh Gordon, p. 53

19. *Yeadon's Register of LNER Locomotives*, Volume 44 (Book Law Publications, 2008), p. 47

20. *Great North of Scotland Railway Locomotives*, Hugh Gordon, pp. 56ff

21. 'John Barr', in *The Railway Gazette*, 17th February 1939

22. Private Correspondence, J.F. McEwan to C.P. Atkins, 12th October 1987

23. Caledonian Railway, Staff Emoluments 1920-1923, NRS, BR/CAL/15/15

24. 'William Pickersgill', ILocoE Obituary, 1928

25. *The LMS Magazine*, September 1931, report on the retiral of Mr Irvine Kempt, p. 292

26. *The Caledonian Dunalastairs*, O.S. Nock (David & Charles, 1968), p. 21

27. *Scottish Locomotive History 1831-1923*, Campbell Highet (George Allen & Unwin, 1970), p. 188

28. 'Scottish Topics – Past and Present', O.S. Nock, in *The Railway Magazine*, January 1965, pp. 20ff

29. 'W.E. Dalby (1868-1936)', Obituary, The Royal Society, 1936

30. *Master Builders of Steam*, H.A.V. Bulleid (Ian Allan 1963), pp. 53, 77

31. PRC, Locomotive Testing Plant, Altoona, Bulletins, E2A-1910: K29-1912: E6S-1913: K2SA-1914, etc

32. Article by David Pawson, *SLS Journal*, March/April 2013, pp. 51ff

33. *Locomotive Performance*, Prof. W.F.M. Goss (John Wiley, New York, 1911)

34. *Locomotive Boilers & Engines*, Prof L.V. Ludy (American Technical Society, 1918)

35. 956 Class piston valves compared to PRC design and specification, per J.H. Yoder and G.B. Wharen textbook, *Locomotive Valves and Valve Gears* (PRC, 1917)

36. 'New Three-Cylinder 4-6-0 Type Locomotives, Caledonian Railway', in *The Railway Engineer*, October 1921, pp. 36ff

37. 'Y125 – And All That', A.G. Dunbar, in *SLS Journal*, August 1948, pp. 192ff

38. Campbell Cornwell Collection of CR 956 Class drawings, Caledonian Railway Association, CRA6/1/3/2, Archive Group 48

39. Jim MacIntosh Collection, private collection

40. Montague Smith Collection, NRS, GD456, RHP136355, Pickersgill Locomotives, 956 Class

41. Alan Dunbar papers: NRS, GD344/6/12/1-7, Private Correspondence; NRS, GD344/4/32, 956 Class Boiler Record Cards

42. LMS Engine Test Reports, ID685, NRM ALS3/7/4/G

43. Tender History Cards, 956 Class Tender No. 6240 etc, NRS, GD344/4/22/68, etc

44. A.J. Powell papers, NRM, 956 Class Material, uncatalogued

45. Philip Atkins Collection, private collection

46. John G. Barr papers, courtesy the Scottish Railway Preservation Society

47. A.E. Glen Collection – private collection, courtesy Dr Ann Glen

48. St Rollox Drawing Register, NRS, BR/CAL/5/56

49. St Rollox Drg No 21020, '2-6-0 Express Goods Engine', NRS, RHP132337

Plate 7
'Dunalastair I' Class locomotive, CR No. 723, *Victoria*, at St Rollox works in 1896. These most efficient and successful engines were first employed on the southern main line between Carlisle and Glasgow Central, working the heavy West Coast Joint Stock trains to and from England. Later, several were allocated to the northern section for working to Aberdeen. The name *Victoria* was removed on the Queen's death in 1901, the locomotive being withdrawn as LM&SR No. 14313 in August 1933.

NRM/SRX140

CHAPTER 2
THE MCINTOSH LEGACY

BACKGROUND

No assessment of William Pickergill's progress at St Rollox and the '956' Class in particular would be complete without some appreciation of the legacy bequeathed to the Caledonian company by J.F. McIntosh, through the experience and capabilities of his senior staff, both in the drawing office and in the works. Pre-1914, the Caledonian technical team and their achievements were certainly in the van of UK railway company locomotive developments, and the extent to which Pickersgill was able to capitalise on this legacy and direct it – as a less empirical approach to locomotive engineering emerged – would be an indicator of his success in motivating his team. Additionally, his vision in determining how emerging new concepts could be applied, keeping future Caledonian locomotive design and performance in a pre-eminent position, would be one of his more significant challenges. Of course, the 1914-18 war intervened, with the attendant disruption it brought, and this would undoubtedly have influenced the resources at Pickersgill's disposal and the opportunities for investment, particularly in the recruitment of qualified staff.

McIntosh's legacy had its roots in Dugald Drummond's locomotive building programmes started on the latter's joining the Caledonian company from the North British in August 1882, and for a more complete assessment of the McIntosh era at St Rollox the reader should consult the excellent *Forty Years of Caledonian Locomotives 1882-1922*.[1] The building blocks of Drummond's success at St Rollox were founded with his '294' Class 0-6-0 goods engine, introduced in 1883. In this locomotive class, inspired cylinder design, well laid out valve motion and a free-steaming appropriately proportioned boiler provided a type to be found in daily service for almost eighty years after the first one turned a wheel, and for which replacement new boilers were still being built post 1935.[2]

For the cylinders, appropriate attention was given to exhaust passages, ensuring sufficient area was provided to allow free passage for expanded steam, with minimised back pressure and clearance volumes. For the Stephenson's valve gear, maximum use was made of available space to provide longest practical eccentric rods, providing a smaller increase in lead as the gear was notched up and, equally importantly, providing a reduction in potential angularity. This latter phenomenon causes valve event distortion, the more noticeable effects being encountered as shorter eccentric rods are used.

The '294' Class boiler was outstanding for its time, having an L/D ratio (tube length divided by tube internal diameter) of 85:1, which conformed to the accepted norms of the time, as set out in Wolff's 1907 text, *Modern Locomotive Practice*.[3] For the grate, Drummond selected an area of approximately seven times the tubeplate free-gas area, i.e. the ratio of free-gas area to grate area was 14 per cent, which gave acceptable heat transfer with economy in coal consumption. The same cylinders and boiler were perpetuated in the Caledonian '66' Class 4-4-0s, introduced in 1884, though the eccentric rods had to be shortened to 4 ft 7 ins due to the space constraints associated with the bogie. However, a smaller wheeled version of the '66' Class, the '80' Class, had the 5 ft 6 ins eccentric rods restored when it was introduced in 1887.

THE 'DUNALASTAIR' SERIES AND 4-6-0 CLASSES

Additional developments by Hugh Smellie and John Lambie culminated in the McIntosh '721' or 'Dunalastair I' Class,

introduced in 1895, the heating surface being 19 per cent greater[4] than previous classes and the tubeplate free-gas area to grate area ratio being set at 16.1 per cent;[4] L/D was again 85.[1] The third engine in the '721' Class, No. 723 *Victoria*, is shown in Plate 7 at St Rollox works when almost new. Successive developments resulted in the building of the '766' and '900' classes, with the use of 5 ft 6 ins eccentric rods and equivalent boiler parameters for free-gas areas being retained from the '721' Class.[1] L/D for the '766' Class was increased to 91, with the tubeplate free-gas to grate area ratio being 15.7 per cent. For the '900' Class, L/D was retained at 91, the free-gas to grate area ratio being 14.4 per cent.[1] L/D ratios around 90 showed that these boilers still had development potential, since ratios approaching 100 were seen as near the top end of the spectrum for efficient heat transfer with the technology of the day.

The performance of the '766' and '900' classes when later superheated by the Caledonian company could be quite exceptional, as shown by the performance of engine No. 772 in September 1915,[5] when handling a 395 ton (gross) train between Carlisle and Strawfrank Junction, on substituting for a failed '903' Class 4-6-0 engine. The 39.7 miles from Carlisle to Beattock station was covered in 47 minutes, against a scheduled 45 minutes, speeds of 66 mph being recorded. On the section from Beattock Summit to Strawfrank Junction (where the Edinburgh portion was detached), a small amount of time was again lost, though speeds in the mid to high 60s were again recorded. Calculations by Cecil J. Allen, who timed the working, suggest that No. 772 was developing around 955 equivalent Draw Bar horsepower (DBHP) – a quite phenomenal effort, with the boiler perhaps being mortgaged in the process.

Indeed, McIntosh expanded engine output power capability further in his '49' Class 4-6-0s of 1903, which, when built, were the most powerful express locomotives in Great Britain – No. 49 in original form being shown in Plate 8 at the head of express stock. In their final 200 psi saturated form, they were capable of developing approximately 1,300 Indicated horsepower[6] (IHP) when handling express passenger trains over Beattock without banking assistance. In 1906 there followed the celebrated 'Cardean' or '903' Class, carrying a 200 psi, 5 ft 3 ins diameter boiler with a heating surface in excess of 2,100 sq. ft and a 26 sq. ft grate. The '903' Class boiler design had an L/D of 114, which was perhaps marginally too high, suggesting the tube bundle was slightly too long; the tubeplate free-gas to grate area was 15.5 per cent. Interestingly, C.J. Allen[7] noted that there was little difference in running performance of the '903' Class before and after superheating, though the edge probably lay with the engines as originally built. This was perhaps to be expected, the greater efficiency under superheated conditions being offset by a boiler pressure reduction to 175 psi and 7.6 per cent increase in cylinder area.[8] Naturally, coal consumption was reduced on the superheated engines.

In designing the '140' Class, known as the 'Dunalastair IV' type, McIntosh, in 1904, raised the L/D to 92, with the tubeplate free-gas to grate area ratio being 16.5 per cent. It was thus apparent, in moving from the 'Dunalastair I' Class to the 'Dunalastair IV',[1] by which the tube heating surface (THS) had increased by 14.5 per cent and the firebox heating surface (FHS) by 22 per cent, McIntosh had achieved significant increase in engine power between these 4-4-0 classes, yet retained the L/D ratio in the 85 to 92 range and the tubeplate free-gas to grate area ratios in the 14.4 to 16.6 per cent band.

There has been the suggestion that McIntosh's success in the '721' Class to '140' Class progression was achieved using little

Plate 8
CR No. 49 when almost new, with its original 200 psi boiler in a 1903 posed photograph near Polmadie shed. When built, the '49' Class were the most powerful locomotives in the UK and, owing to their great length, engine and tender had to be separated at Carlisle prior to turning. No. 49 was rebuilt with a superheated boiler and piston valves in 1911, being withdrawn as LM&SR No. 14750 in 1933.   *NRM/SRX49a*

appreciation of the technical criteria noted and might have arisen just by chance, but the author would not support this contention. Thomas Weir, the Chief Draughtsman, and William H. Moodie, the Locomotive Leading Draughtsman, seem to have well understood the constituent elements for continuing success in boiler development, indeed Weir and Moodie were very much the unsung technical heroes of McIntosh's tenure.

Of course, in the introduction of any new locomotive class, teething troubles were to be expected and McIntosh himself was not immune from such occurrences. J.F. McEwan[9] instances an article in the April 1896 issue of the *Railway Herald* in which it was reported the 'Dunalastair' Class *'is not all that it might be'*, the wording suggesting there had been some initial trouble with No. 721 itself. It would seem that No. 721 was returned to St Rollox early in February 1896, being put back to traffic in late March. Whilst noting that St Rollox records are silent on the problem, McEwan suggests there was an initial problem with the valve gear setting, which was modified on all other members of the class, with the exception of No. 725, prior to their entering traffic. McEwan[9] records that No. 725 may have been used for some experimental work before it finally returned to service workings.

SUPERHEATING

In the introduction and application of superheating, McIntosh's policy seems very clear. In accepting Dr Schimdt's advice,[10] he chose long return loop elements and engineered solutions where the percentage of superheater surface area (SHS) was invariably in excess of 20 per cent of the total of the evaporative heating surface (THS plus FHS). McIntosh also followed the Schmidt arrangements using piston valves with the well-known segmented ring design having Trick ports, an arrangement also adopted successfully by others. The Caledonian arrangement of the Trick ported piston valve is shown as Figure 6, this being St Rollox drawing No. 15545[11] dated the 19th October 1910.

For the Trick ported system, steam is admitted to the cylinder simultaneously in two ways: first, directly past the admission end bobbin edge, as in the ordinary piston valve, and second, through a sleeve connecting the bobbins, from the opposite end bobbin, by a series of slots in its packing ring which align with secondary ports in the liner. Thus steam from the non-admission end passes through the sleeve and enters the cylinder via slots in the admission end ring.

Additionally, on the '49', '903' and '139' classes, McIntosh used superheater elements having a 1¼ ins bore and a radial wall thickness of No. 10 IWG (Imperial Wire Gauge), giving an outside diameter of just over 1½ ins; the 1¼ ins bore ensured a low pressure loss in the superheater circuit. St Rollox drawing No. 15461,[10,12] showing the elements and arrangements for the '139' Class, is typical of the very satisfactory superheating schemes engineered by McIntosh.

Tests on engine No. 139,[13] the first superheated 'Dunalastair IV' Class, showed steam temperatures of 650 °F plus were obtained with these arrangements, leading to most economical working. The table below gives boiler ratios for McIntosh superheated locomotives.[14]

BOILER RATIOS – McINTOSH SUPERHEATED LOCOMOTIVES									
CLASS	**WHEEL ARRANG.**	**THS*** (TUBES AND FLUES)	**FHS*** (FIREBOX)	**(THS + FHS)*** (EVAP. SURFACE)	**SHS*** (SUPERHEAT)	**SHS**** (OF EVAP.)	**L/D**	**FREE-GAS/GRATE****	**FLUES/FREE-GAS****
766	4-4-0	1094	119	1213	214	17.6***	91	15.9	41.0
900	4-4-0	1094	138	1232	214	17.4***	91	14.3	41.0
903	4-6-0	1666	148	1814	515	28.4	114	15.5	44.5
139	4-4-0	1220	145	1365	330	24.2	92	18.0	47.0
34	2-6-0	1071	119	1190	267	22.4	85	17.1	45.0
179	4-6-0	1439	128	1567	403	25.7	102	18.9	45.0

NOTES:
*   All values in square feet.
**   All values are per cent.
***   Fitted with short return loops on rebuilding from saturated arrangements.

In putting forward his designs of piston valves for superheated locomotives, Schmidt[15] adopted the single, wide ring concept, having considered and rejected the use of narrow split rings. In conjunction with others, including Gresley, Schmidt[15] found that the narrow rings wore the bridges on the valve liners quicker than the remaining areas, resulting in increased likelihood of ring seizure and fracture. In retrospect, some railways, including the Great Western, rejected the Schmidt single ring arrangement, whilst others seemed to use the design with considerable success, including the L&NW and SE&C companies, as well as the Caledonian.

Of course valve and cylinder lubrication was always likely to be more difficult the higher the degree of superheat employed. Carbonisation of the passages in the valve bobbins with increasing service mileage suggested to some that the value of the Trick ports became questionable. As ever in locomotive engineering matters, there was no uniformity of view on valve bobbin design, on the effectiveness of Trick ports, on the degree of superheat to be used and even on the composition of oil used for cylinder lubrication.

Interestingly, in pursuing a policy during the 1909 to 1914 period which raised the SHS to evaporative surface ratio to around 25 per cent, McIntosh showed no inclination to revisit this approach, which might have been necessary should difficulties have arisen, for example with lubrication, resulting in excessive wear. In this period, as far as can be established, there seem to be no reports of major cylinder and valve lubrication problems, or excessive carbonisation related to superheat conditions, at least none have come to light and the subject was not raised by contemporary commentators. A paper on the lubrication of Caledonian engine piston valves was read to the ILocoE in 1921 at Glasgow by Irvine Kempt (junior), in which Kempt,[16] in subsequent discussion with R.H. Whitelegg of the G&SWR, said that whilst the Caledonian experienced carbonisation on all of its locomotives, *'the carbonisation depends on the way the driver works his engine and on the amount of oil which he allows to pass through. If he allows too much, he gets excessive carbonisation'*. This admission by Kempt suggests that carbonisation problems with superheated St Rollox locomotives were in large measure related to drivers using too much cylinder oil.

PROPOSALS NOT PROGRESSED

McIntosh, in addition to constructing the above-noted locomotives, undertook preliminary work on various schemes which were not progressed beyond the development stage. In the 1901 to 1906 period, four 4-4-2 schemes were investigated, one of which was a 4-cylinder compound, using Walschaert's valve gear, the un-superheated boiler having an L/D of 107 and a free-gas to grate ratio of 15.4 per cent. These ratios should have provided the necessary steam output, assuming appropriate draughting was applied. Using a boiler pressed to 200 psi and a 26 sq. ft grate, this compound proposal was outlined in St Rollox drawing No. 13019,[17] dated the 4th April 1905, a sectioned front elevation being shown in Figure 7. In one of his few public comments, McIntosh[18] is recorded as noting *'the Atlantic type had not been a conscious success elsewhere'*, which he associated with its limited adhesive weight and alleged heating troubles with the trailing carrying axle.

In parallel with the design and construction of the superheated '34' Class, five of which entered traffic towards the end of 1912, McIntosh schemed out a further 2-6-0 superheated express goods engine having outside cylinders. Options on cylinder diameter and stroke were given, possibly to ensure the Chief Engineer could be satisfied on lateral loading gauge limits, particularly on throw-over. The proposed SHS was 22.6 per cent of the evaporative surface totals, the outline arrangement being shown on St Rollox drawing No. 16284,[19] dated the 17th February 1912. Additionally, in 1911 an outside-cylindered superheated express passenger 4-6-0, having 6 ft 6 ins diameter wheels, was schemed out, details being given in St Rollox drawing No. 15701,[20] dated 1st February of that year.

Whilst this 6 ft 6 ins wheeled engine, having 21 in. x 26 in. cylinders, was subsequently developed by Pickersgill as the '60' Class, there has been the suggestion that these McIntosh outside-cylindered 2-6-0 and 4-6-0 schemes may have been prompted by the spectacular crank axle failure on No. 903 in April 1909. Indeed, another outside-cylindered 4-6-0 express goods engine was schemed out in August 1912, the details being given on St Rollox drawing No. 16505. This latter proposal had 20½ in. x 26 in. cylinders and 5 ft 9 ins driving wheels, the SHS being 19 per cent of the evaporative surface. None of these McIntosh outside-cylindered proposals were taken beyond the embryonic stage.

Surprisingly, in mid-1913, a 4-cylinder 4-6-2 was laid out, which itself had been immediately preceded by another 4-cylinder 4-6-2 scheme. St Rollox drawing No. 17161, dated the 30th September 1913, outlines the earlier scheme for a 6 ft 6 ins wheeled locomotive having over 3,100 sq. ft of heating surface (including the SHS at

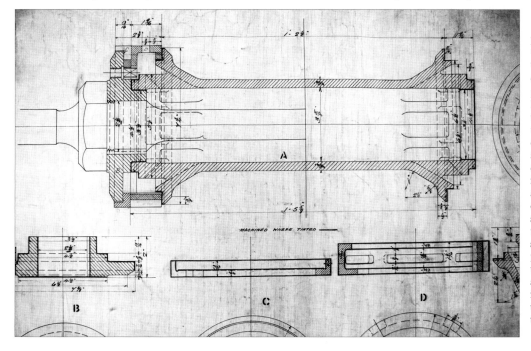

Figure 6
'139' Class. Trick Ported Piston Valve, Drg No. 15545, dated the 19th October 1910. This drawing was prepared for the manufacture at St Rollox of the piston valves to be fitted to superheated engine No. 139. These valves, used by Dr Schmidt as part of his superheating arrangements, allowed steam to be admitted to the cylinder simultaneously in two ways: first, directly through the normal admission edge, and second, from the opposite end of the valve via a series of slots in its packing ring which aligned with secondary ports in the liner. The steam from the non-admission end passes through the sleeve and enters the cylinder through slots in the admission end ring. Not all companies favoured this arrangement, though the CR, L&NWR and SE&CR used them with success.
NRS: GD456, RHP136346/41

19.6 per cent of the evaporative surface totals) and a 27 sq. ft grate. With a 20 ft 6 ins distance between tubeplates, plus an L/D of 140, together with a narrow firebox and higher than acceptable free-gas to grate area ratio, this proposal, had it been implemented, would probably not have influenced McIntosh's reputation for the better. The second 4-cylinder 4-6-2 proposal, outlined in St Rollox drawing No. 17168,[21] had a more acceptably proportioned boiler, using a wide firebox and 37 sq. ft grate, with L/D still rather too high at 132.

In effect, this latter 4-6-2 scheme was no more than an enlarged '903' Class. The four 16 in. x 26 in. cylinders and the standard 6 ft 6 ins coupled wheels[21] would have given a tractive effort of only around 4,500 lbs greater than No. 903 at 85 per cent of the 180 psi boiler pressure. The proposed boiler would have had a tube heating surface of 1,750 sq. ft and a firebox heating surface of 158 sq. ft, with the SHS being set at 526 sq. ft. Taking an overview on this proposal, the justification for the building of an engine weighing around 90 tons[21] – some 16 tons more than the '903' Class, yet having only a marginally increased adhesive weight – seems problematic. Again, it is perhaps fortunate this latter scheme also failed to pass from the embryonic stage.

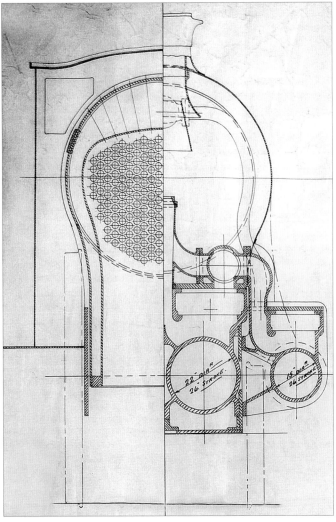

Figure 7
McIntosh Proposed Compound Atlantic. Sectioned Front Elevation, Drg No. 13019, dated the 4th April 1905. This proposal, using a boiler pressed to 200 psi, a 26 sq. ft grate and Walschaerts' valve gear, was one of four 4-4-2 schemes investigated at St Rollox in the 1901-6 period. None of the schemes passed beyond the embryonic stage, McIntosh noting *'the Atlantic type has not been a conscious success elsewhere'*, which he associated with its limited adhesive weight and alleged heating troubles with the trailing carrying axle. *NRS: RHP132378*

A QUESTION OF SUCCESS

From time to time the question arises as to the general success, or otherwise, of locomotives produced at St Rollox during McIntosh's tenure. A point is sometimes made that whilst his 4-4-0 locomotives were exceptional, the 4-6-0s were not quite in the same league and, of the goods engines, only the '812' Class were worthy of any merit. Whilst there is a vestige of truth in these assertions, the author would not wholly support them, though like all Locomotive Superintendents, McIntosh had his comparatively less successful products.

The '55' Class 4-6-0s, designed specifically for Callander & Oban route operation, were most successful, notwithstanding their restricted grate and ashpan arrangements. Equally successful were the '49' and '903' classes, in both their final saturated and superheated forms. Less success could certainly be claimed for the '918' Class, where non-idealised boiler proportions led to poor combustion conditions, high coal consumption and early withdrawal, though two of the boilers were subsequently fitted to '55' Class locomotives for use on the C&O route. The poor combustion conditions are well illustrated in Plate 9, showing accumulated ash and unburned coal in the smokebox of No. 921.

The '908' Class were regarded as well suited for the operation of express passenger services between Glasgow, Perth and Aberdeen, also being successfully employed on the short distance, smartly timed services from Glasgow to the Clyde coast, though they again could be faulted for grate and ashpan restrictions and would have benefitted from superheating. Actually, in early 1914, McIntosh did prepare proposals to superheat the '908' Class, St Rollox drawing No. 17336[22] of the 30th March laying out the details, though wartime materials shortage thwarted the scheme. The superheated '179' Class gave very acceptable performance on express goods and passenger traffic, though again might have been improved with larger fireboxes.

Interestingly, when the Belgians, at the beginning of the twentieth century, adopted the designs of McIntosh, they evidently realised at once the essential shortcomings of these otherwise excellent locomotives, namely insufficient grate area. In at least two of the adaptations, the 0-6-0 and the 4-6-0 mixed-traffic engine, the Belgians increased the grate areas from 20.6 to 27.2 sq. ft[23] in the case of the former, and from 21 to 30.6 sq. ft[23] in the case of the latter. Only the 4-4-0 grate remained unaltered at 22 sq. ft.[23] There were in all some 750 of these Belgian McIntosh engines of the three classes, all except the first five 4-4-0s being built on the Continent.[23] A side elevation of the Belgian State Railways' mixed-traffic 4-6-0, dimensionally close to the McIntosh '908' and '179' Class designs, is shown in Figure 8.

In J.F. McEwan's papers,[9] there is a reference to McIntosh having obtained a detailed drawing for a Belgian State Railways 4-4-2T locomotive, which was very similar to a McIntosh 4-4-2T proposal of 1910 (St Rollox drawing No. 15315). McIntosh had the Belgian tank locomotive construction costed by St Rollox, the intention being a comparison with the CR '439' Class standard 0-4-4T. According to McEwan,[9] any thoughts of investing in the larger locomotive were dropped since build costs were predicted at almost twice that of the '439' Class. The NBR of course invested in 4-4-2T locomotives for their suburban passenger traffic, perhaps inspired by the Belgian engines.

Additionally, when one considers that around 2,500 tons of locomotive coal was moved weekly to Perth from Ross yard, and additional amounts had to be moved to Dundee and Aberdeen, it was only natural that McIntosh turned his attention to the most cost-effective way of handling this and similar mineral traffic, intending to avoid the use of double heading. In a Sunday trial, with loaded 30 ton bogie coal wagons (total train weight around 900 tons), Stirling based 0-8-0 engine No. 602 worked from Stirling to Perth and found no difficulty in climbing Dunblane bank, demonstrating the McIntosh 0-8-0s could handle this traffic unassisted.[24] Unfortunately,

Plate 9
Built primarily to work express goods traffic, the CR '918' Class were occasionally called upon to haul heavy passenger trains. One of the less successful of McIntosh's designs, CR No. 921 is shown with a significant accumulation of ash and unburnt coal in the smokebox. No. 921 was the first of its class to be withdrawn by the LM&SR, as No. 17903, in 1929. Boilers from two member of the class were used to rebuild two '55' Class engines. *NRM/SRX86*

BELOW: **Figure 8**
Belgian State Railways 4-6-0 No. 3218. Side Elevation. The Belgians adopted the designs of McIntosh at the beginning of the 20th century, building 4-4-0, 0-6-0 and 4-6-0 classes. They increased the grate areas on the latter two types, appreciating the shortcomings of the smaller grates used in the UK. There were in all some 750 of these Belgian McIntosh engines of the three classes, all except the first five 4-4-0s being built on the Continent. The 4-6-0 type illustrated was dimensionally similar to the McIntosh '908' and '179' classes. *Author*

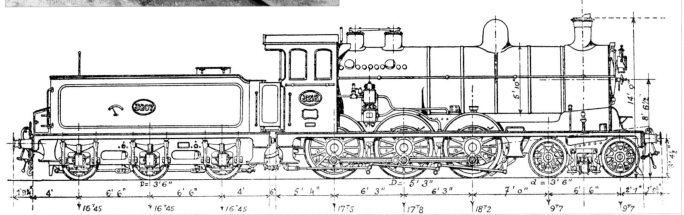

refuge loops and siding accommodation were unable to deal with the workings, hardly a matter that could be laid at McIntosh's door.

It was against this legacy of McIntosh's generally well designed express passenger 4-6-0s and 4-4-0s – where a well driven superheated 'Dunalastair IV' engine would ultimately be seen to run an LM&SR 3-cylinder compound very close on a hard and fast run – that the Caledonian Directors tasked Pickersgill to take the breed forward as traffic loads increased and more demanding timetable schedules were projected. One of the superheated '140' Class engines, No. 147, is shown in Plate 10 at Stirling in 1923, heading a southbound express working.

Surprisingly, on the introduction of superheating, a misconception arose in which boiler efficiency was seen as being determined only by the highest and lowest temperatures in the cycle. In effect, superheated steam locomotives were initially considered as working on the Carnot Cycle, in which theoretical boiler efficiency was independent of steam pressure. As a consequence, a recommendation to reduce boiler pressure when superheating locomotives was enthusiastically seized by some Locomotive Superintendents as a method of reducing boiler maintenance and the associated costs. For example, the Midland Railway reduced boiler pressure, whilst the Lancashire & Yorkshire Company maintained the saturated boiler pressure in its superheated engines.[25] This misconception was laid to rest fairly quickly by showing that boiler efficiency was more accurately described by the Rankine Cycle, where steam pressure is appropriately accounted for.

However, as noted by Professor Goss[26] and others, evaporative efficiency is but slightly affected by changes in pressure, Goss demonstrating by trials that increasing pressure from 180 to 200 psi provided only between 2 and 3 per cent reduction in steam consumption and an even lower percentage reduction in coal consumption per DBHP-Hr. More power was of course available in the locomotive having the higher working pressure.

THE EXTENDED LEGACY

One part of the McIntosh legacy is mirrored in Plate 11, which shows former CR No. 769 as LM&SR No. 14431 at Burghmuir shed, Stirling, in 1933. Entering traffic in 1898, No. 769 was superheated in January 1915 and remains attached to a bogie tender; withdrawal came in 1936 after thirty-eight years sterling service. The gentleman with the cap, sitting on the tender front plate, is Alan Dunbar.

So successful and useful to the LM&SR were these McIntosh superheated 4-4-0 locomotives that, when the original superheated boilers became worn out, some were replaced by superheated boilers of Pickersgill design. Plate 12 shows former CR No. 772 (referred to earlier for its spectacular running when substituted for a failed '903' Class engine in September 1915), as LM&SR No. 14433, again at Burghmuir shed, Stirling, in 1934. No. 14433, which entered traffic in 1898, was superheated by McIntosh in 1914 and then fitted by the LM&SR with a Pickersgill '300' Class superheated boiler in

Plate 10
A rebuilt CR '140' Class engine, No. 147 on a southbound express working at Stirling station in 1923. Built in 1905, this engine was rebuilt with a Pickersgill boiler and Robinson superheater in 1922, the original cylinders and slide valves being retained. As LM&SR No. 14356, it was destroyed by enemy action in an air raid at Greenock in 1941.
R.D. Stephen, NRM/RDS C13

1933, being withdrawn in 1937. The locomotive behind No. 14433 is non-superheated No. 14332, which also entered service in 1898, but remained a saturated locomotive, being fitted with a McIntosh '812' Class boiler in 1931. No 14332 was the penultimate survivor of the 'Dunalastair II' series, being withdrawn in 1946 after some forty-eight years in service.

Some would maintain the apogee of McIntosh's reign at St Rollox was reached with the superheating of the '49' and '903' classes and the working of the 'Corridor' expresses between Glasgow and Carlisle, when trains, at times over 400 tons (gross), were worked, with powers of 1,300 IHP being developed.[5,6,27] At times, loads of 330 tons (gross) were taken unaided over Beattock from the south by these competently handled McIntosh 4-6-0s.[28] Indeed, even prior to superheating, when tested against an L&NWR 'Experiment' Class 4-6-0, the power output of *Cardean*, recorded in the L&NWR dynamometer car, showed the superior quality of the Scottish engine. During these trials, on the ascent from Penrith to Shap Summit, the 1 in 125 climb was accomplished at a sustained 44 mph, with a drawbar pull of over 4 tons, equivalent to 1,390 DBHP,[29] though this figure has been questioned. Plate 13 shows former CR No. 903 *Cardean* as LM&SR No. 14752, standing at Stirling station No. 1 platform in 1929. Built in 1906, No. 903 was superheated in 1911 and withdrawn in 1930, the smokebox wingplates being retained to the end.

Even in British Railways' days the McIntosh superheated 'Dunalastair IV' locomotives could, in emergencies, turn in a sparkling performance. Just such an emergency occurred on the 12th December 1952,[30] when the Up 'Postal' arrived at Forfar some 7 minutes late, the working being headed by Class '5' 4-6-0 No. 45469 which, suffering from injector trouble, had to be taken off the train. A McIntosh 4-4-0, No. 54454, working an Up goods, was substituted and produced a quite stunning exhibition of high speed running, harking back to those runs of Caledonian days on the same stretch. No. 54454 left Forfar in foul weather and ran to Perth with the load of 302 tons in 32 minutes – 2 minutes inside the scheduled 34 minutes allowed for a Class '5' to cover the 32½ mile route. At an average speed greater than a-mile-a-minute, the performance was quite extraordinary for a forty-year-old engine and, recognising that Class '5s' commonly ran at speeds above 70 mph between Glamis and Stanley Junction, and regularly exceeded 80 mph at Cargill, No. 54454 must have sustained this level of working to improve on the tight schedule.

SUPPORTING STAFF

Writing just before McIntosh's retirement in 1914, C.J. Allen noted that McIntosh *'has probably done more than any other locomotive engineer living to influence the general trend of design in this country'*.[31] In paying this tribute, Allen must surely have been aware of the hugely significant influence and contributions made by Chief Draughtsman Thomas Weir and Leading Locomotive Draughtsman William H. Moodie in securing this Caledonian pre-eminent position.

Both Weir[32] and Moodie[33] had been employed as draughtsmen in the Atlas Works of Sharp, Stewart & Co. in Springburn, Glasgow, though both had quite different family backgrounds. They had been recruited[34] to the St Rollox drawing office in 1891 and 1896 respectively, Weir being appointed Chief Draughtsman in 1897.

Whilst Thomas Weir was born in Dublin in March 1860,[35] the 1881 Glasgow Springburn Census[32] records him, aged 21, as an *'Engine Fitter at Works'*; on the same return, his father is noted as *'Iron Slotter at Works'*. By 1891,[32] he was married and living in Flemington Street, Springburn, his employment being recorded as *'Engineering Draughtsman – Locomotives'*. Thereafter, in 1911[32] Weir was living with his wife and mother at Whitehill Street, Glasgow, his employment then being noted as *'Engineering Draughtsman, Railway Co'*. As will be recounted later, Weir resigned as Chief Draughtsman from the Caledonian company in 1920. He had no family and died,[32] aged 87, in July 1947 at Edinburgh, his usual residence being in Peebles.

By contrast, William Henry Moodie was born in Kilmarnock in November 1863,[32] he being the first child of parents who, by 1891,[32] lived in some style at Springhill House, Pollockshaws Road, Glasgow. The Census for that year[32] records William H. Moodie, aged 27, living there with his parents, ten siblings and two domestic servants; his occupation is given as *'Locomotive Draughtsman'*. Moodie married later in 1891, and by 1911[32] was living at Cardowan Drive, Stepps, Glasgow, with his wife and family of five plus domestic servants. Whilst Moodie's occupation at that time is recorded as *'Engine Draughtsman, Loco Dept, Railway Co'*, none of his family entered railway service. It is surmised Moodie retired, aged 65 in 1928; he died in 1942, aged 78,[32] at his house at Stepps.

Whilst it is generally accepted that McIntosh's relationship with his staff was characterised by reciprocated respectful cordiality and

Plate 11
Rebuilt 'Dunalastair II' Class engine CR No. 769, as LM&SR No. 14431 at Burghmuir shed, Stirling, in 1933. Several engines of this class were superheated and in their rebuilt form were capable of quite exceptional performance. This locomotive, superheated in 1915, was withdrawn in 1936. Alan Dunbar, a respected commentator and author on Scottish railway matters, sits on the tender front plate. *CRA440003n*

Plate 12
Former 'Dunalastair II' Class engine, CR No. 772, which was superheated in 1914, is illustrated as LM&SR No. 14433 at Burghmuir shed, Stirling, in 1934. In 1933 this engine was rebuilt using a CR '300' Class superheated boiler and withdrawn in 1937. Behind No. 14433 is un-superheated No. 14332, formerly CR No. 776, which was rebuilt with a CR '812' Class boiler in 1931 and survived until withdrawn in 1946 as the penultimate survivor of the 'Dunalastair II' Class. *CRA440006*

Plate 13
Former '903' Class locomotive, CR No. 903 *Cardean*, as LM&S No. 14752, at Platform 1, Stirling station in 1929. Built in 1906 using a 200 psi boiler, the engine was rebuilt in 1911 with a Schmidt superheater and enlarged cylinders with piston valves. On rebuilding the steam pressure was lowered to 175 psi. Mainly used on the southern main line, they gave a very good account of themselves, being capable, without banking assistance, of taking 330 ton trains over Beattock from the south. No. 14752 was withdrawn in 1930, retaining its smokebox wingplates to the end.
*J.F. McEwan,
Author's collection*

appropriate deference, it appears from notes made by J.F. McEwan[9] that there was some tension, through a clash of personalities, between the Locomotive Superintendent and R.W. Urie. Urie, seemingly a man of unusual ability, had been recruited to St Rollox as a general draughtsman by Dugald Drummond in 1885 and had advanced to Chief Draughtsman in 1890, then to Works Manager in 1895. According to McEwan,[9] McIntosh tended to operate through Peter Drummond, whom the former considered *de facto* deputy Works Manger.

When Dugald Drummond offered the post of Works Manager at Nine Elms to R.W. Urie in 1897, the latter had no hesitation in accepting the position. A question arises here; why did Drummond not offer the Nine Elms post to his younger brother Peter? The

answer, one suspects, is that the technically talented Urie was seen as having a fairly direct and forceful personality – perhaps just what Drummond needed at Nine Elms, a position reinforced by Urie's son J.C. Urie.[36] Whilst quite different in temperament to Drummond, Urie was accepted as a trusted aide, arising from a row between the two men when the latter was Chief Draughtsman at St Rollox. According to J.C. Urie,[36]

'*Drummond had an argument with my father and left the office in bad humour. My father discovered later that they had both been wrong and went to Drummond's office and told him so. Drummond growled at him and told him to get out of his office, but from that day they never had any hard words.*'

McEwan[9] records an incident of public disagreement between McIntosh and R.W. Urie, arising when the latter was Chief Draughtsman. Unbeknown to McIntosh, Urie had apparently schemed out in some fair detail a 4-6-0 proposal using outside cylinders. When this came to McIntosh's attention, he forcefully condemned it, noting that 'outside cylinders and long connecting rods were not wanted on the CR', and ordered that the drawings were to be 'buried'. Seemingly the Urie proposal would not have been as large as the '49' and '903' Classes, but when the time came to build the Oban 4-6-0s ('55' Class), the boiler used was based around the earlier rejected Urie proposal.[9]

As noted previously, whilst McIntosh schemed out several outside cylindered express passenger and goods locomotives, none were in fact built at St Rollox during his tenure, suggesting he may have had an aversion to the basic concept. This position seems to be confirmed by McIntosh's writing that whilst outside cylinders had 'apparently some decided advantages', he had concluded that the 'greatest steadiness of running' of the inside cylindered engine 'due to the closeness of the centres of the cylinders, probably balances all other defects'.[18]

Also, all McIntosh engines carried round-topped fireboxes, though a Belpaire arrangement may have been under consideration at St Rollox in 1911. A drawing,[37] showing a 5 ft diameter boiler with Belpaire firebox arrangement, carrying the 'CR Loco Dep.' logo and dated 17th June 1911, exists. Drawn by W. Hain, the drawing carries no number or title and, though a great deal of information on outer plate-work, detailing of riveted joints and firebox staying has been worked up, the inner firebox is only roughly sketched in. There is no mention of this drawing in the St Rollox drawing register.[38]

The distance between the frame plates on this Belpaire arrangement,[37] at 4 ft 8 ins, points to a rail gauge of 5 ft 3 ins or greater. Perhaps St Rollox had borrowed a Belpaire layout drawing from the North British Locomotive Co. to investigate the options for future use of this firebox arrangement.

Intriguingly, the date of June 1911 and the 5 ft diameter boiler seem significant, in that the details of boiler changes for the superheating of '49' and '903' classes were being worked out in June 1911. Indeed, Mr Hain had been working on the new boiler for No. 49, several entries in the drawing register from May and June 1911 bearing his name. These include drawing No. 15812[38] for the new firebox tubeplate, drawing No. 15819[38] for the new smokebox tubeplate and several others for superheater flues, smokebox details and so forth.

Circumstantial evidence of timing, plus the same draughtsman's involvement in the production of detailed drawings for the superheating of No. 49, suggest that, either officially or otherwise, a Belpaire arrangement may have been looked at. Whilst we know that '49' and '903' Class superheating proceeded using round-topped firebox arrangements and the Belpaire scheme was discarded, if it ever was a real option, the fact that the drawing survived points to Thomas Weir at least wishing to retain it. McIntosh's views are unknown and the enigmatic status of this drawing must remain unresolved *sine die*.

As an aside, one has to record that Mr Hain seemed to have been transferred to carriage and wagon draughting work post June 1911,[38] and thereafter to design work for coal handling plant at Grangemouth docks.[38] Mr Hain's name is absent from the St Rollox drawing register from early 1912, though strangely it reappears in the Pickersgill era,[38] post the retiral of McIntosh and Weir. Indeed, on being re-engaged, Mr Hain was responsible for some of the drawings relating to the application of Stephenson's link motion to the '956' Class.

LM&SR Postscript

Writing some years into the LM&SR regime, John Barr noted[39] that around 1910 'the situation on the Caledonian Railway was such that the passenger and freight train loads on the Main Line had exceeded the locomotive capacity' for single engine working. This, according to Barr, was 'in part due to the gradients and the matter was only saved for the time being by adopting superheating, both for new and reconstructed locomotives, and thus the building of heavier units was put off for at least a number of years'.[39]

References

1. *Forty Years of Caledonian Locomotives 1882-1922*, H.J. Campbell Cornwell (David & Charles, 1974)
2. Boiler Record Cards ex CR 294 Class, NRS, GD 480/2/1/2
3. *Modern Locomotive Practice*, C.E. Wolff (Manchester Scientific Publishing Company, 1907), pp. 69-71
4. *Scottish Locomotive History 1831-1923*, Campbell Highet (George Allen & Unwin, 1970) p. 188
5. *The Caledonian Dunalastairs*, O.S. Nock (David & Charles 1968), pp. 83ff
6. Indicator Diagrams Engine No 49, circa 1906, on 08.20 pm 'Corridor', Glasgow-Carlisle, NRS, RHP136340/38/1-7
7. C.J. Allen in *The Railway Magazine*, June 1914, pp. 484ff, noted in *The Scottish 4-6-0 Classes*, C.P. Atkins (Ian Allan, 1976), p. 68
8. *The McIntosh Locomotives of the Caledonian Railway 1895-1914*, A.B. MacLeod (Ian Allan, 1948), p. 21
9. J.F. McEwan papers, William Patrick Library, Kirkintilloch, ref. T25, etc
10. *The Use of Superheated Steam in Locomotives*, Dr W. Schmidt (1908)
11. St Rollox Drg No. 15545, dated 19th October 1910, NRS, RHP136346/41
12. Campbell Cornwell Collection of CR Locomotive Drawings, CRA6/1/3/2
13. Trials Data & Indicator Diagrams, Engine No 139, Glasgow to Perth 16th August 1910, Montague Smith Collection, GD456, NRS, RHP136436/95, etc
14. *Forty Years of Caledonian Locomotives 1882-1922*, H.J. Campbell Cornwell (David & Charles, 1974), Appendices 2 & 3
15. *The Application of Highly Superheated Steam to Locomotives* (Schmidt Superheater Co., London, 1911), p. 27
16. Irvine Kempt, ILocoE Paper No 97, Glasgow, 10th January 1921, and discussion chaired by R.H. Whitelegg of the G&SWR
17. St Rollox Drg No 13019, dated 4th April 1905, NRS, RHP 132378
18. *Cassier's Magazine*, March 1910, also noted in *The Scottish 4-6-0s at Work*, C.P. Atkins (Ian Allan, 1976), p. 40
19. St Rollox Drg No. 16284, dated 17th February 1912, NRS, RHP132338
20. St Rollox Drg No. 15701, dated 1st February 1911, NRS, RHP132389
21. St Rollox Drg No. 17168, dated 6th October 1913, NRS, RHP132404
22. St Rollox Drg No. 17336, dated 30th March 1914, NRS, RHP136343/9
23. Private Correspondence, E.S. Cox to A.G. Dunbar, 6th May 1965, NRS, GD344/6/12/5
24. *Fifty Years with Scottish Steam*, Alan G. Dunbar and I.A. Glen (Bradford Barton), p. 76
25. *A Defence of the Midland/LMS Class 4 0-6-0*, Adrian Tester, (Crimson Lake, 2011), Chapter 1, p. 4
26. *Locomotive Boilers and Engines*, Prof. L.V. Ludy (American Technical Society, 1918), Prof. Goss paper quoted p. 58-60
27. R.E. Charlewood timing of No 907, noted in *The Scottish 4-6-0 Classes*, C.P. Atkins (Ian Allan, 1976), p. 65
28. *Trains Illustrated*, October 1953, Montague Smith letter to the Editor
29. *Scottish Locomotive History 1831-1923*, Campbell Highet (George Allen & Unwin, 1970), p. 203
30. 'The Dunalastair and Superheated 4-4-0 Classes (9)', David Hamilton, in *The True Line*, No 120, April 2013, p. 30
31. 'Eight Years of British Locomotive Practice', C.J. Allen, in *The Railway Magazine*, February 1914, pp. 123ff
32. Scotland's People: Births, Deaths & Marriages Records, plus Census Returns (http://www.scotlandspeople.gov.uk/)
33. Caledonian Railway, Employees Database: CRA
34. Caledonian Railway, Staff Emoluments (1904-1920), NRS, BR/CAL/15/14
35. Ancestry: Births, Deaths & Marriage Records, England, Wales & Ireland (http://www.ancestry.co.uk/)
36. *The Drummond Brothers, A Scottish Duo*, J.E. Chacksfield (The Oakwood Press, 2005), p. 58
37. St Rollox drawing, no number, no title, Montague Smith Collection, NRS, GD456, RHP136362/1
38. St Rollox Drawing Register, NRS, BR/CAL/5/56
39. John G. Barr papers, courtesy of the Scottish Railway Preservation Society

CHAPTER 3

WILLIAM PICKERSGILL AT ST ROLLOX

Now there grew up a new king over Egypt, which knew not Joseph
Exodus Ch. 1, v. 8

FIRST LOCOMOTIVES

William Pickersgill's tenure at St Rollox from 1914 until the Caledonian company was absorbed within the LM&S grouping in 1923, together with the locomotives he designed and various developments undertaken by the St Rollox team under his leadership, have been well chronicled by a number of authors. Particularly notable are Campbell Cornwell's most informative and well researched, *Forty Years of Caledonian Locomotives 1882-1922*, and various publications by Philip Atkins, including *The Scottish 4-6-0 Classes* and *West Coast 4-6-0s at Work*. Additionally, over many years, commentators, including C.J. Allen, E.S. Cox and O.S. Nock, have provided a significant amount of data and opinion on Pickersgill's locomotives in operation, there being many comparisons with contemporary locomotives from other companies. Indeed, Pickersgill 4-4-0 and 4-6-0 designs figured in comparative LM&SR locomotive type trials south of Carlisle in 1924 and 1926, which have been well documented by O.S. Nock and others.

To place Pickersgill's work at St Rollox in context, and to offer some comparison with the McIntosh era, a brief summary of certain of the former's designs is given in the following paragraphs, together with some observations on each locomotive class. The '956' Class is not included in this summary.

It is also useful to consider Graeme Miller's views of this period on his return from service with the Royal Engineers in France (he enlisted on the 6th December 1916 and returned to Caledonian company service on 25th November 1919),[1] recognising his having worked as a pupil under McIntosh. Miller[2] was quite clear that the Pickersgill era changed many things, the new Locomotive Superintendent being very much an administrator, only visiting the shops infrequently compared to McIntosh. Additionally, Miller[2] points out that Pickersgill, by virtue of his technical education, *'could afford to be less dependent on his technical staff'* than was McIntosh, and it would have been inevitable that he might question, and perhaps even alter, the recommendations of his Chief Draughtsman and the drawing office personnel. Recognising that Thomas Weir had been, *de facto*, the senior technical authority for most of the McIntosh years, this rearrangement of ultimate technical responsibility could, if handled insensitively, have led to internal tensions in the drawing office.

Pickersgill's first design, a 4-4-0 in the McIntosh mould, but sturdier, had been authorised in October 1914, but it was May 1916 before the six locomotives, all built at St Rollox to order Y113, were ready for traffic. Plate 14 shows No 114, the second locomotive of this batch, when new at St Rollox in 1916. Comment has been made that labour shortages at St Rollox were so critical in 1915[3] that ten

Plate 14
CR No. 114, the second member of the '113' Class, is illustrated when new at St Rollox works in 1916. Whilst authorised in October 1914, wartime pressures delayed production and it was May 1916 before all six locomotives of this class, built to St Rollox order Y113, were in traffic. No. 114 was withdrawn as BR No. 54462 in 1960.

NRM/SRX239

further 4-4-0 engines of similar design were, of necessity, built by the North British Locomotive Co. at their Atlas Works, Glasgow, the tenders being built at St Rollox. It has not, however, been satisfactorily explained why St Rollox seemed so severely afflicted by labour shortages, whereas the North British Locomotive Co., in the same city, were seemingly spared such acute deprivation.

These sixteen new 4-4-0 locomotives, all of which were in service by the end of 1916, differed very little from their immediate predecessors, though Pickersgill moved away from the McIntosh superheat policy. For this new class, the double ported piston valves were increased to 9 ins diameter and a lower degree of superheat, using short return loops in place of the previous full length variety, was employed, giving an SHS of 15.0 per cent of the total evaporative surface (Tube HS plus Firebox HS).

Moreover, Pickersgill reduced the bore of superheater elements from the 1¼ ins of the McIntosh era. Details of the elements for the '113' and '72' classes are set out in St Rollox drawing No. 18560,[4] dated May 1916, in which flue diameters are reduced to 4⅝ ins I/D from the 4¾ ins of the McIntosh era. Pickersgill superheater elements were formed from 1⅜ ins O/D drawn steel, the radial section width being either No. 9 or No. 10 IWG, giving respective bores of around 1¹⁄₁₆ ins and 1⅛ ins. For elements with No. 9 IWG section and 1¹⁄₁₆ ins bore, the pressure loss in the superheater circuit would be almost 70 per cent higher than in the McIntosh arrangements, for identical steam flows and taking account of the shorter return loops in the Pickersgill schemes.

Boiler heating surface ratios were broadly similar to their McIntosh predecessors, with L/D of 92 and tubeplate free-gas area to grate area of 18.0 per cent, the latter figure suggesting a slightly larger grate area would have been of some benefit, with in-service coal consumption perhaps being higher than for the McIntosh locomotives. The free-gas area ratio between flues and total free-gas area, set at 48 per cent, points to an adequate and acceptable flue gas flow regime, likely to achieve the required superheated steam temperatures, albeit slightly lower than in the McIntosh locomotives.

Pickersgill was given authority in future Caledonian company renewals programmes[3] for the construction of an additional thirty-two broadly similar 4-4-0 locomotives, which were put into service between May 1920 and December 1922. Of this number, ten were supplied from St Rollox in 1920, ten from Armstrong, Whitworth in 1921, and the remaining twelve from the North British Locomotive Co. in 1922. These final thirty-two varied from the earlier sixteen through having slight increases to both cylinder diameter and boiler pressure.

Over the years commentators have been divided in their opinions of these Pickersgill engines when compared to the higher superheat McIntosh equivalents. The provision of larger diameter piston valves should have contributed to freer running, but contemporary commentators noted the Pickersgill engines as comparatively sluggish and not being as lively as their predecessors, part of the explanation perhaps being increased pressure loss in the superheater and a lower degree of superheat. This opinion, on comparative sluggishness, was

Plate 15
Design work on what was to be the Pickersgill '60' Class started in June 1914, based on a McIntosh 4-6-0 proposal. Construction of the first was authorised in October of that year, with authority for a further five in March 1915, though the six locomotives entered service between November 1916 and April 1917. CR No. 64, which entered traffic in March 1917, is illustrated at Perth shed in 1921. No. 64 was withdrawn as BR No. 54654 in 1952.
A.W. Croughton, CRA460213

given to the author's father by a former Stirling-based LM&SR company employee who fired and drove both types[5] – though this view was not universally held by all enginemen, but was supported by O.S. Nock.[6] Uphill work was usually acceptable, but downhill running was often uninspiring, a condition explained by some commentators as reflective of a change in the company's running policy, which, certainly in the 1914 to 1918 period, could well have been a result of wartime conditions in which passenger timetabling schedules were relaxed.

THE '60' CLASS

In reviewing the need for a larger powered passenger locomotive, Pickersgill revived the McIntosh 1911 scheme for an outside-cylindered 4-6-0, as set out in drawing No. 15701 dated the 6th February of that year. The McIntosh proposal, with 6 ft 6 ins driving wheels and 21 in. x 26 in. cylinders, had been provided with a bogie tender, the evaporative heating surface being 1,726 sq. ft and SHS 487 sq. ft. Interestingly, this 1911 proposal, with SHS set at 28 per cent of evaporative surfaces, had the same driving wheel diameter, cylinder size and SHS ratio as the G&SWR '128' Class built by the North British Locomotive Co. in the same year. There is just the possibility that McIntosh's thinking had been conditioned by the performance of these most successful G&SWR engines.

Design work on the Pickersgill version recommenced in June 1914, the general arrangement being detailed on St Rollox drawing No. 17458,[7] dated the 8th August 1914. Construction for the first of the class was sanctioned in October 1914, with authority for a further five being given in March 1915.[3] The previously selected 6 ft 6 ins driving wheel diameter was reduced to 6 ft 1 in. and, as on the 4-4-0s, a lower superheat regime was applied, with superheater elements reduced to 1¹⁄₁₆ ins bore, as detailed in drawing No. 17972. As with the 4-4-0s, 9 ins diameter double ported piston valves were used, the overall construction being heavily engineered, with 1¼ in. frame plates; a 6-wheeled tender was substituted for the original bogie variety. These new 4-6-0s, the '60' Class, all built at St Rollox, entered service between November 1916 and April 1917, there again being delays in their construction programme. Plate 15 shows No. 64 at Perth in 1921.

In boiler terms, the L/D was 105 and the tubeplate free-gas to grate area ratio 15.5 per cent, with the flue to total tubeplate free-gas area ratio being 45 per cent, the latter perhaps being marginally on the low side. The SHS was 15.4 per cent of the total evaporative heating surface. Whilst the L/D and free-gas parameters are within the range of normal practice of the day, and should have provided a free steaming boiler with adequate draughting, a marginal increase in both flue diameter and grate area would have been of benefit. Steam temperatures, measured in May 1917 trials[8] on engine No. 60 averaged 610°F, with a peak at 640°F, when working a 337 tons (gross) train from Buchanan Street to Perth.

Once again, opinion is divided on their performance compared to the McIntosh '49' and '903' classes, though it is clear that on the most prestigious workings – between Glasgow and Carlisle, and Glasgow and Aberdeen – the new '60' Class engines never equalled, far less out-performed, the achievements of the earlier McIntosh superheated 4-6-0 classes. Both O.S. Nock and E.C. Poultney[9] are recorded as making unfavourable comparisons of the '60' Class running and haulage performance compared to the McIntosh engines, the main criticism again being sluggish downhill running, perhaps because the fitting of cylinder by-pass valves allowed the regulator to be closed. The increased superheater pressure loss and lower steam temperature would not have assisted running conditions and potentially prejudiced coal consumption.

C.J. Allen[10] recorded a post-war working by No. 61 on the 3.50 pm Glasgow to Carlisle express train, which was delayed for operational reasons at Carstairs for some twenty minutes. On restart, with some

380 tons (gross) behind the tender, several minutes were recovered by Beattock Summit which, unfortunately, was *'nullified by very slow running down Beattock Bank to the extent that no time had been recovered on reaching Carlisle 20 minutes late'*. Allen noted that the loss of his connection to the south at Carlisle had possibly jaundiced his view of the working, which *'he found disappointing in the circumstances'*. Those favouring the Pickersgill engines usually point to their rugged construction and immunity from frame fractures in service, leading to lower maintenance costs, as outweighing the locomotive's sluggish response and poor downhill performance.

Interestingly, whilst there seems to be a general opinion that the '60' Class were immune from frame fractures, *The Locomotive News and Railway Notes* in 1919[11] mentions early frame fractures on the '60' Class. Perhaps owing to some transfers by the LM&SR authorities to lower speed freight traffic, '60' Class frame stressing was reduced, leading to an apparent immunity from fractures.

Coal consumption was always a concern, particularly to the LM&SR accountants. In May 1934, E.S. Cox,[12] writing to R.A. Riddles, quotes the accountants' returns for 1933 which show individual '60' Class engines having a coal usage of between 57 and 73 lbs per mile, the average being 62.4 lbs per mile. By comparison, the 'Royal Scot' Class locomotives on the Northern Division averaged 55.4 lbs per mile. From trials results, quoted in the same memo,[12] the '60' Class engines' coal consumption averaged 4.85 lbs per DBHP per hour, the equivalent figure for the Northern Division 'Royal Scot' Class engines being 3.20.

The LM&SR authorities altered the '60' Class tubeplate drawings (No. 17972 and No. 17977 in June 1931) to change the gas flow regime in favour of the flues, the original 2¹⁄₈ ins O/D tubes being reduced to 2 ins and the flues increased from 5¹⁄₈ ins to 5⁵⁄₁₆ ins O/D. These modifications would have permitted the fitting of 1¼ ins I/D superheater elements, as well as increasing the superheat temperature and hopefully improving coal consumption. Such proposed new arrangements would presumably have been introduced at boiler retubing.

The '60' Class were certainly rugged machines. Engine No. 64 (LM&SR No. 14654, subsequently BR No. 54654),[13] delivered in April 1917, cost £5,646 including tender, and accrued 1,115,364 miles prior to withdrawal in January 1952.

THE '938' CLASS

In November 1915, through a most unfortunate set of circumstances, the Caledonian company acquired six new mixed traffic 4-6-0 locomotives, bought from the Highland Railway where they had been deemed too heavy, in axle loading terms, for the latter company's permanent way. The design and working drawings for these engines had been prepared at the North British Railway Co. works at Cowlairs, under contract to the Highland Railway, William Whitelaw being on the boards of both the North British and Highland companies. The engines were built by Hawthorn, Leslie & Co. of Newcastle.

Of thoroughly modern design, with 21 in. x 28 in. outside cylinders, fed by 10 ins diameter piston valves actuated by Walschaert's valve gear, these locomotives seemed ideally suited to the Caledonian company's immediate needs. The boiler, having an L/D of 101, with free-gas to gate area ratio at 15.5 per cent, together with flue to total free-gas area ratio of 45.2 per cent, seemed well proportioned, though it would have benefited from a marginal increase in flue diameter, thus assisting the superheat.

Full return length superheater elements were initially provided, the North British Railway Co. prepared general arrangement drawing[14] titled 'Highland Railway No 1' noting 448 sq. ft of SHS, this being 28 per cent of the total evaporative surfaces. Moreover, draughting arrangements in the smokebox were rather different to Pickersgill's approach to these matters, with the '938' Class chimney

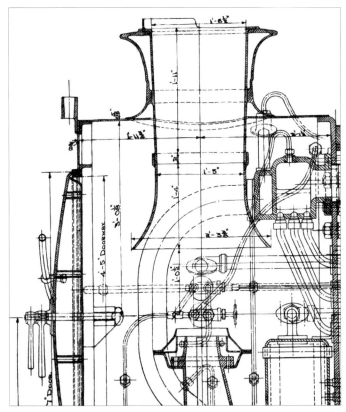

Figure 9
HR 'River' Class. Smokebox Cross Section, North British Railway Co. Cowlairs, General Arrangement, 'Highland Railway No. 1'. This GA drawing, a section of which illustrates the draughting arrangements in the 'River' Class, was prepared by the NBR under contract to the HR. These arrangements, using the smokebox layout developed by Professor Ludy at Purdue University in the USA, were somewhat different to those used by Pickersgill. Whilst other CMEs used these Purdue arrangements most successfully, the CR did not.

NRS: GD456/3

BELOW: **Plate 16**
Acquired through unfortunate circumstances from the HR in 1915, the CR '938' Class was a well-designed modern locomotive which was used initially on express passenger duties and ultimately on fast fitted freight workings. The illustration shows No. 938 passing Beattock Summit from the south with a freight working in April 1922, the engine finally being withdrawn as LM&SR No. 14756 in November 1939.

Henry L. Salmon, A.G. Ellis 16435

having an appropriately tapered liner, integrated with a fully flared and radiused bell-mouthed internal chimney structure – the detail, taken from the NBR Co. drawing,[14] being shown in Figure 9. These chimney stack arrangements mirrored the criteria set down by Professor Ludy.[15] Additionally, the '938' Class ashpan was much deeper than Caledonian contemporary standards, an area of design where St Rollox practice suggested the need for some improvement; the initially provided NBR designed rocking grate and operating mechanism was removed.

On Caledonian metals, the engines were used on fast goods traffic, Plate 16 showing No. 938 breasting Beattock Summit from the south in April 1922, although for the first year in service, two locomotives regularly worked the 10.00 am and 5.00 pm expresses to Perth from Glasgow Buchanan Street.[16] On these workings they are said to have at least equalled, and sometimes bettered, the performance of a superheated '903' Class, a position never achieved by the '60' Class.[17]

In addition to a series of changes to the '938' Class to allow conformity with the Caledonian company's loading gauge, Pickersgill changed the superheater arrangements within the class, by substituting short return loop elements in place of the original full length ones. This reduced the SHS to 350 sq. ft, or 21.9 per cent of the total evaporative surface, the details being given on St Rollox drawing No's 18960 and 18961, dated February 1917. By this change, Pickersgill brought the SHS arrangements on the '938' Class into broad conformity with his ostensible requirement for a lower superheat regime throughout the Caledonian company, a policy which seemed to be retrograde for a variety of reasons. The internal diameter of the superheater elements on the '938' Class locomotives was, however, retained at 1¼ ins, as shown on drawing No. 19493[18] for class N79 boilers in the LM&S boiler book.

Few commentators have anything but the best to say of the '938' Class, the question in many minds being why the class was not significantly expanded in numbers, since they were superior, both for express goods plus passenger workings, to anything the Caledonian company then owned, and indeed were to own – O.S. Nock noting the '938' Class as being *'the best 4-6-0s the CR ever had'*.[19] Suggestions of a *'not invented here'* attitude at St Rollox, tinged with *'professional jealously'* have been made,[20] though the Caledonian company's footplate staff were very appreciative of these new and powerful locomotives. Seen by the LM&SR authorities as a non-standard class, though provided with replacement fireboxes in the 1928 to 1933 period, the largest recorded mileage accrued by a '938' Class engine was 737,826, for No. 14760, which was withdrawn in December 1946.[21]

Plate 17
The CR '944' Class 4-6-2 tank locomotives were used initially on Glasgow to Edinburgh express passenger workings, though are usually associated with the Wemyss Bay route and banking at Beattock. Of handsome design, No. 953 awaits duty at Beattock shed in 1919 and would be the last survivor of the class, being withdrawn as BR No. 55359 in 1953.
H. Gordon Tidey, NRM/LPC43956

THE '944' CLASS

For the remainder of the Caledonian company's existence, only one new class of tank locomotive was built, this being a tank engine version of an earlier McIntosh 4-6-0 proposal, set out in St Rollox drawing No. 16505 of the 15th August 1912. Cylinder diameter was set at 19½ ins and a trailing radial truck added to give a 4-6-2T arrangement. Valve arrangements again used the Schmidt single broad ring fit with Trick ports, detailed design work on the main frames starting in December 1914. The engines were authorised in November 1915, a contract being placed with the North British Locomotive Co. in December 1915 for twelve locomotives to be delivered by October 1916. The actual deliveries of the '944' Class were made in the March to May 1917 period, some six months late. Plate 17 shows No. 953 at Beattock circa 1920.

The class initially worked on Glasgow to Edinburgh passenger traffic, some members being allocated to Beattock for banking duties, whilst others were used on the Gourock and Wemyss Bay services. Strangely, the coal carrying capacity of the class seemed artificially restricted for no good reason, the bunker holding only 3 tons, whereas the McIntosh '439' Class 0-4-4T carried 2½ tons. Recognising the 1910 McIntosh 4-4-2 tank engine proposal – outlined in St Rollox drawing No. 15315,[22] dated the 10th March 1910 – also had a 3 tons coal capacity, Pickersgill seems to have perpetuated this capacity, yet the 4-6-2 tank locomotive was a much more powerful proposition. By extending the bunker laterally to the same width as the side tanks, around a further one ton of coal could have been accommodated, giving an axle weight profile still within the company's axle loading limit, plus providing increased locomotive availability.

Interestingly, the NBR 4-4-2 tank locomotives, supplied by the Yorkshire Engine Co. from 1911 to 1913 (L&NER 'C15' Class), had a 4 tons coal capacity,[23] and the superheated 'C16' Class, built by the North British Locomotive Co. had 4½ tons capacity,[24] suggesting again that the '944' Class was under-provisioned in that regard.

The '944' Class boiler had an L/D of 116, which is perhaps a little too high, the tubeplate free-gas to grate area ratio being 15.3 per cent. The ratio of flue free-gas area to total free-gas area at 40.5 per cent was on the low side, inhibiting superheat temperature achievement. The boiler would have benefitted from an increase to 5¼ ins in the flue diameter, raising the flue gas flow, accompanied by an increase in grate area. Compared to the '60' Class boiler, the '944' Class boiler had 91 per cent of the former's THS, yet only 84 per cent of the grate area and 83 per cent of the FHS, again pointing to both the grate

and FHS being on the small side. A grate area increase to 24 sq. ft, with a corresponding FHS of 135 sq. ft, would have produced a more balanced boiler design, with the potential for improvement in coal consumption. It is felt these changes, which would have resulted in a flue to total free-gas area ratio of 48 per cent, could have been implemented without exceeding the company's axle loading limits, the recorded adhesive weight for the class, in working order, being 55 tons.

For the '944' Class superheater elements, Pickersgill provided only 77.5 per cent of the '60' Class SHS, against 91 per cent of THS capacity, which, with the provision of only eighteen flues, suggests that a further conscious reduction in superheat temperature was being designed into the class, compared to the McIntosh era. Moreover, '944' Class SHS was reduced to 13.2 per cent of the total evaporative heating surfaces. Superheater elements used 1⅜ ins O/D tubes with No. 9 IWG section, giving a 1¹⁄₁₆ ins bore; a 1¼ ins bore would have been more satisfactory, providing reduced superheater pressure loss.

In summary, the '944' Class was marginally under-boilered, though, to fit a larger, more appropriately proportioned boiler, the weight balance in the design would have needed alteration, if axle loading limits were not to be exceeded. The cost per locomotive was £5,693, one of the longest survivors being ex CR No. 954 (BR No. 55360), which had run 960,022 miles[25] when withdrawn in February 1952.

THE '191' CLASS

In 1919, Pickersgill considered the need for more powerful locomotives on the Callander & Oban (C&O) section, proposing a 4-6-0 locomotive, without superheater and using slide valves, the outline of which was shown on drawing No. 19873,[26] dated the 18th March 1919. This proposal, using 20½ in. x 26 in. cylinders, 5 ft 6 ins diameter driving wheels and a 5 ft diameter boiler, proved too heavy for the Oban line, where a particularly severe weight restriction of just over 15 tons per axle was applied, the main constraints being two wrought iron, bow-string girder bridges in the Pass of Leny.[27] The adhesion weight for this initial proposal was approximately 50 tons, or just under 17 tons per axle.

A modified version of the initial 4-6-0 proposal, with reduced weight, was schemed out, being shown on drawing No. 20488,[28] dated the 5th March 1920, which met the Civil Engineer's axle loading limits. Cylinder diameter was reduced to 19½ ins and the boiler barrel to 4 ft 9 ins, giving an adhesion weight of 45¼ tons, or just over 15 tons per axle. A non-superheated boiler using slide valves was retained. Initially it had been intended to build these engines at St Rollox under orders Y128 and Y129, but in the event what became the '191' Class were built by the North British Locomotive Co., eight being delivered in December 1922. The builder's '191' Class general arrangement drawing, No. G27219,[29] gives the maximum axle load, with the locomotive empty, as 14 tons 16 cwt, and in working order as 15 tons 14 cwt, figures which were acceptable to the Chief Engineer. Plate 18 shows No. 197 at Balornock in 1923.

The '191' Class boiler, which was considered by most commentators and drivers to be of insufficient capacity for the intended duty, had an L/D of 108 and a free-gas to grate area ratio of 15.4 per cent, and should have steamed reasonably well with adequate draughting. Most commentators judge the performance of the '191' Class to have been no better and sometimes inferior to that of the McIntosh '55' Class, which was designed in 1902 and was capable of smart running at speeds in excess of 60 mph between Dunblane and Glasgow.[30] A Stirling driver,[31] who fired and drove both classes, claimed the '191' Class could become 'winded' very quickly on the C&O severe gradients, particularly climbing Glen Ogle and Glen Cruitten, and also had difficulty keeping time between Dunblane and Buchanan Street.

Recognising that the Highland Railway Co. had acquired a class of eight 4-6-0 superheated locomotives with 5 ft 3 ins diameter wheels in 1916 from Hawthorn, Leslie & Co., within a maximum adhesion weight of 14 tons per axle,[32] makes the Pickersgill '191' Class seem a feeble effort. Indeed, these most successful Highland company superheated goods locomotives were followed in 1919 with the delivery, again from Hawthorn, Leslie, of further 4-6-0 superheated locomotives with 6 ft driving wheels, this time within a maximum axle loading of 15 tons 3 cwt.[33]

The real problem with the '191' Class, if one excludes the indifferent steaming, was the weight balance in the design. The structure and engine should have been lightened and sufficient weight saved to cover the fitting of a superheater in a slightly enlarged boiler, plus the use of piston valves. If Hawthorn, Leslie could meet these objectives twice for the Highland company, and within the C&O stringent axle loading limit, it would seem reasonable to suggest St Rollox should have been able to follow suit three years later.

Moreover, the '191' Class suffered mechanically from recurring failure of the valve rods,[34] in much the same way as the '956' Class. These valve rods, detailed on St Rollox drawing No. 21006,[35] had under-cuts at the section between the combination lever input and the rear circular section sliding in the support bearing. These under-cuts removed 25 per cent of the cross section of the rod at a point where bending stresses were likely to be maximised. Repeated stressing in the 8Hz bandwidth may have led to fatigue failures at the under-cut section.

In 1933, the LM&S authorities trialed both the ex HR 'Superheated Goods' and 'Clan' Class locomotives on the C&O line, the engines involved being respectively No. 17957 and No. 14768 *Clan MacKenzie*, which were transferred to Burghmuir shed, Stirling, for some weeks in July and August of that year – both locomotives being recorded at Burghmuir shed on the 4th August by Dr J.T. Rutherford.[36] No. 17957 returned north to Perth on the 4th August, acting as banking engine from Stirling on a passenger working to Inverness, the train engine being McIntosh 4-4-0 No. 14447.[36] The result of these trials was the transfer of the eight members of the ex HR 'Clan' Class to the C&O section in 1934/35 to take over the principal passenger workings, since the '191' Class engines were not then capable of handling normal loads without piloting. The ex HR 'Clan' Class axle loadings were within the C&O line restrictive limits.

Withdrawals of the '191' Class commenced in 1939 and, but for the 1939-45 war, all would probably have been withdrawn within a further two years. By comparison, the last of the ex HR 'Clan' Class engines, No. 54767 *Clan Mackinnon*,[37] which with its tender had

cost £8,882 in 1921, accrued 804,134 miles prior to withdrawal in February 1950. The ex HR 'Superheated Goods' Class faired even better, with engine No. 57951[38] – which, in 1918, with its tender had cost £5,215 – accruing 858,990 miles prior to withdrawal in May 1951.

SOME PICKERSGILL LOCOMOTIVE BOILER RATIOS

The table below gives various boiler ratios for Pickersgill superheated locomotives,[39] the GNR 'K3' Class[40] being noted for comparison.

BOILER RATIOS – PICKERSGILL LOCOMOTIVES					
CLASS	WHEEL ARR.	SHS/EVAP*	L/D	FREE-GAS/ GRATE*	FLUES/ FREE-GAS*
113	4-4-0	15.0	92	18.0	48.0
60	4-6-0	15.4	105	15.5	45.0
944	4-6-2T	13.2	116	15.3	40.5
956	4-6-0	11.4	110	18.6	34.8
938	4-6-0	28.0 (21.9)**	101	15.5	45.2
K3 (GNR)	2-6-0	21.4	96	19.3	49.0

NOTES:
* Figures are given as per cent.
** Reduction in superheat by Pickersgill.

DIFFERENCES BETWEEN PICKERSGILL AND McINTOSH DESIGNS

The overall designs of Pickersgill and McIntosh locomotives had many factors in common, including the Trick ported piston valves and the use of broadly similar boiler heat transfer proportions. Moreover, for the 4-4-0 locomotives, the valve settings were initially to all intents similar, the Pickersgill engines being provided with larger diameter piston valves and being a little more rugged in construction than their McIntosh predecessors. In several areas the machinery was made heavier and more robust, the frames being made from 1¼ ins plate,[41] as compared with the McIntosh engines at 1 1/16 ins. Additionally, by moving the cylinder centres 3 ins closer,[41] a substantial increase in coupled axle bearing journals in the Pickersgill 4-4-0s was facilitated.

The degree of superheat designed into the Pickersgill classes and the bore of superheater elements was, however, different from the McIntosh era. Additionally, the fitting of by-pass valves below the cylinders on the Pickersgill engines, to facilitating cylinder end-to-end connection when coasting with the regulator shut, was a change. These by-pass valves were closed by steam pressure when the regulator was opened, though if the valves did not seat properly, power would be lost through direct escape of live steam to the exhaust for some part of the cycle. The LM&SR removed the by-pass valves from all classes of Pickersgill engines on the basis that a by-pass valve failure resulted in a direct and total locomotive failure.

As previously noted, McIntosh consistently used a higher degree of superheat than Pickersgill. There seems to be an enigma here, in that, as far as is recorded, there are no suggestions of McIntosh having any technical concerns, reservations, problems, or reflections on the use of the higher superheat levels. However, in the Pickersgill regime, there is the guarded suggestion of lubrication difficulties,[42] perhaps partially self-inflicted. As a consequence, Pickersgill, concerned at the reduced availability of skilled labour in wartime conditions, may have selected the lower superheat option in an attempt to remove potential lubrication problems, an approach quite different to the stance of other CMEs, including Gresley.

Whilst there is no direct evidence that he did so, Pickersgill may well have instructed Thomas Weir to implement a reduced superheat policy. Left to his own devices, Weir would, in all probability, have

Plate 18
Built to operate on the Callander & Oban section, the '191' Class 4-6-0 locomotives were one of the least successful Pickersgill designs. CR No. 197, only a few months old, is illustrated at Balornock shed in 1923. After a short working life of only seventeen years, No. 197 was withdrawn as LM&SR No. 14625 in 1939.
Blencowe WD1196

remained with the McIntosh higher superheat regime as advocated by Dr Schmidt, which had served the company very well. The influence of John Barr in such matters is unknown, though O.S. Nock[43] records he was one of the strongest *'powers behind the throne'* in the Pickersgill era.

Whether this lower SHS approach, which resulted in around 100°F reduction in steam temperatures (from averages of around 650°F in the McIntosh era to approximately 550°F in the '956' Class trials) made any significant difference to valve wear is now difficult to determine and must remain a matter of conjecture. However, the reduction of only 100°F in average superheat temperature is unlikely to have greatly diminished any oil carbonisation in valve and steam passages *per se*, since the 550°F average temperature recorded on No. 956 trials[44] actually maximised on one occasion at 590°F.

In his textbook, *Steam Power*,[45] Professor Dalby drew attention to steam leakage phenomena across engine valves and pistons, noting that whilst rings appeared steam tight when stationary, they were often subject to leakage whilst in operation, there being a direct passage of steam from steam chest to exhaust without entering the cylinder, or leakage across piston rings. The phenomenon was explained in terms of a water film formed by condensation of steam on surfaces which previously had been in contact with exhaust steam, the water film being forced through the sealing arrangements.

This leakage is very much conditioned by steam chest pressure (which determines the saturation temperature) and the temperature of surrounding components, plus superheat conditions. If component parts of the system are near or below the saturation temperature, the effect seems to increase markedly, though the effect will be reduced as the degree of superheat is increased. Moreover, such potential leakage conditions are likely to be experienced in the locomotive warming-up period of around 20 minutes at full power, or when the locomotive is operating only intermittently at higher power, or where the steam chest pressure is artificially lowered due to poor steaming or other effects. At a boiler pressure of 200 psi, to eliminate initial cylinder condensation at 10 per cent cut-off requires 250°F of superheat, the corresponding figures at 20 per cent cut-off being 190°F of superheat and at 30 per cent cut-off being 150°F, these figures[46] demonstrating the necessity for a high degree of superheat with locomotives intended to run at early cut-offs.

However, if the degree of superheat was deliberately depressed by design, a position may well have been inadvertently set up whereby what previously had been beyond the cusp of unacceptability, in condensation terms, could now have been moved to the wrong side of the critical cusp point. Pickersgill, by using smaller bore superheater elements, with resultant higher pressure loss and subsequent reduction in steam chest pressure, would not have assisted any condensation problems. Lower superheat conditions would have exacerbated the position and not have assisted coal consumption figures.

Examination of various St Rollox drawings, such as No. 18560,[4] indicates Pickersgill had introduced lower superheat conditions and reduced element bores in the McIntosh '30' and '34' classes. Similarly, for the '179' Class the same reduced conditions were applied as noted on drawing No. 18548.[4] No reason for these changes has emerged, though it seems the '139' Class was not affected. Interestingly, the extraordinary performance[47] in 1952 of McIntosh 4-4-0, No. 54454, referred to earlier, when the forty-year-old locomotive sustained a period of high speed running on being substituted for a failed Class '5' on the Up 'Postal' at Forfar, attests to the superiority of the McIntosh engines over the Pickersgill type and may be a direct function of superheat provision and element design.

In similar fashion, the performance of the G&SWR high superheat '128' Class 4-6-0s could be exceptional, No. 128 having been timed in ordinary passenger train service at 85 mph between Stewarton and Kilmarnock.[48] The key to successful running again seemed directly related to superheat conditions with a free-steaming boiler. C.J. Allen recorded the running of G&SWR No. 129 on a St Enoch to Carlisle working with a 220 tons (gross) train.[49] Allen noted that *'on the descent to Kilmarnock 83.3 mph was touched - - - had not the brakes been applied, 85 mph would have probably been recorded'*; he also noted *'a maximum speed of 75 mph between Sanquhar and Carron Bridge'*. These G&SWR '128' Class engines[50] were provided with an SHS of 28 per cent of the boiler evaporative surface and a superheater circuit with 4⅞ ins I/D flues. These could accommodate 1¼ ins bore elements, thus minimising the related pressure loss. Plate 19 shows No. 129, renumbered No. 513 in 1919, on an express passenger working at St Enoch station circa 1920.

As regards smokebox and draughting layout, there were subtle differences between McIntosh and Pickersgill designs. For his initial non-superheated locomotives, McIntosh favoured a tapered chimney liner integrated with a well-radiused bell-mouth internal chimney structure, used at times in conjunction with a truncated cone shield plate, known as a 'hood'. The 'Dunalastair I', 'Dunalastair II' and '812' classes had the radiused bell-mouth only, without the cone, whilst the non-superheated '900', '49', '903', '908', '492' and '140' classes initially had a well-radiused bell-mouth plus cone combined with tapered chimney liner. These chimney arrangements accorded broadly with the results of Professor Ludy's work,[15] though the influence of the 'hood' used by the Caledonian company was difficult to appreciate.

In 1908 McIntosh introduced a spark-arrester and a redraughting of the company's locomotives was put in hand, this being undertaken in parallel with the introduction of superheating to some classes. As a result of the redraughting exercise – which, according to Alan Dunbar,[51] had an adverse effect on locomotive steaming – McIntosh removed the cones and introduced an almost parallel chimney liner. The pronounced bell-mouth entry petticoat was replaced by a truncated conic section. Further modifications were needed, again according to Dunbar,[51] to regain acceptable steaming.

As part of these attempts to improve steaming, McIntosh conducted smokebox vacuum and blast viewing trials on the then-saturated 4-4-0 No. 147, Plate 20 showing the locomotive fitted with an indicator shelter: the well-radiused bell-mouth is apparent, the cone having been removed. The manometers used to measure vacuum conditions are shown in Plate 21, as is the glass viewing window in the smokebox waist used to monitor the blast, the observer's position being particularly cramped. Whilst no smokebox vacuum data has come to hand for these trials, any resultant reduction in steaming capacity on the McIntosh '139' Class was probably masked by the higher level of superheat used.

Some results of the blast evaluation trials were published in an Institution of Engineers & Shipbuilders in Scotland, Student Section, paper of March 1910,[52] the paper being read by a Mr Thomas Thompson who was employed in the St Rollox drawing office at that time. Whilst not being involved in the actual trials work, Mr Thompson was provided with much data by McIntosh, one conclusion in the paper being the 'complicated double cone casting below the chimney was abolished as unnecessary', and the almost parallel chimney liner with a truncated cone at its lower end adopted as being satisfactory. Whilst this form of chimney liner was used in the '139' and subsequent classes, the paper makes no mention of the smokebox vacuum achieved under these apparently 'satisfactory' spark suppression conditions.

In the discussion on a 1917 ILocoE paper entitled 'Locomotive Blast Pipes and Chimneys',[53] the taper for the chimney liner, as advocated by Professor Ludy,[15] was endorsed, it being suggested the blast, with an 8 degree enclosed taper, should impinge on the liner near the top to obtain maximum exhaust gas entrainment. In further discussion, the SE&CR company representative noted Ashford's significant doubts on the effectiveness of the parallel liner and associated truncated cone, Ashford having demonstrated by trials that removal of the cone seemed to significantly improve steaming, so long as the radiused bell-mouth petticoat was substituted with the appropriately tapered chimney liner. This latter point, of course, again accorded with Professor Ludy's views.[15]

Pickersgill, however, on all of his locomotives, including the '956' Class, used a shortened form of the almost parallel chimney liner coupled with what appears to be a more finely tapered cone, which suggests a move marginally further away than McIntosh from the geometry advocated by Professor Ludy. So, on the '113', '60', '944', '956' and '191' classes, Pickersgill broadly followed a smokebox layout which seemed not to accord with acknowledged best practice of the time, though which mirrored that used on the '139' Class.

Plate 19
G&SWR '128' Class engine No. 129, renumbered No. 513 in 1919, waits to leave St Enoch station on an express working in 1921. Whilst technically a most successful design, this 4-6-0 class, having only two engines, could not survive in the LM&SR standardisation era and was withdrawn as LM&SR No. 14674 in 1934. Both engines of the class were timed at speeds in excess of 80 mph, a maximum of 85 mph being recorded on one occasion. *Author*

Among CMEs, he was not alone in this approach. It may be that the shortening the '956' Class exhaust stack height to accommodate loading gauge imperatives, which itself might have prejudiced complete exhaust gas entrainment, may have significantly interfered with the steaming.

A somewhat similar position on the GWR is recalled by L.A. Summers.[54] When Churchward acquired the first of the De Glehn compounds, the engine was one of a type supplied to the Nord Railway and was followed by two more, derived from the 'PO 3001' Class, which were slightly larger. However, according to Churchward's report on the comparative running, the latter two *'were disappointing in not giving greater hauling power'*.[54] Various explanations were advanced for this disappointing performance, one opinion being that the shorter chimney stack ordered by Swindon to suit the GWR loading gauge may have interfered with the steaming. It needs, as S.O. Ell was later to show, only the most trivial of alterations to chimney sizing to make a substantial change in boiler performance.

Unfortunately, little definitive data has survived with respect to any smokebox vacuum trials which might have been undertaken on the various Caledonian company locomotive classes, and which could throw some light on the indifferent steaming referred to by Alan Dunbar. A St Rollox drawing, No. 21746[55] of March 1922, showing manometers connected to smokebox tapping points does exist, this allowing measurement of smokebox vacuum for various conditions including blower use, but no data on the locomotive class application is given. Recognising the date of this drawing, it is very likely a '956' Class engine could have been the potential recipient.

Interestingly, in reducing the SHS on the '938' Class locomotives, the well-radiused bell-mouth petticoat plus tapered chimney liner shown on the general arrangement,[14] as illustrated in Figure 9 and conforming to Professor Ludy's criteria,[15] was retained. This may unintentionally have ensured little difference to the '938' Class

overall steaming performance with reduced superheat, since the basic draughting geometry conformed to established best practical criteria. Moreover, even after the reduction in SHS, the '938' Class still retained an SHS of 21.9 per cent of total evaporative heating surface and of course used the larger 1¼ ins bore for superheater elements.

As regards potential leaks between live steam and exhaust sides in the cylinder via the by-pass valves, plus any difficulties with piston valve sealing, these could only have been investigated by taking indicator diagrams and making comparisons on locomotive performance with and without the valves fitted. No evidence has been discovered pointing to any trials in this regard, though, as the by-pass valve seats themselves might be assumed to wear at the same rate and manner as a snifting valve, by-pass valve leakage can probably be discounted.

E.S. Cox,[56] who was no fan of by-pass valves, wrote that:

'another way to reduce the vacuum was to connect the two sides of the piston while coasting ... on which however, the connecting passage was too small to be of the slightest use, except at very low speeds.'

As one might imagine, not everyone agreed with Cox,[57] it being argued that the MR Fowler-Anderson by-pass valves, when properly maintained, benefitted engine performance and reduced piston valve carbonisation.

Due to wartime coal supplies not being up to the quality normally purchased by the CR, J.F. McEwan[58] noted that *'Pickersgill and Moodie altered the valve gear from the position set in the days of McIntosh'*, with the intention of reducing the blast and to stop the throwing of semi-burned coal from the chimney. Also, McEwan[58] points out that the St Rollox-built engines had their valve settings changed prior to entering service, whilst those built by contractors

Plate 20
CR '140' Class engine No. 147 is illustrated fitted with an indicator shelter at St Rollox works circa 1909. Blast monitoring and smokebox vacuum trials were conducted on this engine in an attempt to improve steaming after the fitting of McIntosh's spark arrestor. No. 147 was rebuilt with a Pickersgill boiler and Schmidt superheater in 1922, retaining its original slide valves and cylinders.   *NRM/SRX165*

Plate 21
The indicator shelter with smokebox manometers and blast viewing aperture in the smokebox waist of CR No. 147 is illustrated at St Rollox works circa 1909. The space available to the observer is particularly cramped.

NRM/SRX174

to the McIntosh era criteria seemed free of steaming problems until shopping at St Rollox, when valve gear modifications were made. It is not clear if McIntosh era builds were altered, but '60' Class and all the Pickersgill 4-4-0 classes seemingly were so treated, which again might have contributed to their comparative lack-lustre performance.

At this time there also seemed to be a difference of opinion at St Rollox as to valve setting principles,[58] with instructions from the drawing office apparently being disregarded by the valve setter, who used his own ideas as to how the task should be carried out. Apparently the problem of poorly set valves was only noticed by officials around 1924 when questions were asked as to why coal consumption of repaired engines had not improved after shopping.

LM&SR Changes to Tubeplates and Superheater Elements

It would seem that the LM&SR authorities, recognising some shortfalls in the Pickersgill superheat regime, and perhaps concerned with coal consumption figures, changed the tubeplate drawings on all the Pickersgill passenger engines, this work being carried out between 1928 and 1931. The flues on the '113' and '72' classes (drawing No. 17742,[4] originally dated December 1914) were increased from 5⅛ ins O/D to 5⁵⁄₁₆ ins, as were those on the '60' Class (drawing No. 17977,[4] originally dated May 1915) and those on the '944' Class (LM&SR drawing No. 24919,[4] of October 1929). Additionally, the tubes on each class were reduced from 2¹⁄₁₆ ins O/D to 1⅞ ins. As boilers were retubed the revised arrangements presumably would be installed.

By these modifications, the LM&SR authorities seemingly planned the restoration the McIntosh superheat regime, which, with the fitting of the larger 1¼ ins bore and full length superheater elements, would have raised steam temperatures to around 650-675°F and reduced superheater pressure losses. By adopting this change, the LM&SR mirrored broadly the superheater fit in the G&SWR '128' and CR '139' classes.

LM&SR Tests on Scottish Coal Calorific Values

In the same time frame as these changes to former Caledonian company engine superheater arrangements, in 1929 the LM&SR authorities commenced a series of tests to establish the calorific value of locomotive coal supplied by various collieries in the Scottish central belt.[59] Some fifty-nine collieries were initially examined, three tests being run for each colliery, the results being graded as 1, 2 or 3, depending on the calorific values established. Results for fifty-

four collieries were documented,[59] giving the following data, though it is unclear if composite amalgams were tested, or whether the better coal from each colliery was put forward for analysis.

Grade 1: Calorific Value Range 13,450-12,900 BTU/lb
Grade 2: Calorific Value Range 12,700-11,500 BTU/lb
Grade 3: Calorific Value Range 11,500-10,250 BTU/lb

Noticeably, the collieries providing the highest value energy levels[59] (all Grade 1) were Cardowan, Kingshill, Polkemmet and Climpy, all being connected to the former CR rail network, and presumably being used by the CR and the succeeding LM&SR. The South Lanarkshire area collieries tended to produce outputs in the range 12,300 to 12,700 BTU/lb, whilst the Ayrshire basin values were lower, being 11,700 to 12,200 BTU/lb. To get consistent results for specific areas seems to have been difficult, the seams varying in quality from area to area and colliery to colliery.

In comparing the coal consumption of LM&SR Northern Division locomotives in this publication, the author has used engine performance data derived from the LM&SR Scottish area accountants' returns, which has been analysed by a number of commentators. This data, when used, is specifically referenced, much of the day-to-day data being held at the NRM.

Writing just after his retirement in 1939, John Barr referred to LM&SR experience gained from experimental runs from London to Crewe, Crewe to Carlisle and Carlisle to Glasgow, on actual passenger trains operating under comparable conditions of locomotives, loads and coal calorific values.[60] According to Barr, it was found that a *'higher coal consumption, at times upwards of 4 lbs per mile, was required on the Northern Division comparable duties, as opposed to the two sections of the line in England'.* He noted the increased Northern Division figures were attributable to general working conditions and lower ambient temperatures, *'but more particularly to the gradients and even more so to the many curves or absence of long straight sections, on which easy running can be made'.*

Proposed Eight-Coupled Engine

Seemingly, Pickersgill[61] was asked by his Board about providing an 8-coupled engine for Caledonian mineral traffic and replied that, until the Civil Engineer (Paterson) could lengthen the refuges and sidings, there was no work for an engine of this type on the main lines. No doubt Pickersgill would have been aware of the '600' Class having already demonstrated this point. Whilst the Civil Engineer reported that he could lengthen the tracks appropriately,

Plate 22
GCR 'MM' Class 2-8-0 No. 2077 at Balornock shed in 1920. Fifty ex-ROD 2-8-0 locomotives were hired by the CR from August 1919 until 15th August 1921, when government control of the railways ceased. Engine No. 2077, which was built by the NB Locomotive Co. in August 1919, arrived on CR metals in the following month. Returned to the government in August 1921, No. 2077 was one of five of this type sold to the Peking-Mukden Railway in October 1926.
G.P. Keen, courtesy Jim MacIntosh

he also noted that ground would need to be acquired to enable the lengthening to proceed and gave an estimate of related costs, which shook the Board. So the matter was dropped.

If serious consideration was being given to the acquisition of 8-coupled goods engines, one might have anticipated comparative trials of competing types, and trials did in fact take place, in November 1919 and January 1920.[62] The engines involved in this trial were GCR 'MM' Class 2-8-0 No. 2078 and L&NWR 'G1' Class 0-8-0 No. 2421, the workings being from Glasgow (Mossend) to Carlisle (Kingmoor).

The trials were conducted on Sundays, when anticipated main line traffic would be relatively light, the L&NWR dynamometer car being attached for both workings. The intention in the trials was to establish respective locomotive performance when working mixed goods trains between Mossend and Kingmoor. Additionally, a number of train restarting trials were conducted on the 1 in 143 and 1 in 116 up gradients at Motherwell,[62] which may well have been related to the working of heavy coal trains. Details of the events on the 9th November 1919 with the GCR 2-8-0, and on 18th January 1920 with the L&NWR 0-8-0 were written up by St Rollox,[62] with conclusions.

The Caledonian representatives[63] attending the trials included W.H. Moodie from the drawing office, William Drummond, Chief Locomotive Inspector, and John Menzies, Chief Mechanical Inspector. Menzies[64] would travel on engine No. 956 on its first day in steam on 21st July 1921, when the brand new 4-6-0 made a return trip from St Rollox to Glenboig. Crewing for the GCR 2-8-0 was provided by driver William Smith and fireman Alexander McGregor from Motherwell,[62] the L&NWR locomotive being crewed by driver J. McCall and fireman W. Bell from Upperby,[62] a Caledonian footplate conductor being provided on the L&NWR engine. The weather was similar for both trips, being noted as 'bad rail and little wind'. Stops were made at various points to photograph the trials, but unfortunately these have not, to date, been located. Plate 22 shows GCR 'MM' Class 2-8-0 No. 2077 at Balornock, whilst on loan from government to the CR for wartime traffic. Extracts from the trial records[62] give the comparative data shown in the table below.

The results suggest that the L&NWR engine put up a better all-round performance in terms of running traction power, drawbar pull on starting and overall train working times, though coal consumption figures were not recorded. It should also be noted the L&NWR 'G1' Class had an adhesion weight of 60 tons, compared to 67 tons for the

GCR engine, the L&NWR engine boiler pressure being 160 psi as opposed to 180 psi for the 2-8-0. Additionally, the L&NWR engine, whilst having a lower starting tractive effort, had 17 per cent greater boiler heating surface and a larger superheater, again ostensibly demonstrating the advantage of higher superheat conditions. A further trial on Sunday the 25th January 1920 was undertaken,[63] using an unknown GCR 2-8-0, but results from this trial have not been located.

The St Rollox drawing register[65] indicates that drawings No. 20533 and No. 20532 (both dated the 26th March 1920) were prepared for 'MM' Class No. 2078 and 'G1' Class No. 2421 respectively, and are most likely to have been related to the presentation of trials results; unfortunately, the drawings have not been located.

J.F. McEwan[58] mentions a further series of trials involving 'MM' Class No. 2125 and 'G1' Class No. 2430 in the summer of 1920 – the trials, over three successive Sundays, being run on the 12½ mile gradient from Motherwell to Graigenhill Summit. McEwan notes he had examined the related inspectors' reports from which it seems that the 'G1' Class was prone to slipping badly, perhaps due to its lower adhesion, and was worked at 50 per cent cut-off during the whole of the 12½ mile climb to Graigenhill. On the other hand, the 2-8-0 'MM' Class was more sure-footed, was worked at 35 per cent cut-off throughout and averaged 36 minutes for three successive trips, against 39 minutes for the 'G1' Class. The 0-8-0 was heavier in water consumption, though coal usage was broadly similar. No corroborating evidence for these latter trials has yet been located.

Nothing seems to have come of these various trials, possibly because the Caledonian company could handle[58] the traffic with their standard '812' Class locomotives, double headed if needed. Also, whilst the company was operating a number of GCR 2-8-0s, hired from government, a financial case for their purchase would have been difficult to sustain at the government's inflated asking price and taking account of post-war reduced traffic conditions.

Early LM&SR Experience

In his 1946 ILocoE paper,[66] E.S. Cox drew attention to LM&SR locomotive developments in the 1923 to 1932 period and contrasted the designs and associated performance of the stock inherited from the constituent companies. Cox[66] singled out John Barr for special mention, along with Hughes, Fowler, Anderson and Beames, noting

Eight-Coupled Goods Engine Trials		
	GCR 2-8-0 No. 2078 9th November 1919	L&NWR 0-8-0 No. 2421 18th January 1920
Train weights in tons:*		
(1) Mossend to Carstairs	884.5	892.75
(2) Carstairs to Beattock	751.0	765.0
(3) Beattock to Kingmoor	751.0	765.0
Timings in minutes:		
(1) Mossend to Law Junction	65.25	55.00
(2) Law Junction to Graigenhill S/B	55.50	45.50
(3) Graigenhall S/B to Carstairs	16.00	17.50
(4) Carstairs to Summit	92.00	71.25
Train Starting Trials:		
(1) Maximum drawbar pull, tons, on 1 in 143 up gradient	11.50	13.50
(2) Maximum drawbar pull, tons, on 1 in 116 up gradient	13.75	16.50
DBHP**		
Mossend to Law Junction	225.0	267.0
Law Junction to Graigenhall S/B	142.0	173.0

Notes:
* Refers to weight behind the tender.
** DBHP figures calculated from train plus locomotive weights together with vertical height differential and average speeds to give DBHP due to gravity only.

'the influence of these men was great'. Clearly, Barr's position as Northern Division Motive Power Superintendent carried significant weight in those early years and he was undoubtedly the principal decision taker in such matters.

For Caledonian company engines in general, Cox noted that *'all the more recent types gave high fuel consumption because the effect of short travel valve gear was enhanced by insufficient grate area, giving low boiler efficiency'*. In concluding his remarks on design matters, he wrote: *'the influence of Caledonian company design in the wider field of the LMSR turned out to be small'*.

From an operational and standardisation position, Cox recorded:[66]

'mechanically the Caledonian engines were very robustly constructed and frame fractures were almost unheard of, but hot bearings were a frequent trouble. A stout fight was made north of the border for the retention of the Caledonian types, which were claimed to be specially suited to Scottish conditions.'

This policy, coupled to a somewhat ruthless approach to standardisation, resulted in 12.7 per cent of Caledonian locomotive stock being scrapped in the ten years to 1932, compared to 79.4 per cent and 36.4 per cent respectively for ex-G&SWR and ex-HR locomotives, Cox noting: *'none of the former G&SWR locomotives measured up to LMS standards of effectiveness and efficiency'*.

In concluding his remarks on Scottish constituent company engines (presumably referring to the 'River', 'Superheated Goods' and 'Clan' classes – all built by Hawthorne, Leslie and Co.), Cox wrote:[66]

'Highland Railway engines were probably, on the whole, the best Scottish types of all, particularly the three most recent superheated outside-cylindered types, and these engines continued throughout these ten years to work the difficult Highland section, supplemented only by a few of the Horwich 2-6-0 type engines.'

REFERENCES

1. Caledonian Railway, Staff Emoluments 1900-1920, NRS, BR/CAL/15/14
2. Private Correspondence, Graeme Miller to CP Atkins, 1978
3. Caledonian Railway, Directors' Reports & Minutes of Board Meetings, NRS, BR/CAL/1/67, held as CRA2/3/1/10
4. Campbell Cornwell Collection of CR Locomotive Drawings, CRA6/1/3/2
5. Author's father's notes of conversations with Peter Todd, LM&S engineman, Burghmuir, Stirling
6. *The Caledonian Dunalastairs*, O.S. Nock (David & Charles, 1968), p. 94
7. St Rollox Drg No. 17458, dated 8th August 1914, NRS, RHP132390
8. Trials data, Engine No. 60, on Buchanan Street to Perth working, 18th May 1917, Montague Smith Collection, NRS, GD 456, RHP136352/49
9. Article by E.C. Poultney in *The Engineer*, 15th October 1920, as noted in *The Scottish 4-6-0 Classes*, C.R. Atkins (Ian Allan), pp. 67-8
10. 'British Locomotive Practice & Performance', C.J. Allen in *The Railway Magazine*, January 1921, pp. 25ff
11. *The Locomotive News and Railway Notes*, 24th May 1919
12. E.S. Cox memo to R.A. Riddles, dated 24th May 1934, accountants' figures for '60' Class coal consumption, NRM ESC2/1/9
13. LMS Engine Record Card, No. 14654, NRS, GD480/2/1/1/4
14. NBR Co., Cowlairs Drg, Highland Railway No. 1, NRS, Montague Smith Collection, GD456/3
15. *Locomotive Boilers & Engines*, Prof. L.V. Ludy (American Technical Society, 1918), pp. 85, 86
16. *Forty Years of Caledonian Locomotives 1882-1922*, Campbell Cornwell (David & Charles, 1974), pp. 161, 186
17. *The Scottish 4-6-0 Classes*, C.P. Atkins (Ian Allan, 1976), p. 15
18. LMS Northern Division, Engine Boiler Book, for Class 79 boilers, NRS, BR/LMS/5/131A, Drg No. 19493
19. Private Correspondence, O.S. Nock to A.G. Dunbar, 1st April 1964, NRS, GD344/6/12/2
20. 'The CR 938 Class 4-6-0s', A.G. Dunbar comments in *The True Line*, No. 71, December 2000, pp. 14ff
21. Boiler Record Card No. 14760, NRS, GD344/4/34/17
22. St Rollox Drg No. 15315, dated 10th March 1910, NRS, RHP132379
23. *Scottish Locomotive History 1831-1923*, Campbell Highet (George Allen & Unwin, 1970), p. 177
24. *Scottish Locomotive History 1831-1923*, Campbell Highet, p. 218
25. Engine Record Card No. 55360, NRS, GD 480/2/1/1/4
26. St Rollox Drg No. 19873, dated 18th March 1919, NRS, RHP132394
27. E.S. Cox memo to R.A. Riddles, dated 12th July 1933, giving axle loads for C&O and Highland lines, NRM, ESC2/2/13/2
28. St Rollox Drg No. 20488, dated 5th March 1920, NRS, RHP132395/1
29. NB Loco. Co. Drg No. G27219, NRS, BR/CAL/LOC/43
30. *McIntosh Locomotives of the Caledonian Railway 1895-1914*, A.B. MacLeod (Ian Allan, 1948), p. 22
31. Author's father's notes of conversations with Peter Todd, LM&S engineman, Burghmuir, Stirling
32. *Highland Railway Locomotives*, Book 2, Cormack and Stephenson (RCTS, 1990), pp. 117ff
33. *Highland Railway Locomotives*, Book 2, Cormack and Stephenson, pp. 129ff
34. *Forty Years of Caledonian Locomotives 1882-1922*, Campbell Cornwell, p. 186
35. St Rollox Drg No. 21006, Montague Smith Collection, NRS, GD456, RHP136356/13
36. Dr J.T. Rutherford, Notes on visit to LMS shed, Burghmuir, Stirling, 4th August 1933, courtesy R.W. Lynn
37. Engine Record Card No. 54767, NRS, GD480/2/1/1/4
38. Engine Record Card No. 57951, NRS, GD480/2/1/1/4
39. *Forty Years of Caledonian Locomotives 1882–1922*, Campbell Cornwell, Appendix 2
40. *The LNER 2-6-0 Classes*, John F. Clay and J. Cliffe (Ian Allan, 1978), Appendices, p. 64ff
41. *Scottish Locomotive History 1831-1923*, Campbell Highet, p. 224
42. Irvine Kempt, ILocoE paper No. 97, 20th January 1921, and subsequent discussion chaired by R.H. Whitelegg of the G&SWR
43. *The Caledonian Railway*, O.S. Nock (Ian Allan, 1963), p. 143
44. See Appendices 1-3
45. *Steam Power*, Prof. W.E. Dalby (Arnold, London, 1915), pp. 228ff
46. *Steam Locomotive Design, Data and Formulae*, A.E. Phillipson (The Locomotive Publishing Co.) pp. 156-9; Steam Tables from Greer, *Proceedings* (ILocoE, 1927)
47. 'The Dunalastairs and Superheated 4-4-0 Classes (9)', David Hamilton, in *The True Line*, No. 120, April 2013, p. 30
48. *Locomotives of the G&SWR*, David L. Smith (David & Charles, 1976), p. 113
49. 'British Locomotive Practice & Performance', C.J. Allen, in *The Railway Magazine*, January 1912, pp. 48ff
50. NB Loco. Co., G&SWR '128' Class Drg, No. L440/12-802, courtesy Stuart Rankin, G&SWR Association Archive
51. *Caledonian Cavalcade*, E.A. Glen, I.A. Glen, with A.G. Dunbar (Ian Allan, 1979), p. 95
52. Notes of Experiments Upon Locomotive Spark Arrestors, IESES Student Section, Thomas Thompson, 28th March 1910
53. J. Maxwell Dunn, ILocoE paper No. 56, 24th November 1917, and discussion thereafter
54. *Swindon Steam, A New Light on GWR Locomotive Development*, A.L. Summers (Amberley Publications, 2013), pp. 104ff
55. St Rollox Drg No. 21746, dated 7th March 1922, NRS, RHP132416
56. *British Railways Standard Steam Locomotives*, E.S. Cox (Ian Allan, 1966), p. 189
57. A Breath of Steam, Vol. 1, W.G.F. Thorley (Ian Allan, 1975), p. 96
58. J.F. McEwan papers, William Patrick Library, Kirkintilloch, ref T25, etc
59. LMS Coal Tests for Scottish Collieries – Notes Book of Inspector W. Dunsmuir, LMS Running Dept, 302 Buchanan St, Glasgow, Courtesy Stuart Rankin, G&SWR Association
60. John G. Barr papers, courtesy the Scottish Railway Preservation Society
61. Private correspondence, J.F. McEwan to C.P. Atkins, October 1987
62. Comparison of Experimental Trips between Mossend and Kingmoor, Caledonian Railway Report, NRM, Test/Misc/3
63. 'Sunday 18th January 1920', A.G. Dunbar, in *The True Line*, No 16, February 1987
64. 'Y125 – And All That', A.G. Dunbar, SLS Journal, August 1948, pp. 192ff
65. St Rollox Drawing Register, NRS, BR/CAL/5/56
66. 'A Modern Locomotive History: Ten Years' Development on the LMS 1923-1932', E.S. Cox, *Journal of the Institution of Locomotive Engineers*, March 1946, vol. 36, pp. 100-170 (republished by the RCTS, April 1946 and Supplement No. 6 to the *Railway Observer*)

CHAPTER 4
1914-1918 WARTIME CONDITIONS AT ST ROLLOX

GENERAL

It is certainly the case that the war had an impact on the Caledonian company, and on St Rollox in particular, but how this should be assessed and calibrated is now difficult to determine. Records from the period are sketchy, though examination of various company documents, including Board minutes[1] and the St Rollox drawing register[2] does assist in developing some understanding of the position.

Several major consequences of the war affected all railway companies: the loss of staff, as employees enlisted in the armed services, despite government discouragement; increases in traffic as the movement of troops and services' supplies were hugely increased; and the use of railway workshops for the manufacture of armaments and related war materiel. In Scotland, the Highland company was particularly affected almost immediately, with much increased northbound stores and services' personnel traffic. The Board minutes record, in October 1914,[1] that the Caledonian company was prepared to repair various Highland company locomotives at Perth, a position which suggests that staff resources at Perth were not then unduly stretched and might have been made available to relieve pressures at St Rollox.

The usual six-monthly renewal programmes for rolling stock continued to be addressed by the Board,[1] with 1915 renewals noting the receipt of quotations for 4-4-0 tender engines and 4-6-2 tank engines from the North British Locomotives Co., without comment on St Rollox work loading or shortages. However, the difficulties in obtaining timely deliveries of steel for the construction of goods rolling stock was minuted, and in February 1916 the attention of the Board was drawn to the scarcity of fitters at St Rollox,[1] leading to the improbability of properly undertaking repairs to locomotives. Arising from this latter position, the Board acknowledged receipt of tenders for locomotive repairs from Robert Stephenson's at Darlington, plus Hawthorn, Leslie at Newcastle, and the Yorkshire Engine Co. at Sheffield.[1] In the period March 1916 to December 1918, some twenty CR locomotives were repaired by the Sheffield firm.[3]

In attempting to order new carriages, the Board minutes[1] record that in April 1916 an objection was received from the Ministry of Munitions and the orders were cancelled, indicating that non-essential work was being deferred, priority being given to the use of scarce materials for munitions production. Lack of materials for locomotive repairs, in addition to skilled labour shortages, continued to cause Directors concern and in September 1916 the need to acquire twenty-five new 0-6-0 goods tender engines was minuted, noting the impossibility of building more than ten at St Rollox.[1] Moreover, in the following month, October 1916, the Directors instructed the company's General Manager to confirm arrangements with the Railway Executive to secure the delivery of materials for the repair of engines, emphasising the repair position, rather than for new construction.[1] Seemingly, the shipbuilding industry had a higher priority for the supply of steel plate from Scottish rolling mills than the locomotive building and repair sector.[3]

In early 1917, both steel and labour resources continued in short supply, which prejudiced St Rollox's ability to build rolling stock suitable for the movement of munitions. Board minutes for January 1917[1] note the placing of orders for 150 wagons for the conveyance of explosives with R.Y. Pickering, with an additional 180 wagons of similar type being ordered from Clayton & Shuttleworth. Such material and labour shortages continued into 1918, with Board minutes noting the receipt of quotations for ten locomotives with

tenders from Armstrong, Whitworth & Co., plus authority being requested to send locomotives to William Beardmore & Co. for repair.[1]

Review of the St Rollox drawing register suggests that limited design work was put in hand for the government until May 1915, when a significant amount of drawing effort was focused in the detailing of an Ambulance Train[4] to be built at St Rollox. This train, for use in France, was complete with wards, operating tables, pharmacy and internal water supplies, and contained facilities for the treatment of infections. Full sewerage and drainage facilities were provided, as was accommodation for medical and nursing staff. The train was used in France and Belgium, though whether it returned to Caledonian metals remains in doubt. Design and production for special rolling stock vehicles, including those for the movement of explosives and large naval guns was also undertaken. In 1915, despite pressure on its own resources, the Caledonian company sent seven locomotives to help the hard pressed Highland company, one of which did not return until 1922. Strangely, neither the Board minutes,[1] nor the St Rollox drawing register,[2] make any mention of the manufacture by the Caledonian company of munitions of any type.

MOTIVE POWER SUPPORT

At Carlisle, locomotive servicing facilities were significantly enhanced by the rebuilding between 1915 and 1917 of the engine shed at Etterby, the existing structure being in a poor state of repair. The new brick-built complex on the same site, now renamed Kingmoor, replaced the previous wooden one, a sum of £22,000 being approved for the works.[5] At the same time, a proposal was seriously considered to build a locomotive repair workshop alongside the new shed,[6] utilising two overhead travelling cranes which had been displaced from St Rollox. Unfortunately, due to wartime shortages the idea was shelved, although arrangements were made to double the facilities for locomotive lifting using electrically operated engine hoists.

Additionally, a further new engine servicing complex was built at Balornock to replace the old St Rollox shed, the new facilities being opened in November 1916, the price quoted for the works being £28,000.[7] On a more sombre and melancholy note, the drawing register for the 24th May 1915 records, in the simplest of terms, the four drawings prepared by Alexander Linn, setting out the composition of the three trains involved in the 'Quintinshill Accident' and the layout of the accident site.[8]

The motive power position was certain not improved in 1917 when the government requisitioned twenty-five '294' Class 0-6-0s for use overseas by the Royal Engineers ROD, the Railway Executive Committee having to draft four Fletcher 0-6-0s from the North Eastern company and seven 0-6-0s from the Great Central to help make good the loss.[9]

Pickersgill, according to McEwan,[3] on joining the company in 1914, seems to have considered expanding the pool of available boilers, with the intention of expediting the repair of locomotives, but wartime conditions made this impractical due to materials and labour shortages. Additionally, and again due to these shortages, it was decided that older engines would not be given heavy repairs,[3] being allowed to 'work themselves out', recognising the need for assimilation (cannibalisation) of parts of older engines to keep other class members working. Shortages of materials also resulted in the decision to discontinue[3] the superheating of further

'Dunalastair II' Class locomotives and may well have been the reason for the Pickersgill '300' Class 0-6-0 freight engines being initially laid out as saturated locomotives.[3]

Moreover, it would seem that Pickersgill had proposed using Belpaire firebox arrangements on his '72' Class 4-4-0s built in the 1920 to 1922 period,[3] but, with escalating costs, the extra expense ruled out such improvements and the class had to be built with round-topped fireboxes. Further, the Civil Engineer was doubtful about the additional weight bearing on the track,[3] recognising wartime arrears in maintenance.

The time taken for engine erection at St Rollox was also subject to review, it being noted that outside builders were able do the work much more quickly, the North British Locomotive Co.[3] being cited as an example, even taking account of war work and other orders they had in hand. One reason for the better efficiency at North British Locomotive was their use of 'piece work' rates, and this approach was introduced at St Rollox, though not all employees were empathetic to it.

BOILER SHOP STRIKE AND THEREAFTER

The Caledonian company's boiler provision position was not assisted in Pickersgill's first few days at St Rollox, as the whole of the boiler shop was brought to a standstill through a strike of employees which lasted for five weeks.[6] Running shed staff fortunately were not affected by the strike, but it was a very serious matter for the operating department, since the strike ended just before the period of annual holidays, when the workshops were normally idle and traffic was at its peak with increased demand for engine power for passenger workings.

Following the outbreak of this labour trouble, Pickersgill[6] asked the running department to do everything possible by way of repairs at engine sheds, thus removing the need for engines to go out of traffic or to visit the works. The necessary repair work was undertaken at various sheds where appropriate facilities were available.

These arrangements made by Pickersgill to reduce the impact of the boiler shop strike had direct application[6] during the war years, since increasing workload was focused on the running sheds. Assistance was given to the sheds by the provision of a few additional machine tools and an increase in unskilled local labour. Eventually, only heavy boiler work was carried out at St Rollox, with such facilities as tyre turning being available at Kingmoor, Motherwell, Polmadie

and Perth. Additionally, 30 ton engine hoists were provided at most major depots, and by the end of hostilities there were separate locomotive repair works,[6] under the control of the respective running shed foremen, at Kingmoor, Dalry Road, Balornock, Dawsholm, Greenock, Aberdeen, Motherwell and Hamilton.

To assist with shortages of fitters at individual sheds, able drivers and firemen were given the opportunity to come off the footplate, without loss of status, and worked in their respective sheds as examining fitters.[6] Most returned to footplate grades on the cessation of hostilities.

WOMEN EMPLOYEES

As one might have anticipated, male employees in the locomotive and clerical grades at individual sheds, St Rollox works and other company establishments had enlisted in significant numbers, with the result that women were employed to fill the gaps. To cater for this change in employee gender numbers, drawings were prepared at St Rollox for women's canteen, lavatory and other facilities, these being built at various depots such as Polmadie, Balornock and Motherwell, as well as at the works itself. The St Rollox Works Staff Ledger, which excluded foremen and clerical staff, treats the employment of women in a slightly dismissive way, by simply, though prominently, recording:

'Women employees were introduced on the 8th March 1917 and dispensed with on the 31st December 1919.'[10]

REFERENCES
1. Caledonian Railway, Directors' Reports & Minutes of Board Meetings, NRS, BR/CAL/1/67, held as CRA2/3/1/10
2. St Rollox Drawing Register, NRS, BR/CAL/5/56
3. J.F. McEwan papers, William Patrick Library, Kirkintilloch, T25/1, etc
4. St Rollox Drawing Register, NRS, BR/CAL/5/56, drawings in range No's 17981-18070, May-August 1915
5. *LMS Engine Sheds*, Hawkins and Reeve (Wild Swan Publications, 1987), vol. 5, p. 83
6. John G. Barr papers, courtesy the Scottish Railway Preservation Society
7. *LMS Engine Sheds*, Hawkins and Reeve, vol. 5, p. 21
8. St Rollox Drawing Register, NRS, BR/CAL/5/56, drawings No's 18013-18016 inclusive
9. *British Locomotive Catalogue, 1825-1923*, Baxter (Moorland Publishing, 1984), vol. 4, p. 13
10. St Rollox Works Staff Ledger, NRS, BR/CAL/15/21

No. 957 at Kingmoor in 1922.

G.P. Keen

CHAPTER 5
POST-WAR DEVELOPMENTS AT ST ROLLOX

DEVELOPMENTS LEADING TO THE '956' CLASS

Locomotive development on the CR, as on other companies, had been frustrated by war effort demands and it was only on the cessation of hostilities that serious thought could once again be given to new locomotive designs, in anticipation of increased passenger traffic and train loadings, presupposing labour and material resources were available. As noted earlier, McIntosh had schemed out two Pacific type locomotives for express passenger duties just before his retirement, though Pickersgill, in considering the need for new locomotives for that type of duty, probably preferred the 4-6-0 option. Based on the performance of the '938' Class, acquired from the HR in 1915, plus his own '60' Class, introduced in 1916 and itself the development of an earlier McIntosh proposal, a Pacific option for express passenger workings was probably seen as an overly complex and costly solution.

During the war years, St Rollox prepared two proposals for outside-cylindered 4-4-0s, the first being shown on drawing No. 19225,[1] dated the 21st September 1917. This was in effect a scheme using the same superheated boiler as on the '113' Class 4-4-0s, steam distribution being via piston valves and internal Stephenson's link motion, in the style of the '60' Class layout; the SHS and grate area were identical to the '113' Class. As with the '113' Class, SHS was 15 per cent of the evaporative heating surfaces, though, most unusually, the drawing also gave outline details of a non-superheated boiler option having an evaporative heating surface of 1,614 sq. ft.

The second scheme, prepared in January 1918 and shown on drawing No. 19346,[2] again carried a boiler identical to the '113' Class. The 20 in. x 26 in. outside cylinders were driven by external Walschaert's valve gear, using 11 ins diameter piston valves. This second outside-cylindered 4-4-0 design was worked up in some detail, calculations being prepared to demonstrate a factor of safety of 5.76 for the ⅝ in. plates proposed for the 175 psi boiler, the SHS again being 15 per cent of the evaporative surface. Side and sectioned front elevations for this second 4-4-0 proposal is shown in Figure 10, although neither of these outside-cylindered schemes progressed further than the drawing board.

In July 1917, St Rollox prepared a scheme for a 2-6-0 superheated express goods engine, having inside valve chests and Stephenson's link motion, again in the '60' Class mould, this proposal being shown on drawing No. 19161.[3] Surprisingly, the superheater was very small, the elements being only single pass and carried in 3¼ ins diameter flues. SHS at only 9 per cent of the evaporative surface total was surely a retrograde step. Significant detail was worked up, with variants having 5 ft 8 ins, 6 ft 1 ins and 6 ft 6 ins driving wheel diameters being included, together with 26 ins and 28 ins strokes being noted as options for the 21 ins diameter cylinders. Boiler details indicated a factor of safety of 5.2 for the ⅝ in. boiler shell plates, the working pressure being 175 psi.

It may have been that this 2-6-0 express goods engine proposal was prepared in support of the Association of Railway Locomotive Engineers' (ARLE) attempts to introduce standard locomotive designs for post-war use. However, Alan Dunbar noted that serious consideration was given to building this 2-6-0 class at St Rollox,[4] though it is not clear which of the options outlined would have been selected.

Towards the end of 1918, a series of drawings was prepared at St Rollox for locomotives which appeared to be more than marginally outside the company's loading gauge. The need for a heavy goods locomotive was seemingly under investigation, drawing No. 19696, prepared in November, indicating that a 2-10-2 arrangement had been considered in outline. This need for a powerful goods locomotive was further considered in the same month, schemes for both 2-8-0 and 2-8-2 proposals being outlined in respective drawing No's 19718 and 19720 for the former and No. 19722 for the latter type. The drawing register entries are illustrated in Figure 11.

The proposed 2-8-0, outlined in St Rollox drawing No. 19718, is shown as Figure 12,[5] the locomotive having 23 in. x 30 in. cylinders, a 200 psi boiler, a maximum axle load of 20 tons and a height above rail level of 13 ft 5 ins. Whilst there would be some merit in considering a 2-8-0, thereby increasing haulage capacity per train, with consequent potential reduction in double heading and overall footplate costs, this proposal, having 20 ton axle loads on adjacent axles at 5 ft 6 ins or even 6 ft 6 ins centres, would not have been acceptable to the Civil Engineer, a position noted by E.S. Cox.[6] Cox also pointed out 'that 2-8-0s with reasonably widespread running have not usually exceeded 16/17 tons per axle',[6] which was the axle loading position on the Robinson GCR 'MM' Class 2-8-0s.[7] Moreover, such a proposal may have found little support in the operating department, where, as previously noted, standard refuge loop lengths most probably could not accommodate the lengthened trains.

An additional drawing in the same series, No. 19726, dated the 22nd November 1918 and also noted in Figure 11, outlines an arrangement for a 4-6-0 express passenger engine. This proposal, again using 23 in. x 30 in. cylinders, would almost certainly be outside the CR loading gauge. Individual axle loading at 22 tons and an adhesion weight of 65 tons on a 15 ft 9 ins span, plus a maximum height above rail level of 13 ft 5 ins, would not have passed the Civil Engineer's filter. For the record, the boiler had 2,550 sq. ft of evaporative surface, an SHS at 11 per cent of that, and a grate area of 30 sq. ft.

Whilst these four strange proposals would certainly not fit the Caledonian company loading gauge, there is just the possibility they also may have been prepared for ARLE purposes, to review what might be possible if loading gauge enhancement was intended. Since the St Rollox drawing register makes no further mention of them, it can be assumed that any ARLE initiative was not taken further.

In early 1919, further consideration was given to a new express locomotive, an outline arrangement drawing No. 19828,[8] dated the 6th February, referring to a 4-6-0 'Express Passenger Engine'. The first mention of the expression '3-Cylinder Passenger Engine' in the register[9] also comes in February 1919 with drawing No. 19836, dated the 18th February, which refers to the reversing shaft bracket, and drawing No. 19848, dated the 27th February, which refers to the crank axle. By March 1919, the choice of a 3-cylinder 4-6-0 seemed to have been underwritten, all related drawing work thereafter[9] carrying the annotation '3-Cylinder Passenger Engine'.

However, 4-cylinder propulsion was also considered, since drawing No. 19825,[9] dated the 11th February 1919, prepared by W.H. Moodie, and titled 'Torque Diagrammes, 4 & 3 Cylinder Engines', was produced for comparative purposes. Indeed, Thomas Weir, the St Rollox Chief Draughtsman, spent several days at Crewe[10] evaluating the L&NWR 4-cylinder, 4-6-0 'Claughton' Class design. From this visit, two schools of thought emerged at St Rollox:[10] Weir and Kempt seemingly favouring the 4-cylinder arrangement, whilst Pickersgill and Barr apparently considered a 3-cylinder arrangement was all the CR required.

Hoped-for advantages from the use of four cylinders included a reduction in stresses together with a simpler balancing regime;

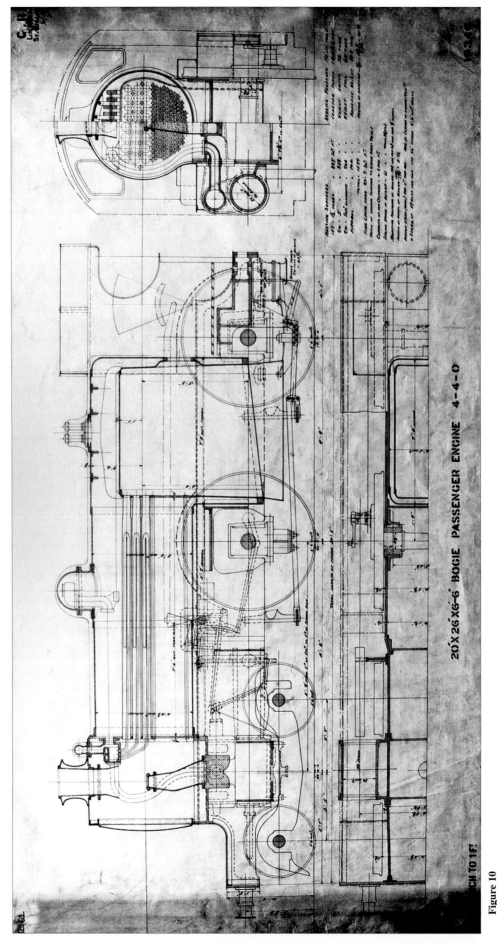

Figure 10
Pickersgill Proposed Outside-Cylindered 4-4-0. Elevations, Drg No. 19346, dated the 30th January 1918. During the war years, St Rollox prepared two proposals for outside-cylindered 4-4-0s, the second of these being shown on this drawing. Carrying a boiler identical to the '113' Class, the 20 in. x 26 in. cylinders were driven by external Walschaerts' valve gear using 11 ins diameter piston valves. This proposal was worked up in some detail, calculations showing a factor of safety of 5.76 for the ⅝ in. plates used in the 175 psi boiler. Neither of these outside-cylindered 4-4-0s progressed further than the drawing board.

NRS: RHP132352

Figure 11
St Rollox Drawing Register Entries, November 1918, Drg No's 19718 and 19720 for 2-8-0 goods engine, No. 19722 for 2-8-2 goods engine and No. 19726 for 4-6-0 passenger engine. This page of the drawing register shows the dates, drawing numbers, titles and draughtsmen concerned with outline proposals for three types of locomotives, all of which were outside the company's loading gauge. There is just the possibility the drawings were prepared for ARLE use, but there is no further reference to them in the register. The register also notes Drg No. 19709, dated the 8th November, for 'Proposed Alteration to Loading Gauge'.
NRS: BR/CAL/5/56

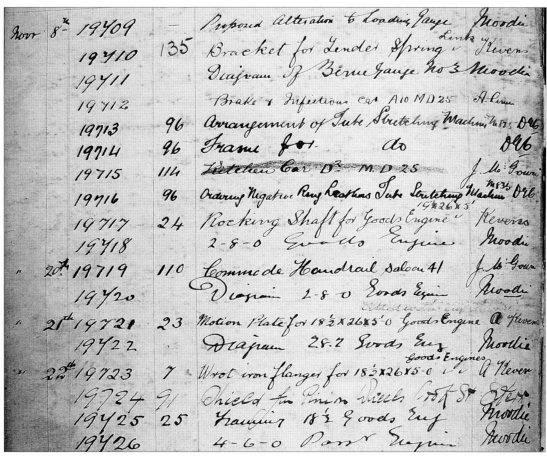

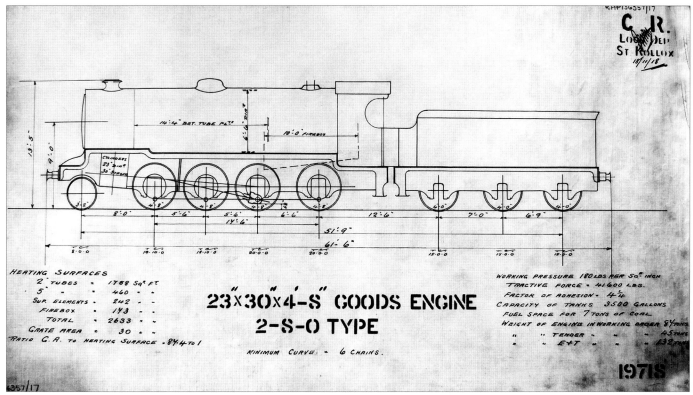

Figure 12
Proposed 2-8-0 Express Goods Engine. Side Elevation, Drg No. 19718, dated the 18th November 1918. The drawing illustrates the outline schematic for a 2-8-0 goods engine, the locomotive having 23 in. x 30 in. cylinders, a 200 psi boiler, a maximum axle loading of 20 tons and a height above rail level of 13 ft 5 ins. In height, width across cylinders and axle loading terms, this proposal was outside the company's loading gauge. At the time, it was recognised that 2-8-0 locomotives with reasonably widespread UK route running availability did not exceed a loading of 16 to 17 tons per axle.
NRS: GD456, RHP136357/17

disadvantages included inaccessibility of the inside motion and increased complexity, though little comparative difference would be obvious for a 3-cylinder fit. Interestingly, some UK CMEs went to considerable lengths to obtain connecting rods of equal length on all four sets of motion. On the GWR, Churchward secured it by setting the inside cylinders forward to drive the leading axle, whilst the outside cylinders were set back level with the rear bogie axle and drove the middle set of coupled wheels. On the other hand, Bowen Cooke on the L&NWR selected his layout with all cylinders in line and all four drove the leading coupled axle.

Clearly some major points of design principle were at stake here, leading in some cases to divided drive, which found no support in other quarters. In setting out the arrangements for his 3-cylinder 'S3' Class 4-6-0s on the NER, Sir Vincent Raven opted for all cylinders in line and all connected to the leading coupled axle. Three separate sets of Stephenson's motion (six eccentrics) had to be accommodated on the leading crank axle, which, with crank webs and the provision of adequately sized journals, made things somewhat tight.

In the final analysis at St Rollox, in the post-war CR straightened financial circumstances, the solution may have predicated on the 3-cylinder option being seen as less costly. It was, perhaps, 'three cylinders or not-at-all'.

In parallel with the choice of the 3-cylinder arrangement, the type of valve gear was clearly under consideration and to assist this evaluation Drawing Office Motion Models were constructed, the details being covered in drawing No's 19840, 19841 and 19843, all dated February 1919.[9] Unfortunately the drawings covering the motion models and the torque diagrams for 3- and 4-cylinder propulsion options have not been located.

The suggestion has been made that having belatedly recognised the constraints of the CR loading gauge, St Rollox set out to design and build as powerful a passenger locomotive as could be accommodated within the then Caledonian company loading gauge limits. There is more than an element of truth in this assertion, since the St Rollox drawing register contains references to a number of drawings and analyses related to loading gauge matters. Drawing No. 19487, dated the 27th May 1918, lays out the 'Maximum British Loading Gauge', whilst drawing No. 19682, dated the 12th October 1918, lays out proposals for a 'New Loading Gauge', followed by drawing No. 19709, of the 8th November 1918, suggesting 'Alterations to the Loading Gauge'.[9]

The 'Berne No 3 Gauge' was laid out in drawing No. 19711, also shown in Figure 11. However, one suspects that in the end, the maximum loading gauge, as underwritten by the company's Chief Engineer, would ultimately have proscribed the St Rollox drawing office '956' Class starting point, though the various loading gauge investigative drawings may well have been prepared for ARLE use.

Whilst extending the power of currently operating locomotive classes by extrapolation was an obvious and well-tried method of developing enhanced tractive capability, the basic requirements for what became the '956' Class would have been determined by anticipated train loadings and required journey times, taking account of the proposed routes' topologies – factors usually set by the operating department and endorsed by the Board. However, if the locomotive department proposed a major new engine type, able to deal expeditiously with the company's anticipated traffic demands, the Board would be more than likely to endorse such a proposal, especially if more efficient working, such as the reduction of piloting, was a demonstrable advantage. Additionally, in such a proposal the latest schemes in engine development would be incorporated, as appropriate, to increase operating efficiency, reduce engine running costs and keep the company on the forefront of current locomotive technology.

A successful high-powered passenger locomotive could bring acclaim to the company, its Directors, the Locomotive Superintendent, and to all associated with the construction programme.

At St Rollox, over the period March to November 1919, the drawing effort for what became the '956' Class was by-and-large completed, the table below setting out some of the major items and the draftsmen involved.[9]

In addition to these drawings, many more were produced in the 1919 to 1920 period for the '956' Class by a number of other

'956' CLASS – MAJOR DRAWINGS			
DRG NO	TITLE	DATE*	DRAFTSMAN
19828	4-6-0, Outline, Express Passenger Engine	6th February 1919	W. Moodie
19848	Crank Axle, 3-Cylinder Passenger Engine	27th February 1919	A. Kevens
19887	Driving Coupling Rods, 3-Cylinder Engine	26th March 1919	A. Kevens
19912	Tube Plate, 3-Cylinder Engine	18th April 1919	G. Kerr
19915	Front Tube Plate, 3-Cylinder Engine	28th April 1919	G. Kerr
19921	Inside Cylinder, 3-Cylinder Engine	30th April 1919	A. Linn
19932	Valve Motion Rods, 3-Cylinder Engine	5th May 1919	A. Kevens
19940	Outsides Cylinders, 3-Cylinder Engine	7th May 1919	A. Linn
19942	Framing Arrangement, 3-Cylinder Engine	7th May 1919	W. Moodie
19947	Valve setting (o/s cylinders), 3-Cylinder Engine	8th May 1919	A. Linn
19968	Motion Arrangement, 3-Cylinder Engine	22nd May 1919	W. Moodie
19970	Boiler Arrangement, 3-Cylinder Engine	22nd May 1919	G. Kerr
20007	Smoke Box Arrangement, 3-Cylinder Engine	11th June 1919	A. Kevens
20082	Main Frames, 3-Cylinder Engine	6th August 1919	A. Kevens
20107	Crank Axle Detail, 3-Cylinder Engine	20th August 1919	A. Kevens
20118	Superheater Elements, 3-Cylinder Engine	22nd August 1919	G. Kerr
20210	Horn Blocks, 3-Cylinder Engine	10th October 1919	W. Moodie
20267	Bogie, 3-Cylinder Engine	5th November 1919	G. Kerr

NOTE:
* The dates quoted are from the drawing register, and probably infer the date on which the particular drawing number was allocated, not when the drawing was completed.

draughtsmen,[9] including G. Miller, N. Donaldson, G.B. Grafton, A. Arnold, L. Armstrong, J.A. Cook and J. Mackie. Moreover, further drawings were prepared in the 1921 to 1922 period, when various valve gear modifications were made, these being noted later in the text.

Referring to the company Board minutes,[11] there is no specific date recorded authorising the construction of the four '956' Class locomotives, though it is likely that instructions to proceed would have been given in late 1919 or early 1920.

POST-WAR PROBLEMS FOR THE CALEDONIAN COMPANY

It is quite clear from the Caledonian company Board minutes in the 1919 to 1922 period,[11] a series of major post-war difficulties continued to weigh heavily on the Directors' decisions and the company's future. Moreover, the wartime shortages of manpower and materials could not immediately be rectified, as instanced by the sending of locomotives to William Beardmore & Co. for repair in 1919. In 1920, the continued external construction of carriages was authorised by the Board, since it appeared that St Rollox itself could not meet the renewals demands.

In an early 1921 reference to the overall carriage construction programme, the minutes record that, of the carriages authorised by the Board since 1916, 171 had not yet entered traffic.[11] Of these, St Rollox currently had forty-two in hand, whilst fifty-three were being built by outside contractors. On the basis of that data, the Board then authorised a further sixteen carriages to be constructed at St Rollox, but only when the backlog of forty-two had been cleared.

Additionally, and more seriously, in June 1921 the Directors instituted an immediate policy[11] to reduce stores on order and in hand, plus deferring renewals work on both permanent way and rolling stock. The related minute is headed 'Reduction in Stores Inventory' and clearly points to the conservation of cash, through what appeared to be a drastic restriction on capital and revenue expenditures.

This course of action seems directly related to protracted compensation negotiations with government for use of the railways during the period of hostilities, the associated delays no doubt leading to cash-flow difficulties for the Caledonian company and many others, compounded by significant inflationary pressure on the companies' costs. The seriousness of this is brought into focus by a minuted instruction of the 12th July,[11] which directs all construction in the companies' workshops was to be delayed until after the 15th August 1921, the inference being staff were to be laid off. In the same minute, an order for 400 off 16 ton mineral wagons, previously placed with the Motherwell Wagon & Rolling Stock Co., was cancelled, costing the Caledonian company significant compensation.

By the first week in August 1921, the position had become so serious that the chairman instructed locomotive construction work at St Rollox would be stopped from the 15th August,[11] but carriage and wagon work should continue. The St Rollox Staff ledger[12] gives details of individual named employees laid off from the loco works, the records showing reductions under that heading for 1920, 1921 and 1922.

Interestingly, this date of the 15th August had great significance, as it was the date on which the wartime government control of the railways, which had been exercised under the Regulation of the Forces Act, 1871, came to an end. Further, the Railways Act, 1921, under which the four amalgamated railway groups were to be formed, was to receive the Royal Assent on the 21st August 1921. Moreover, in the run up to the August the 15th date, government and the railway companies had been locked in difficult and sometimes acrimonious negotiations to settle the compensation issue. At the eleventh hour, and by statute, the government imposed a compulsory settlement of £60 million to cover total claims, amidst much concerted railway company anger.

The Caledonian Directors' collective anger was manifest in their return to government of all ROD 2-8-0s which had been on loan. Moreover, the company refused to buy any at the government's inflated asking price – and indeed at midnight on the 14/15th August all the 2-8-0s on Caledonian lines were chained and padlocked[10] to the rails at their various depots, and remained thus until removed to either of the Gretna dumps.

At the Caledonian company Annual General Meeting, held in Glasgow on the 28th February 1922,[13] which covered the previous year's financial position to 31st December 1921, the Chairman, Henry Allan, reported on the compulsory settlement between the various British railway companies and the government. He noted the sum of £60 million, payable by government in two tranches over two years, observing that the first payment of £24,500,000 had been received, the Caledonian's share being £1,126,618, of which £16,608 was payable to the C&O company.

Prior to these unparalleled events, the Board minutes note the half-yearly rolling stock renewals programme to 31st December 1921 was to be delayed until further instructions were given.[11] The minutes do not indicate when the halt in construction on these renewals was lifted. Furthermore, by February 1922 the position remained extremely tight, the minutes noting that since certain materials were to hand at St Rollox, construction of ten passenger engines and seven mineral tanks was authorised.[11] The minute is unequivocal: 'no more locomotives were to be constructed after these materials had been used'.

Concurrent with these difficult government negotiations, the uncertainties of the railway amalgamations would have added to the Directors' burdens, as would on-going doubts on their own respective positions in the new company. Even though seemingly not directly affected by these turbulent events, Pickersgill and the St Rollox drawing office staff would have been unavoidably subject to the same concerns and pressures as other employees, which cannot have added to their collective esprit-de-corps. Moreover, Pickersgill's personal position was by no means secure or certain: it could not have been easy for him to accept a subsidiary position after some twenty-seven years of 'being in charge'.

Whilst the '956' Class locomotives had been completed by June/August 1921, it seems clear, from the financial position outlined, there would be difficulty in obtaining authorisation for expenditure relating to any modifications arising from identified trials shortcomings.

Interestingly, around this time St Rollox started working up the design of a powerful 2-6-0 express goods engine, which in LM&SR days formed the basis of the George Hughes' designed Horwich mogul, of which 245 were built by the LM&S company. The St Rollox scheme used 21 in. x 28 in. cylinders and 11 ins diameter piston valves, the LM&SR changing the stroke to 26 ins. With good valve events this would have given a powerful engine, though Horwich did not include the proposed cylinder by-pass valves. St Rollox drawing No. 21020,[14] produced under LM&S auspices and dated the 16th October 1923, sets out the detail of this final St Rollox scheme, which is shown as Figure 13.

Whilst the St Rollox boiler proposed for this 2-6-0 had an L/D of 76, the initial Horwich boiler L/D was 97, the grate areas being almost identical at 27 sq. ft. For the CR design the SHS was only 10.2 per cent of the evaporative heating surface, the Hughes-built superheater providing an SHS of 21 per cent, housed in 5¼ ins I/D flues. Superheater elements, with full extension loops, having approximately 1½ ins O/D, were used in the LM&SR Horwich locomotive, ensuring a low steam circuit pressure loss with high superheat.[15]

With a calculated tractive effort of 28,600 lbs, the overall boiler proportions proposed by St Rollox were far from being ideal and the low superheat would have again prejudiced overall efficiency. Using an ashpan of '956' Class proportions, a shallow sloping grate

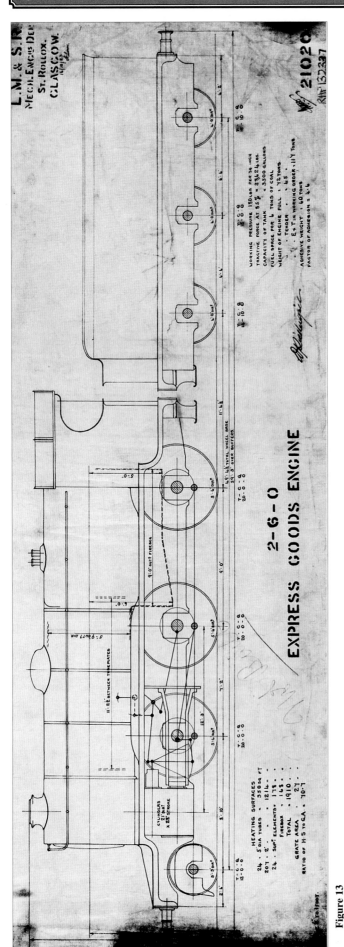

Figure 13
Pickersgill Proposed 2-6-0 Express Goods Engine. Side Elevation, Drg No. 21020, dated the 16th October 1923. This 2-6-0 proposal formed the basis of the George Hughes LM&SR 2-6-0, of which 245 were built by the company, though the LM&SR engine had a much improved boiler and valve gear. E.S. Cox covered the story of his examination of well-advanced production drawings for this St Rollox proposal, noting the best features were the extremely robust main frame and structure. However, Cox felt the tube layout would have led to low boiler efficiency which, with small and tortuous steam passages and short travel valve gear, would have produced a sluggish and wasteful locomotive.

and similar smokebox draughting arrangements, it is very likely the steaming and performance problems of the '956' Class would have been perpetuated in this 2-6-0 proposal. The proposed outline suggests the use of a Belpaire firebox.

E.S. Cox covered the story of his examination of well advanced production drawings for this 2-6-0, sent from St Rollox early after the grouping, in his *Locomotive Panorama, Volume 1*, 1965 and '*Chronicles of Steam*', 1967, both published by Ian Allan. Cox[16] noted the:

> '*best features were the extremely robust main frame and structure. On the other hand, the use of 2in. diameter tubes only 11ft 2½ in. long would have assured low boiler efficiency which, with small and tortuous steam passages and short lap, short travel valve gear would have produced a locomotive which would have both been sluggish and wasteful.*'

REFERENCES

1. St Rollox Drg No. 19225, dated 21st September 1917, NRS, RHP132373
2. St Rollox Drg No. 19346, dated 30th January 1918, NRS, RHP132352
3. St Rollox Drg No. 19161, dated 26th July 1917, Campbell Cornwell Collection
4. Private correspondence, A.G. Dunbar to C.P. Atkins, 1965
5. St Rollox Drg No. 19718, Montague Smith Collection, NRS, GD456, RHP136357/17
6. Private correspondence, E.S. Cox to A.G. Dunbar, NRS, GD344/6/12/5
7. *Robinson Locomotives – A Pictorial History*, B. Haresnape and P. Rowledge (Ian Allan, 1982), pp. 73ff
8. St Rollox Drg No. 19828, dated 10th February 1919, NRS, RHP132396/1 (the date on the drawing is 10th February 1920)
9. St Rollox Drawing Register, NRS, BR/CAL/5/56
10. J.F. McEwan papers, William Patrick Library, Kirkintilloch, ref. T1/25, etc
11. Caledonian Railway, Directors' Reports and Minutes of Board Meetings, NRS, BR/CAL/1/67, held as CRA2/3/1/10
12. Caledonian Railway, St Rollox Staff Ledger, NRS, BR/CAL/15/21
13. Caledonian Railway, Annual General Meeting, 28th February 1922, CRA 2/3/1/11
14. St Rollox Drg No. 21020, dated 16th October 1923, NRS, RHP132337
15. *The Hughes and Stanier 2-6-0s* (RCTS, 2009), pp. 4-13
16. E.S. Cox remarks, from 'Horwich Built "Caley" 2-6-0s', Jim MacIntosh, in *The True Line*, No 80, April 2003, p. 18

CHAPTER 6

TRAFFIC REQUIREMENTS FOR THE '956' CLASS AND THE DESIGN PROCESS

TRAFFIC REQUIREMENTS

In attempting some assessment of how what became the '956' Class design might have evolved, one has to firstly look at the proposed operational routes, which in this case were principally between Glasgow and Aberdeen and between Glasgow and Carlisle, plus Edinburgh to Carlisle. For the first route, of 146 miles to Aberdeen, the CR normal express train service was timed at 3 hours 55 minutes, with five booked stops and a running time of very nearly 3½ hours.[1] This gave an average speed of approximately 42 mph, though running at in excess of 70 mph could be anticipated and was necessary through the Strathmore area to keep booked time. The steepest grades northbound were encountered just north of Stirling, where an average 1 in 100 gradient from Cornton Crossing for three miles to Dunblane was immediately followed by two miles at 1 in 88, then an average gradient of 1 in 125 to a mile or so south of Kinbuck:[2] an overall hard climb for approximately 6 miles. Banking assistance was always available from Stirling, though its use was left to the discretion of the drivers of individual trains.

Coming southwards out of Perth, there was an equally demanding 7 miles climb from Dunning to just south of Gleneagles, with an average gradient of 1 in 110.[2] Piloting from Perth through to Gleneagles or Stirling was often used with the heavier trains. Additionally, on the northbound route, banking was regularly practised on the grade from Buchanan Street station out to Robroyston West. The standing start from the station itself, up through the tunnel to St Rollox at 1 in 79, was a stiff pull away for heavy trains.

For the Carlisle to Glasgow route, at 103 miles, there was a sustained climb for the northbound 10 miles between Beattock station and the summit at 1,020 ft above sea level,[3] with 1 in 88 for the first 2 miles, followed by 1 in 80 for the next 2 miles, increasing to an average of 1 in 75 for the final 6 miles.[4] The fastest CR express service between Carlisle and Glasgow was timed at 2 hours 15 minutes, with 2 hours 13 minutes running time,[5] the difference being the time allotted to attach the banking locomotive at Beattock station. The average speed for this service was 46 mph – though smart running was called for out of Carlisle, with a timetabled average speed of 55 mph to Beattock station requiring speeds of over 70 mph if booked time was to be maintained. North of Beattock Summit, average speeds in excess of 60 mph were the norm, with 70 mph achieved on the downgrades. Banking assistance for the Beattock climb was invariably used and would be assumed as available, though '903' Class engines were known to tackle the bank unaided with up to 330 ton (gross) trains,[6] and 455 ton (gross) trains with banking assistance,[7] normal passenger timetable schedules being maintained.

On the journey south from Glasgow to Carlisle, a sustained climb for 16 miles, from Uddingston Junction to Craigenhill, at an average gradient of approximately 1 in 125,[4] presented a challenge to both locomotives and enginemen. Piloting was often used with pilots being detached at either Carstairs or Beattock summit. Additionally, the Edinburgh to Carstairs route presented a stiff climb from Merchiston through Midcalder to Cobbinshaw[4] at 880 ft, with an average gradient of 1 in 120 for 17 miles.

Assuming that train loads of around 375/425 tons (gross) would be handled by a single engine on these main routes, and accepting that banking assistance was available for the most severe gradients, it is possible to outline, in simple terms, the technical requirements for an appropriate class of locomotive. These would include, *inter alia*, a principal requirement to haul a 425 ton (gross) train at a speed of, say, 65 mph on the level, and a similar weight on a 1 in 100 incline at, say, 30 mph. From these figures the outline sketch design could start and the route topology would certainly have conditioned St Rollox thinking, irrespective of where the proposal for a new locomotive originated.

THE DESIGN PROCESS

Steam locomotive design has always required a degree of intuition and has never been an exact science, though through the passage of time, coupled with the accrual of experience and operational data, various 'rules' for a reasonably successful outcome were developed and underwritten. Moreover, in the 1905 to 1915 period, the influence of Professor Dalby[8] was extensive in the analytical appreciation of certain cardinal elements of the process, as was the technical output from the Pennsylvania Railroad Company's (PRC) locomotive testing station at Altoona.[9] By 1918, most of these rules and their supporting first level analytical methodologies were sufficiently well understood by innovative CME practitioners such as Gresley, Churchward, Robinson, Bowen-Cooke, Maunsell and others, to allow production of competent designs suiting their respective company's traffic requirements. Furthermore, many CMEs were experimenters and innovators, very focused on pushing steam locomotive technology forward.

The design process was undertaken in individual railway company drawing offices using tables/graphs and standard data built up over many years: design was essentially progressed on an empirical basis, though not always so.

Referring to the design of locomotive frames and the operational stresses arising therein, Vaughan Pendred[10] noted that '*changes in the magnitude and direction of stresses occur on a continuous basis, the cyclic stressing being too complicated to permit of mathematical treatment*'. As such, '*the designer never attempts to calculate their amounts*', but '*adapts the proportions and methods of riveting and bolting, which have been found by experience to be the best*'. He goes on to note: '*Any considerable change in design involves something of an experiment. Risks are got over, however, by the simple expedient of making things very strong*'.

Not surprisingly, frame stressing was not fully understood, even in late LM&SR days, and frame fractures were not uncommon even on LM&SR Stanier Class '5' locomotives.

In these days, before any form of calculator was available, all calculations were done by hand and slide-rule – a time consuming and laborious process – and if a solution was seen as 'having worked last time', then it would invariably be used again, until failure arose, usually through over-stress. Detailed calculations were normally undertaken for boiler stressing, balancing and valve events, though for the latter, use was also made of full-size valve gear models fitted with vernier gauges, from which detailed valve events could be read off. Strength of materials and the associated metallurgy was reasonably well understood, and inertial plus buckling stressing effects for coupling and connecting rods had been appreciated in some detail since the turn of the century.[11] More complex analyses usually only arose when unexplained problems surfaced. Weight control during the design process was important and handled using standard data sheets, as were centre-of-gravity calculations,[12] which were used to set speed limits on curved and/or super-elevated tracks.

REFERENCES

1. Caledonian Railway, Working Timetable No. 537, July 1916, CRA3/1/2/21
2. Caledonian Railway, Glasgow to Perth Gradient Profiles, from 956 Class Trials 1921, Montague Smith Collection, NRS, GD456, RHP136355/27, and Caledonian Railway Gradient Profiles, CRA3/7/2/18
3. Caledonian Railway, Gradient Profiles CRA3/7/2/18 states 1,020 ft; Ordnance Survey height is 1,033 ft; Rail Track sign-board at Beattock Summit states 1,016 ft.
4. Caledonian Railway, Glasgow to Carlisle Gradient Profiles, from 956 Class Trials 1922, Montague Smith Collection, NRS, GD456, RHP136355/31, and Caledonian Railway Gradient Profiles, CRA3/7/2/5
5. Caledonian Railway, Working Timetable No. 550, July 1916, CRA3/1/2/21
6. *Trains Illustrated*, October 1953, Montague Smith letter to the Editor following W.J. Probet article in July 1953 publication
7. *The Scottish 4-6-0 Classes*, C.P. Atkins (Ian Allan, 1976) (report of C.J. Allen timing of No. 903), pp. 66ff
8. Three books by Prof. W.E. Dalby FRS, all published by Edward Arnold, London: *Valve and Valve Gear Mechanisms* (1906), *The Balancing of Engines* (1906), *Steam Power*, 2nd edition (1915)
9. PRC, Locomotive Test Plant, Altoona, reports 1910 onwards
10. *The Railway Locomotive*, Vaughan Pendred, (Archibald Constable & Co., 1908), p. 4
11. *Modern Locomotive Practice*, C.E. Wolff (The Scientific Publishing Co., 1907), chapter IX, pp. 162ff
12. *The Modern Locomotive*, G. Edgar Allen (Cambridge University Press, 1911), chapter VIII, Stability, p. 125

Plate 23
The frames plates for one of the '956' Class locomotives assembled in the Erecting Shop at St Rollox. The plates have been drilled and slotted, with some minor plate work assembled. Whilst horn blocks appear to have been fitted, the main stretchers are absent, the frame plates being held in place by spacer bars.
A.E. Glen

CHAPTER 7

LOCOMOTIVE CONSTRAINTS, POWER REQUIREMENTS, CONSTRUCTION AND INITIAL TRIALS

WEIGHT CONSTRAINTS

For any locomotive design, the civil engineering department axle-loading limitations had to be met, especially in regard to bridge structures, which invariably determined the maximum permissible engine weights. For some years, the Railway Engineers Association (REA) produced graphs of allowable Equivalent Uniformly Distributed Live Load (EUDL, expressed in tons per lineal foot), plotted against Bridge Span (expressed in feet), the analyses being based on given maximum acceptable bending moments at given bridge span centres.[1] A loading profile per axle (20 tons for the heavier laid lines), together with distances between axles, was used to establish the EUDL for a locomotive, this figure being compared with the maximum allowable EUDL derived for the company's bridge structures (calculated from the spans and allowable bending moments), thus allowing the Civil Engineer to assess the impact of locomotive proposals on the company's permanent way.

The '956' Class proposed loading and weight limits were marginally outside the REA 1908 curves,[1] but could be satisfactorily accommodated with a 10 per cent margin over the REA 1920 figures.[1] By the mid-1920s the REA standards had been brought within the British Engineering Standards Association (BESA) remit, the bridge curves being further enhanced in 1925 to take account of increasing locomotive weights.[1]

For the track, the 20 tons limit was derived using a long established empirical relationship for UK, chaired, bull-head rail, with sleepers at 30 in. centres, in which the axle loading limit was determined by dividing the weight of the rail (measured in lbs per yard) by 5, the result being expressed in tons.[2] Thus, for 95 lbs per yard rail, which, in 45 ft lengths was the standard used for permanent way from around 1914 to 1920 or so, the figure of 19.5 tons was obtained, being rounded up to 20 tons.[2]

At this time, these steady state approaches to axle loading design took no direct account of the dynamic interaction and related forces imposed by the locomotive on the track and structures on which it ran. However, the more progressive CMEs, such as Churchward, Gresley, Maunsell and others, recognised the importance of appropriate balancing, and took positive steps to ensure emerging analytical procedures were applied. It was left to the Bridge Stress Committee,[3] set up in 1923 and reporting in 1928, using the locomotive balancing analyses developed by Professor Dalby, to provide a fuller understanding of these matters and to determine appropriate stress level standards, particularly for bridges.

In selecting a 4-6-0 wheel arrangement as the most appropriate for the duties related to their proposed new locomotive, St Rollox faced an overall locomotive weight limit of approximately 80 tons (60 tons adhesion from the coupled axles and 20 tons on the bogie), if maximum axle load was a limiting criteria. For the tender, assuming 7 tons coal capacity and 5,000 gallons of water (22½ tons), together with an empty weight of 20½ tons, a loaded tender weight of 50 tons results – an acceptable 17 tons per axle on three axles, with 6 ft 6 ins between axle centres. The all-up in-service laden weight for the proposed engine and tender combination can be taken as 130 tons.

LOADING GAUGE CONSTRAINTS

Loading gauge considerations would also have figured significantly in the St Rollox design process, since the Caledonian company maximum height from rail level to chimney top was limited to a nominal 12 ft 10½ ins,[4] though the Main Line[5] could accept 13 ft 1 in., whilst between Carlisle and Glasgow, heights up to 13 ft 3½ ins could be accommodated.[5] All of Pickersgill's six-coupled passenger engines were built to the 12 ft 10½ ins height constraint.[6] By comparison, the Highland company height loading gauge, for pre-1918 locomotives, was set at 13 ft 3¾ ins,[6] this dimension being the limit used in the 'Castle' and 'River' Class 4-6-0s, though the 'Superheated Goods' and 'Clan' Class locomotives were built to a 12 ft 10½ ins limit.[6]

Height restriction is most important from the boiler design aspect, for not only does it set a limit on the diameter of the barrel, but, in what is perhaps of greater significance, it increases the difficulties in providing adequate firebox dimensions, especially in the case of 4-6-0 types. The difficulty manifests itself in limiting the firebox heating surface which can be carried above the coupled axles as well as constraining the firebox depth. The latter point might be overcome by using a shallow firebox, but this has its own disadvantages.[4] Whilst it could be argued that adoption of the 4-6-2 wheel arrangement would largely discount these firebox difficulties, the 4-6-0 option is the better arrangement because it offers higher 'power-to-weight' and 'power-to-cost' ratios, noting the maximised adhesion conditions for the 4-6-0.[4] Indeed, on railways with moderate distances between passenger termini, plus more severe gradients and curves, such as the Caledonian company, a strong case can be made for the adoption of the 4-6-0 over a 'Pacific' type.

Additionally, recognising the severe gradients on the CR main lines, the need for tractive effort as opposed to high speed probably suggests a driving wheel diameter at the lower end of the 6 ft 0 ins to 6 ft 6 ins spectrum, and in making the selection at, say, 6 ft 1 in.,[4] the difficulties noted earlier in providing adequate firebox dimensions are eased.

During the McIntosh era, only inside-cylindered express passenger locomotives were built by the company, though Pickersgill, in his '60' and '944' classes, re-introduced the outside cylinder arrangement for various reasons.[4] These include the difficulties in getting larger diameter cylinders fitted between the frames, as well as allowing greater piston thrusts to be transmitted more directly to the coupling rods. In making the change to outside cylinders, further benefits accrue through greater accessibility for maintenance and the availability of increased journal lengths on the coupled axles.

POWER REQUIREMENTS

The power necessary to pull a 425 ton (gross) corridor-stock train together with its 130 ton locomotive and tender at 65 mph on a level track, with clean and dry rails, can be calculated with reasonable accuracy from data prepared pre-1914 by Strahl, Fry, Henschel and others.[7] To derive the required power, the overall train weight, in this case 555 tons, is separated into the various appropriate component parts (engine coupled axles & mechanism, engine bogie and tender, rolling stock, etc) to which a power requirement per ton at specific speeds is applied; further components are added for atmospheric resistance, inclines, any required acceleration, track curvature and so forth.

For what became the '956' Class, the appropriate calculations result in approximately 1,370 horsepower being required to pull the 555 tons total train weight at 65 mph on a straight and level track. Whilst additional components can be added for the resistance of curves and the need for specific acceleration, these latter factors tend to be of second order influence in this case, and can be accounted for by rounding up. With the same train weight, at 30 mph on a 1 in 100 gradient, the required horsepower is around 1,380, again excluding track curvature resistance and acceleration needs. In overall terms, and rounding up, the locomotive cylinders are required to produce, say, 1,500 horsepower, including a margin, which will cover both the level track running and the 1 in 100 incline conditions. This figure is an IHP value, since the resistance of the locomotive and tender has been accounted for in the overall train weight.

It is now required to estimate the boiler requirements, and various 'rules' were available to do this, a position which was reasonably well understood by 1918, certainly by the more accomplished CMEs

and private builders, and which led to the required outputs being obtained with reasonable thermal efficiencies. Moreover, the PRC, amongst other US-based testing facilities, had been producing substantive boiler thermal design data since around 1910,[8] and major papers on the subject thereafter. So that St Rollox could proceed with the design, certain assumptions were necessary, including the calorific value of the boiler fuel, the diameter of the driving wheels, and an indication of piston speed.

The calorific value of Scottish mined bituminous coal at this time could vary between 11,000 to 15,500 BTU/lb,[9] though the collieries usually sold a composite amalgam, varying between 11,500 to 13,500 BTU/lb, ensuring that the lower grades were used. The Douglas 9 ft and 7 ft seams (Lanarkshire) and the Drysart seam (Fife) provided an average value of 12,500 BTU/lb, whilst a lower quality coal, averaging around 11,000 BTU/lb, was obtained from the Ayrshire basin.[9] From this data, it is reasonable to assume an average calorific value of 12,500 to 13,000 BTU/lb being associated with locomotive coal used by the Caledonian company. An express passenger locomotive would be provided with a better quality fuel because of its duties, perhaps around 13,000 to 13,500 BTU/lb. If

Plate 24
Engine No. 956 in an advanced stage of building at St Rollox works, filling and priming work being in progress prior to painting. Motion components, including connecting and coupling rods seem to have been removed and lie beside the locomotive, as do the front buffers. The engine appears under crane lift, possibly to allow wheel rotation to assist painting.   *J.G. Barr/SRPS*

coal of a lesser calorific value was used, more would be consumed for the same duty, with a proportionate increase in ash production.

Additionally, a firebox temperature of around 1,950°F[10,11] and a corresponding smokebox temperature from flue gasses of 660-690°F[12,13] is assumed as reasonably representative of optimised combustion conditions with envisaged firing rates[14] of 100 lbs of coal per hour per sq. ft of grate area, giving most effective heat transfer characteristics, with the locomotive near maximum working conditions.

With a required train speed on straight and level track of 65 mph and a driving wheel diameter in the range 6 ft to 6 ft 6 ins, it is convenient to select a rotational speed of 300 revs per minute (rpm), which gives a wheel diameter of 6 ft 1 in., which in fact was the size selected by the St Rollox team. One should also be mindful that the CR '60' Class locomotives had 6 ft 1 in. diameter driving wheels, so the patterns for these would be available.

Mean piston speeds in the range 1,000 to 1,400 ft per minute[15] would normally be associated with locomotives of this type, and in this case, with a train speed of 65 mph, a wheel diameter of 6 ft 1 in. and a proposed piston stroke in the range 26 ins to 28 ins, the mean piston speed falls in the range 1,296 to 1,396 ft per minute. Allowing the locomotive to run up to around 75 mph raises the mean piston speed to 1,496 ft per minute, and suggests 26 ins for the piston stroke, which is entirely satisfactory.

Based on the assumptions outlined, at 300 rpm, for a simple expansion locomotive operating at 180 psi, a heating surface of approximately 1,900 to 2,000 sq. ft[16] is needed to produce the necessary IHP at 65 mph on level track. On the 1 in 100 gradient, where the rotational speed is around half of that obtained on the level, the heating surface is around 2,200 to 2,300 sq. ft.[16] Heating surfaces quoted include all tubes, flues and firebox areas, but are exclusive of superheater surfaces. These simply and almost empirically determined heating surfaces compare very favourably with the 2,370 sq. ft determined by St Rollox. Moreover, the above outline analyses confirm that the boiler rating of the locomotive is determined by its hill climbing requirements.

For comparative purposes, Pickersgill, through his ILocoE work,

would undoubtedly have been aware of the performances of the GWR 'Star' and 'Saint' classes and the L&NWR 'Claughton' Class where IHPs of 1,500 could be produced and exceeded by these locomotives. Much has been written of the exceptional performances of the GWR locomotives, whilst the 'Claughton' Class was a design of significant potential, which, in the opinion of many, missed greatness by a narrow margin.

Pickersgill would also have known of the well publicised 1913 'Claughton' Class test runs,[17] in which engine No. 1159 *Ralph Brocklebank* worked a 450 ton (gross) Euston to Crewe non-stop train, covering the 158 miles in 158 minutes, an IHP of 1,617 being recorded after Northchurch Tunnel. A few days later a 360 ton (gross) train was worked non-stop by the same engine from Crewe to Carlisle, the 141 miles being covered in 140 minutes, with Tebay troughs being passed at 69 mph, and a recorded 1,669 IHP. The minimum speed over Shap was 37 mph.

CONSTRUCTION AND INITIAL TRIALS

From the production aspect, the Caledonian company locomotive works management at St Rollox would be aware of the design as it progressed. A smooth building cycle would be required and adjustments would inevitably be needed after preliminary steaming. Alan Dunbar,[18] who took part in the class construction, recorded foremen Harry Glow and John Brough dealt with the detailed erection under the supervision of Mr Alexander Hallam, the chief foreman. Each frame was noted as weighing around 3 tons and was cranked inwards 3 ft 9 ins from the front of the first coupled axle to give appropriate valve gear layout clearances. Plate 23, captured by Ernest Glen,[19] shows the frames for one of the '956' Class set up in the erecting shop, whilst Plate 24 shows No. 956 at a more advanced build stage.

The first steaming of No. 956 took place at St Rollox works yard on the 21st June 1921,[18] Plate 25 illustrating this event.[19] On that day, driver MacIntyre and fireman Simpson took No. 956 to Kilgarth, near Glenboig, Alan Dunbar noting: *'John Menzies, an Inspector accompanied them, with Messers Moodie and Urie from the drawing*

Plate 25
No. 956's first official day in steam at St Rollox works yard on the 21st June 1921. On that day driver MacIntyre and fireman Simpson took No. 956 to Kilgarth, near Glenboig, accompanied by Inspector John Menzies, and Messers Moodie and Urie. Pickersgill put in an appearance, but did not travel on the initial trip.
A.E. Glen

office. Mr Pickersgill put in an appearance but did not travel on the initial trip'. [18]

St Rollox finance data of the time indicates the cost of materials for each of the class was £6,375, wages were £2,584 and overheads £723, giving a total of £9,682 per locomotive,[20] including tender. In the St Rollox costing ledger, the Y125 works order entry notes that costs were accrued against this head of charge from 19th December 1918, which presumably would point to the start of design work in the drawing office. Authorisation to build the four engines would follow.

Trials of the new locomotive were put in hand straight away on express passenger workings between Glasgow Buchanan Street and Perth, also between Glasgow Central and Carlisle. Plate 26 shows

No. 956, fitted with the original derived motion and an indicator shelter, at Buchanan Street station on the 2nd August 1921, about to depart on an express working to Perth. The arrangement to drive the indicator mechanism is shown attached to the RHS crosshead just above the union link.

The St Rollox drawing register[21] shows that in April 1921, in preparation for these trials, various drawings were put in hand covering the indicator shelter (drawing No. 21148) and the arrangement of the indicator drive gear (drawing No's 21156, 21158-21161). Most unfortunately, the indicator drive gear arrangement drawings have not been located, though the actual numerate IHP figures are available for some trials conditions and are given in the Appendices.[22]

Plate 26
No. 956 at Buchanan Street station, about to depart with an express working to Perth under trials conditions on the 2nd August 1921. The locomotive is fitted with an indicator shelter, the drive for the indicator mechanism being connected to the crosshead above the union link. The results for this trial working are given in Appendix 1.
Ken Nunn, NRM/LCGB3162

REFERENCES
1. REA Bridge Curve Data, Author's collection
2. *Steam Locomotive Design: Data and Formulae*, A.E. Phillipson (The Locomotive Publishing Co.), p. 9
3. *Bridge Stress Committee Report 1928*, Dept. of Scientific & Industrial Research (HMSO, 1928)
4. 'Caledonian Railway: Six-coupled Express Passenger Locomotives', E.C. Poultney, in *The Engineer*, 4th November 1921, pp. 474ff, Article written after visit to St Rollox Works and discussion with Wm. Pickersgill.
5. John G. Barr papers, courtesy the Scottish Railway Preservation Society
6. *The Scottish 4-6-0 Classes*, C.P. Atkins (Ian Allan), Appendix pp. 87ff
7. *Locomotive Engineers' Pocket Book* (The Locomotive Publishing Co.), Strahl, Fry, Henschel, etc, data, pp. 24-35
8. PRC, Altoona, 'Tests on E2A Locomotive 1910', is typical of PRC output results
9. Data supplied by Scottish Resources Group/Scottish Coal, for Douglas and other coal seams
10. *Locomotive Engineers' Pocket Book*, The Locomotive Publishing Co., Radiant Heat, pp. 44ff
11. *Steam Locomotive Design: Data and Formulae*, A.E. Phillipson, p. 62
12. *Locomotive Boilers and Engines*, Prof. L.V. Ludy (American Technical Society, 1918), Prof. Goss paper, pp. 58-60
13. Locomotive Testing Plant, Altoona, Bulletin No. 31, 1918, fig. 12, p. 26
14. *Locomotive Design: Data and Formulae*, A.E. Phillipson, p. 51 (*The Engineer*, 1913)
15. *Locomotive Design: Data and Formulae*, A.E. Phillipson, p. 29
16. *Locomotive Engineers' Pocket Book*, The Locomotive Publishing Co., (L. H. Fry, *Engineering*, vol. XCV, 1913), pp. 61-3
17. *Jubilees of the LMS*, John F. Clay (Ian Allan, 1970), p. 12
18. 'Y125 – And All That', Alan Dunbar, in *SLS Journal*, August 1948, pp. 192ff
19. A.E. Glen Collection, private collection, courtesy Dr Ann Glen
20. Extract of costs, St Rollox Cost Ledger, NRM
21. St Rollox Drawing Register, NRS, BR/CAL/5/56
22. Appendices in this publication

CHAPTER 8
THE '956' CLASS LOCOMOTIVES AS DESIGNED AND BUILT

From the requirements previously outlined, St Rollox prepared the detailed design for the 3-cylinder '956' Class, which had the dimensions given below. The details have, as far as possible been taken from extant original drawings and other design material for the class[1,2,3], and as such may differ marginally from data quoted by other authors, where rounding may have been applied.

BOILER DIMENSIONS	
Barrel external diameters – front ring	5 ft 6⅜ ins
– middle ring	5 ft 7¹¹⁄₁₆ ins
– rear ring	5 ft 9 ins
Barrel length	15 ft 7¼ ins
Barrel plate thickness	²¹⁄₃₂ ins
Firebox outer wrapper thickness	¾ ins
Length between tubeplates	16 ft 0 ins
Length of firebox outer casing	9 ft 3 ins
Internal steam pipe diameter	5 ins
Centre line above rail level	8 ft 10 ins
Chimney height above rail level	12 ft 10½ ins

Firebox staying used two rows of sling stays from the firebox wrapper (adjacent to the firebox tubeplate) to the outer shell, followed, to the backhead, by direct staying between the firebox wrapper and outer shell.[4,5]

BOILER HEATING SURFACES AND OTHER DATA		
Boiler tubes,	203 x 2¹⁄₁₆ ins O/D*	1,700 sq. ft (based on 2.0 ins)
Flue tubes,	24 x 5⅛ ins O/D**	500 sq. ft (based on 5.0 ins)
Firebox		170 sq. ft
Total evaporative heating surface		2,370 sq. ft
Superheater[7] – 28 Elements (50 per cent return bends, 12 ft length, with 1⅜ ins O/D elements, No. 9 IWG section)		270 sq. ft
Superheater elements I/D[7]		1¹⁄₁₆ ins
Precentage superheat, as ratio to THS + FHS		11.4 per cent
Grate area		28 sq. ft
Working pressure		180 psi
L/D for tubes		110
Free-gas area of tubes		3.39 sq. ft
Free-gas area of flues (ex superheater)		1.81 sq. ft
Total Free-gas area of tubeplate		5.20 sq. ft
Total Tubeplate Free-gas area as ratio of grate area		18.6 per cent
Free-gas area of flues as ratio of total free gas area		34.8 per cent

Notes:
* Original drawing altered from 2¹⁄₁₆ ins to 2⅛ ins for 'future construction' (undated).[6] Original drawing further altered to change tube diameters to 1⅞ ins, dated the 6th June 1931.
** Original drawing altered from 5⅛ ins to 5⁵⁄₁₆ ins for 'future construction' (undated).[6]

CYLINDERS AND MOTION	
Cylinders (3: two outside, one inside)	18½ ins x 26 ins with by-pass valves
Valve gear	
– outside cylinders	Walschaerts' (inside admission)
– inside cylinder*	Pickersgill derived motion (inside admission)
– piston valve bobbin diameter	8 ins
– piston valve type	two rings per bobbin (PRC design)
– valve lap (from combination lever action)	1½ ins
– valve lead	¼ ins
– valve travel in full gear**	5⅞ ins
– valve gear operation	steam assisted lever reverse
Connecting rod lengths	
– outside cylinders	11 ft 0 ins
– inside cylinder	6 ft 6 ins
Eccentric rod lengths (for Stephenson's link motion)	3 ft 11 ins
Cylinders (outside) centre to centre distance	6 ft 9¾ ins

Notes
* Original Pickersgill derived motion removed and Stephenson's link motion fitted, followed by further modified Pickersgill derived motion.
** Restriction applied to limit centre cylinder valve travel. Restriction set at 65 per cent cut-off.

LUBRICATION

One CR-pattern eight-feed mechanical lubricator was provided, the feeds being divided, three for cylinders, one divided for piston glands and four for the leading and centre driving boxes. The trailing axleboxes had ordinary siphon feeds in the cab. The oil for the steam chests was pumped through a non-return atomiser into the steam pipes. Displacement lubricators were fitted on the cylinder covers in order that any deficiency in the supply could be made up, the pistons having no tail rods. The fact that cylinder oil was used to lubricate two sets of driving axleboxes caused most of the hot box cases in the early years to take place at the trailing end.

OBSERVATIONS ON THE BOILER DESIGN

In assessing the '956' Class design against the known criteria of the time, the basic building blocks of the locomotive will be reviewed as separate items, the details being given in succeeding chapters. However, prior to this, it is worth noting a few basic parameters for the '956' Class boiler and judging these against contemporary best practice.

The '956' Class SHS provision at 11.4 per cent of the evaporative surface totals must be regarded as a design shortfall for reasons already given. Additionally, from the ratio of gas flow through the flues to total gas flow, it is clear that Pickersgill, or his staff, even in 1919 to 1920, persisted with this limited superheat provision policy,

WHEELS, WEIGHTS AND OVERALL DIMENSIONS

Diameter of wheels	– bogie	3 ft 6 ins
	– coupled	6 ft 1 ins
	– tender	4 ft 0 ins
Wheelbase	– engine	7 ft 0 ins + 10 ft 3 ins + 7 ft 0 ins + 8 ft 0 ins
	– bogie	3 ft 5 ins + 3 ft 7 ins
	– coupled	15 ft 0 ins
	– tender	6 ft 6 ins + 6 ft 6 ins
	– engine and tender	54 ft 0½ ins
Length over buffers		63 ft 8 ins
Engine frames	– length	37 ft 8 ins
	– thickness	1¼ ins
Weight of engine and tender	– full	129 tons 0 cwt
	– empty	94 tons 15 cwt
Weight of engine	– full	81 tons 0 cwt
	– empty	72 tons 0 cwt
Weight of tender	– full	48 tons 0 cwt
	– empty	22 tons 0 cwt
Weight distribution (full)	– adhesion	60 tons 0 cwt
	– bogie	21 tons 0 cwt
	– tender	48 tons 0 cwt
Tender coal capacity		5 tons 10 cwt
Tender water capacity		4,500 gallons
Minimum radius of curvature		7.5 chains
Tractive effort at 85% boiler pressure		28,000 lbs
Factor of adhesion		4.8

the ratio in this case being 34.8 per cent. When coupled to the low SHS provision, this would suggest average steam temperatures in the range 500-550 °F (actually borne out by trials results[8]).

These decisions on low SHS provision and flue gas ratio may well have been driven by a continuing misguided attempt to limit carbonisation of steam passages and valve liners but, as already pointed out, was unlikely to achieve such an objective, as the upper end steam temperature was still approaching the high superheat bandwidth.

One should recall that in his '113', '60' and '944' classes, Pickersgill had progressively reduced flue gas ratios (flue gas area to total free-gas area ratio) from around 48 per cent for the '113' Class, to 45 per cent for the '60' Class and around 40 per cent for the '944' Class.[2] Whether this was intentional is by no means clear, and the extent to which Thomas Weir, the Chief Draughtsman, or for that matter John Barr, agreed with this progressive reduction is unknown. However, for the '956' Class, the application of this more risk averse, even timid, approach to this important design parameter, coupled to a low SHS as a percentage of the evaporative heating surface, very much flew in the face of contemporary best practice and the criteria set down by Dr Schmidt.[9,10]

Operating in the same time frame, Gresley, for his 'K3' Class boiler,[11] used high superheat provision, the SHS being 21.4 per cent of the evaporation surface totals, with an equivalent flue gas ratio of 49.4 per cent. Moreover, Gresley used 1½ ins O/D superheater elements,[11] which, with No. 9 IWG section, gave 1¼ ins bore, just as on the McIntosh '139' and '903' classes, leading to steam

temperatures in the 650-700 °F range. Clearly, Gresley would have been equally concerned with carbonisation, but this did not deter him providing a 32-element, 407 sq. ft superheater. The 'K3' Class[11] free-gas area through the tubes and flues, at 19 per cent of the grate area, was higher than the 15 to 16 per cent which McIntosh would have recognised, suggesting the 'K3' Class grate could have been beneficially increased to 30 or even 32 sq. ft.

REFERENCES

1. Campbell Cornwell Collection of CR '956' Class drawings, CRA6/1/3/2, Archive Grouping 48
2. *Forty Years of Caledonian Locomotives*, Campbell Cornwell (David & Charles, 1974), Appendices 2-5
3. The Montague Smith Collection, NRS, GD456, RHP136355, Pickersgill Locomotives, '956' Class
4. 'New Three Cylinder 4-6-0 Type Locomotives, Caledonian Railway', in *The Railway Engineer*, October 1921, pp. 365ff
5. St Rollox Drg No. 19948, dated 10th May 1919, Montague Smith Collection, NRS, GD456, RHP136355/8
6. St Rollox Drgs No. 19912 dated 23rd April 1919 and No. 19915 dated 29th April 1919, CRA6/1/3/2, Archive Grouping 48
7. St Rollox Drg No. 20118, dated 22nd August 1919, CRA6/1/3/2, Archive Grouping 48
8. Appendices 1-3 of this publication
9. *The Use of Superheated Steam in Locomotives*, Dr W. Schmidt (1908)
10. *The Application of Highly Superheated Steam to Locomotives*, Dr W. Schmidt (1911)
11. *The LNER 2-6-0 Classes*, John F. Clay and J. Cliffe (Ian Allan, 1978), Appendices, pp. 64-7

CHAPTER 9

PICKERSGILL AND THE ST ROLLOX DRAWING OFFICE STAFF

GENERAL

By all accounts, the drawing office team at St Rollox was unusually small by comparative standards for railways of broadly equivalent size to the Caledonian company. This team carried out all the design and specification work for the company's locomotives, carriages, wagons, docks and plant, under a Chief Draughtsman, referred to by Graeme Miller[1] as *'the frock coated'* Thomas Weir,[2] who had joined the company in 1891. Miller recalled the locomotive team was led by Leading Draughtsman William H. Moodie,[2] who was only three years younger than Weir, the C&W team being led by James McGown and the plant side by David Cowan. Whilst Miller, who became Chief Draughtsman at St Rollox in 1939 on the death of George Kerr,[3] noted the total drawing office team never exceeded nine, this probably refers only to salaried staff, the overall total being perhaps nearer twelve, as attested by draughtsmens' signatures in the St Rollox drawing register.[4]

Thomas Weir, Chief Draftsman until his retiral in February 1920,[5] was a *'much respected figure of exceptional ability'*[1] who, as previously noted, could claim much of the credit for the locomotive successes of the McIntosh era. W.H. Moodie, who succeeded Weir as Chief Draftsman in 1920,[6] together with seniors Alexander Linn, George L. Kerr and Graeme Miller plus others, constituted the locomotive team from the time of Pickersgill's appointment until the formation of the LM&SR company.

Compared to other railways broadly similar in standing to the Caledonian – such as the GNR, MR and GCR, in which CMEs had very able dedicated technical assistants and related support staff – St Rollox appears to have had nowhere near the technical strength in depth enjoyed by its comparable English neighbours. At Doncaster, Gresley[7] had Bulleid, Wintour, Groom, and others; at Derby, Fowler[8] had Anderson, Symes, Henderson, Chambers, Sanford, Parr and several other Whitworth Scholars; at Gorton, Robinson[9] had Thom, Maclure and Rowlands, the latter a Whitworth Scholar and exceptionally talented analytical engineer. Additionally, most of the larger companies had a development and experimental section attached to their respective drawing offices, devoted to the general progression of the related company's locomotive engineering, and not necessarily focused specifically on the design and drawings for a new class. St Rollox had no such development section, which *prima facie*, recognising locomotive technological advances of the time, must be viewed as a major omission on the Directors' part.

Another measure of the engineering strength of the individual railway companies could be gauged by the number of technical papers presented by their employees to the ILocoE, IMechE and the ICE. Gresley and Fowler plus their staffs were frequent contributors, but, as far as is known, only one learned society paper was produced by a Caledonian company technical officer in the Pickersgill era, that being by Irvine Kempt (junior),[10] he, at the time, being Assistant Locomotive Superintendent (Works). Kempt, as previously noted, read his paper on locomotive lubrication to the ILocoE in Glasgow on the 20th January 1921. By his own preamble, Kempt stated his paper *'was not to be considered as a technical treatise'* on lubrication.

When considering St Rollox staff development policy, it is also noteworthy that the English companies mentioned tended to invest in the recruitment, technical education and promotion of staff from within their own ranks and, by so doing, they sustained an internal succession planning regime, something that St Rollox never really achieved at the most senior technical levels on a comparable basis.

Perhaps the staff shortfall here may have been a driving influence in the recruitment of Pickersgill, the Directors becoming aware of their own company's comparatively thinly provisioned technical staff numbers, anticipating that Pickersgill would reinforce his department.

POST DRUMMOND INFLUENCES

Certainly when Dugald Drummond arrived at St Rollox in 1882,[11] he brought a number of experienced Cowlairs men with him, including George Wheatley, William M. Urie and his brother Peter Drummond. Robert W. Urie was recruited externally in 1885[12] as a general draughtsman, subsequently rising to become Chief Draughtsman then Works Manager at St Rollox, thereafter joining Dugald Drummond on the L&SWR in 1897, and eventually succeeding him as Chief Mechanical Engineer. However, with McIntosh's appointment, on the untimely death of John Lambie, and the retiral of Joseph Goodfellow, plus Peter Drummond's moving to Inverness, together with Robert W. Urie's departure, the St Rollox locomotive design team was left much downsized. With the exception of W.H. Moodie, there was no senior external recruitment at St Rollox in McIntosh's tenure, which must be viewed as a significant omission and quite the antithesis to the policy adopted by Drummond in the 1882 to 1890 period.

One has to acknowledge that St Rollox technical strength in depth was visibly lacking, there being no one of Bulleid's or Rowland's abilities in direct support of the Locomotive Superintendent, operating in parallel with the Chief Draughtsman. In these circumstances, the available St Rollox locomotive design staff could, with the exception of Weir and possibly Moodie, perhaps be regarded as having very limited experience and being practitioners of the existing norms, inclined to remain with the *status quo*, and certainly not innovatively inclined.

Against this charge, however, one has to bear in mind that Thomas Weir with Moodie, under McIntosh's direction, led the design of the superheated '903' and '139' classes, which were innovative in their time and most successful. Also, superheating of the 'Dunalastair II' Class had begun, just as McIntosh retired, again with great success, and the superheating of the '908' Class was planned. Of course, Drummond precepts were being relied upon, and superheating using the Schmidt system, with parameters underwritten by Schimdt's development work, noted earlier, proving highly successful. It seems clear that this superheating policy met with Thomas Weir's approval.

PICKERSGILL'S ENGINEERING POLICY AND STAFF RESOURCES

Pickersgill, from the time of his appointment, however, gradually turned his back on the precepts of the McIntosh era, or was persuaded to so do, particularly with regards to superheating. This seems obvious in retrospect, when considering much of Pickersgill's work and the '956' Class design in particular, though there is evidence[13] that escalating materials costs plus their availability in war-time and immediately thereafter significantly influenced events. Perhaps the '956' Class design shortfalls and subsequent operational problems could have been 'designed out' if a stronger and more robust analytical technical presence had been in place alongside the Locomotive Superintendent and his Chief Draughtsman. Interestingly, the use of piston valve sealing arrangements in the '956' Class similar to those used by the PRC suggests at least some at St Rollox were conscious of developing practice elsewhere.[14,15] St Rollox seemingly was not unaware of developments at Altoona.

O.S. Nock wrote of Pickersgill as *'a scholarly man, with a charming, though quiet personality'*,[16] a point endorsed by Alan Dunbar, who remarked that he *'was a reticent individual and took very little part in any publicity'*.[16] By all accounts, Pickersgill's forte was as an administrator rather than as a locomotive designer, Montague Smith noting him to have been *'a brilliant workshop organiser'*,[16] who raised the workshops at St Rollox to a very high standard of efficiency. Being of significantly different temperament to the powerful personality of his predecessor, and focused on administrative matters, Pickersgill may have delegated to the drawing office the detail of designs for which he would ultimately carry responsibility, and perhaps even relied on John Barr, the Assistant Locomotive Superintendent, to deal with drawing office matters on his behalf.

Of course the recruitment of a senior assistant for Pickersgill raises the question of salaries and, as Pickergill's own starting salary suggests a strong measure of Scots' frugality in the CR boardroom, the same parsimony may well have inhibited further senior design staff recruitment. In 1905,[2] Thomas Weir's annual salary had been set at £264, with William Moodie's being £203; by January 1918,[2] Weir had advanced to £334 and Moodie to £265 – hardly large sums, at a time when the average 1918 St Rollox locomotive department 'clerical' salary[2] was in the £150 to £190 range and when skilled craftsmen in the works were paid 8 shillings per day.[17] By comparison, both Barr and Kempt[2] were paid salaries of £450 in 1914 (both advanced to £500 in 1917), so to attract a leading engineer to act as Pickergill's technical assistant, and *de facto* be his deputy, would probably have required a salary of £450 at the very minimum in 1915/16, which may not have been sufficiently attractive to potential candidates of the required calibre.

On his appointment as Chief Draughtsman of the NER in November 1906, George Heppell[18] was paid £300 per annum, about 15 per cent above Weir's rate for the same period. Potentially, any suggestion of an appropriately qualified technical assistant for Pickersgill being paid above £450 per annum was unlikely to have been supported by the Directors, who, in any case, might have been tempted to ask 'what was Pickersgill himself doing?', suggesting they were more than somewhat out of touch with emerging locomotive developments. Also, as one of *'the powers behind the throne'*,[19] Barr may have been more than unsympathetic to such a recruitment, which could have potentially undermined his own position.

The two remaining salaried members of the locomotive drawing office team, Alexander Linn[2] and George Kerr,[2] joined the company in 1894 and 1907 respectively, both aged 16 when they joined, so were again St Rollox experienced only. It seems extraordinary that Kerr,[1] the most junior member of the salaried team, aged 29 in mid-1919, should be tasked with the concept work on the '956' Class derived motion, though the more experienced Linn, aged 41, produced most of the drawings, with Moodie no doubt intimately involved. In 1919,[2] Linn's salary was £170 and Kerr's £120,[2] which seem very much out of line with what seemed equitable, bearing in mind contemporary clerical salaries[2] and Donald Matheson,[20] the General Manager, receiving £2,000 in 1910, advanced to £3,000 per annum in 1916.

One is faced with the inexorable conclusion that the Caledonian company was a 'tightly run ship', both in regard to the recruitment of appropriately qualified staff and their remuneration, with Scot's frugality potentially having overtaken the necessary management imperatives. The unexpected departure of Thomas Weir seemed to have caused significant management reflection, to the extent that Moodie's salary,[6] when taking the post as Chief Draughtsman in 1920, was increased from £265 to £560, with Linn[6] being advanced from £170 to £425 and Kerr[6] from £120 to £325 at the same review. However, it seemed all too little and too late, though the effect of any government restrictions on wartime and immediate post-war drawing office staff recruitment is not known. Such constraints as there may have been seem not to have inhibited Gresley in the recruitment of Bullied in the same period.

THOMAS WEIR'S DEPARTURE

Graeme Miller[1] refers to the sudden retiral of Thomas Weir in enigmatic terms, noting (incorrectly) that Weir's *'retirement late in 1921'* (the date should be the 28th May 1920[5]), was *'co-incident with the derived motion to drawing No 20179* ['Motion Arrangement for 3-Cylinder Engine', drawing No. 20179 dated 2nd October 1919[4]], *being discarded'*. Whilst his date for Weir's retirement is incorrect (almost certainly a memory slip as Miller was referring to an incident almost sixty years previously), and drawing No. 20179 was actually endorsed by Pickersgill, not discarded, Miller nevertheless clearly identifies Weir's unexpected and premature departure with drawing No. 20179, the final arrangement of the initially conceived '956' Class 3-cylinder derived motion.

Recognising that Pickersgill signed the major '956' Class drawings in early 1920, and this undoubtedly would have included No. 20179, there is the implied suggestion that Weir's precipitate departure came about since he could not support the 3-cylinder derived motion arrangement set out on that drawing, and had perhaps been over-ruled. One should also recall that having examined the L&NWR 'Claughton' Class drawings, Weir[13] seemingly favoured the 4-cylinder arrangement, whilst both Pickersgill and Barr regarded a 3-cylinder solution as satisfactory.

Posterity has not been favoured with Weir's thinking at the time, when important technical decisions were made, and the St Rollox drawing register[4] is silent regarding any valve gear options which may have been investigated. It may be that Weir could have supported the 3-cylinder solution, but not the proposed valve gear arrangements.

Miller's[1] notes go to some length to record that Weir was a *'man of high integrity and strong principles and not the person likely to speak of any exchanges which may have occurred with his superiors'*. In short, Weir would *'not tell tales out of school'*. Miller's[1] overall remarks leave one with the distinct possibility of Pickersgill or Barr and Weir having had a major technical disagreement on the '956' Class, ostensibly related to the derived motion. Indeed, this incident could have been the culmination of a series of such difficulties, which, when coupled with Pickersgill's being *'inclined to be a bit regimental'*,[1] prompted Weir's departure. In rounding off his comments in these matters, Miller[1] records that *'Weir left quietly, refusing to be the recipient of any parting gift from the management. Later, a senior member of the DO called at his home with a gift from ourselves, as a mark of our esteem and regard'*.[1]

Caledonian company records relating to Weir's departure initially record that *'Mr Weir desires to retire from the services on the 28th May next and recommending that his retirement allowance of £116 10s 3d from the superannuation fund should be supplemented'*.[5] The resulting finance committee decision noted on the 10th February 1920 was, *'Make up allowance to Mr Weir to £250 per annum (including superannuation)'*,[5] this point seemingly coming from the General Manager. However, it transpired by April 1920 that Weir was not eligible for a pension from the superannuation fund, he finally being given *'an allowance of £165 per annum during the pleasure of the Company, and an honorarium of £250 in recognition of Mr Weir's long and valuable services'*,[5] again at the General Manager's recommendation.

It would seem that Donald Matheson did his best for Weir in the circumstances. For Weir to apparently resign in this manner, having no pension, and to completely rely on the company's benevolent munificence, suggests nothing other than a major rift within the locomotive department. Whilst William Moodie succeeded as Chief Draughtsman, the locomotive drawing office team was now, most unfortunately, deprived of its most experienced member, when the recruitment of an additional senior engineer seemed wholly appropriate, verging on the essential. One wonders what McIntosh or Drummond would have made of all this.

If Pickersgill had understood and accepted the reasons for Gresley's rejection[21] in 1918 of the initial GNR multi-pinned derived motion, it is just possible a more appropriate scheme might have emerged. Unfortunately, however, Pickersgill chose to persevere with 'the wee contraption of his own',[22] selected what turned out to be an unworkable type of motion, and inadvertently may have managed to lose his Chief Draughtsman in the process. If Miller's remarks[1] are to carry any credence, this series of events can hardly be seen as a glowing endorsement of Pickersgill's technical and managerial judgement. Indeed, as noted by E.S. Cox,[23] Pickersgill may well have been suffering from 'an insular and self-satisfied outlook' on his new locomotive.

In his unpublished autobiography, which includes observations on the St Rollox drawing office where he worked in LM&SR days, H.N. Marshall[24] makes a few observations on the '956' Class derived motion. He notes that, aided by Professor Mallenby, George Kerr, to whom he ascribes significant ability, schemed out the derived motion for which Pickersgill and Moodie took credit until its difficulties became apparent, whereupon it became 'your valve gear', the 'your' referring to Kerr. According to Marshall,[24] it would seem that the technically talented Kerr's career suffered through his association with the '956' Class derived motion, and but for that he could have aspired to higher office, and more quickly, though he did succeed Sandy Linn as Chief Draughtsman at St Rollox.

Support from Directors and Assistants

After a series of disappointing trials, Miller notes:[25]

'The outcome was that after a period of close observation, Pickersgill had no hesitation in making the bold decision to abandon the gear in its original form and replace it with Stephenson's independent gear, the only alternative which could be conveniently and quickly applied.'

One wonders what Weir's comments might have been.

Reverting to the need to acquire an experienced senior technical assistant, one could question what support Pickersgill might have secured from his General Manager and the Directors? The post-war environment and the company's financial predicament, together with the impending 1922 amalgamations, may have conspired to place further technical staff recruitment well down their order of priorities. It is just possible that Pickersgill's hands were artificially tied over recruitment, the Directors as a group having failed to grasp the urgency of the need, notwithstanding the loss of Thomas Weir. It is a distinct possibility that senior technical staff recruitment was compromised by war-time constraints arising from government policy.

However, Pickersgill's ostensible rejection of the '938' Class precepts must remain one of the great puzzles of his tenure. The Caledonian company authorities themselves seemed to have little regard for the class, perhaps taking the view that they 'had been saddled with them'. Additionally, the '938' Class may have displayed their NBR pedigree just a little too prominently, with Belpaire boiler and curved smokebox handrail, though it appears Pickersgill's intention to use the Belpaire firebox[13] on the '72' Class 4-4-0s was unfortunately thwarted by post-war cost escalation, materials shortages and arrears of track maintenance. It is possible that the '938' Class's better operational performance on the road upset the St Rollox hierarchy even more, notwithstanding the appreciative footplate crews' comments.

The attitude of John Barr, the Assistant Locomotive Superintendent (Running) to the '938' Class and to the proposed new 4-6-0 also remains enigmatic, in that Barr, having significant 'on the road' experience of the '938' Class workings, should have been in a position to positively endorse their capabilities directly to Pickersgill. O.S. Nock,[19] describing Barr as one of the strongest 'powers behind the throne' in the Pickersgill era, also mentions[26] discussing Caledonian company express train running with Barr, and notes him as being virtually dismissive of the 4-6-0s 'as of little consequence in the working of the main line express traffic'. As Running Superintendent, Barr had clearly placed almost complete reliance on the 4-4-0s and may have been unwilling to endorse the '938' Class, which he may have considered a 'non-standard' type. That the '938' Class was of 'foreign extraction' and appeared a very capable performer, would not have assisted its credentials, suggesting that Barr's objectivity might be questioned.

Moreover, the way in which Pickersgill exercised technical authority over his drawing office staff can be questioned. When signing drawings and therefore accepting responsibility for the emerging design, did Pickersgill question the detail and any supporting analyses put before him, thus accepting his principal role as the company's ultimate technical authority, or did he review his staff output merely in a peripheral way? Did he insist on analyses in the more problematic areas being undertaken, and if this was not within the capabilities of himself and his staff, did he seek external assistance when needed? The only identified external support came from Professor Mallenby[1] and that seems of doubtful consequence.

It is known that senior company management time was continually diverted from railway responsibilities to war related matters, both Pickersgill and Donald Matheson, the General Manager, being so effected: indeed the former was created CBE for his wartime work. In such circumstances, it is understandable that Pickersgill was unable to remain in touch with detailed developments in the locomotive drawing office, and, moreover, much daily oversight of the office technical output would have to be delegated to the available staff, irrespective of their abilities. Post-war, however, Pickersgill should have been prepared to take more cognisance of his drawing office staff advice and worked positively to ensure the company's retention of the redoubtable Thomas Weir.

Summary

It would be quite incorrect to conclude that the Caledonian Directors had been mistaken in choosing Pickersgill to fill McIntosh's shoes. Indeed, for the era in question, when locomotive technical developments and the use of related analytical design tools were expanding rapidly, no one man, on his own, could sensibly have been expected to fulfil the Locomotive Superintendent's remit without the provision of a senior experienced and qualified full-time technical assistant in the Bulleid or Rowlands mould. Whether the Directors recognised this need is not known, but having selected Pickersgill they should have had the foresight to provide the necessary additional senior technical resource to support their Locomotive Superintendent.

However, several enigmas remain: the rejection of Schmidt and McIntosh precepts; the '938' Class experience so readily discarded; Thomas Weir's precipitate departure; and the influence and attitude of John Barr.

When one reflects that superheated '903' Class locomotives could take 330 tons (gross) passenger trains unaided over Beattock,[27] and keep time, something neither the '60' or '956' Classes achieved, one could be forgiven for having some sympathy with John Barr's views in the use of 4-4-0 locomotives for express passenger traffic.[26] Moreover, whilst one might be inclined to conclude that the period of Pickersgill's tenure as Locomotive Superintendent at St Rollox was one of lost opportunity and technical stagnation, the influence of the 1914-18 conflict and its aftermath cannot be over-emphasised. But for that conflict and continuing post-war problems, conditions may have been very different for the Caledonian Company and St Rollox.

How far from the truth is E.S. Cox[23] in his assessment that Pickersgill was suffering from *'an insular and self-satisfied outlook'* on his '956' Class? Cox, of course, was more than somewhat anti-Pickersgill, having written of Pickersgill's designs for outside-cylindered engines in somewhat pejorative terms when commenting that they *'were progressively worse performers, and the fine reputation the McIntosh engines had gained became much blown upon as these later efforts went into traffic'*.[28]

However, of Pickersgill himself, Cox wrote:

'I saw him a number of times during George Hughes' tenure of the office of CME of the LM&SR from 1923 to 1925. Although much too junior then to speak with him, the grapevine which existed among lowly opposite numbers was surprisingly accurate in its assessment of the character of their different "chiefs" at the time. I remember that Pickersgill was held in considerable respect as a level-headed and altogether rational being, without any of the vagaries of some of his contemporaries. This is confirmed by the fact that the hard-headed Caledonian Directors chose him to succeed McIntosh, and they were not the characters to put their investments in jeopardy by employing an incompetent engineer.'[16]

Cox concluded by noting: *'history often commits injustices when it dwells on one aspect only of a career which must have displayed many facets'*.[16]

It was hardly of Pickersgill's choosing that an increasing proportion of his efforts at St Rollox were perforce deployed in refocusing his department to war related work, activities for which he was seemingly given no additional technical staff resources. Having such an imposition followed by harsh and uncertain economic circumstances, on to which was then superimposed the statutory railway amalgamations of 1922 and 1923 may well have led to pressures affecting his general health.

Pickersgill's last years in harness could not have been particularly happy. One cannot help but feel that however justified the changes in management that occurred at grouping in 1923 may have been, it would not have been easy to accept a subsidiary position after many years 'in the top post'. Perhaps this, together with the strain of ill-health, led to his early retirement in 1925, three years prior to his death.

REFERENCES

1. Private correspondence, Graeme Miller to CP Atkins, May 1978
2. Caledonian Railway, Staff Emoluments (1904-1920), NRS, BR/CAL/15/14
3. *LMS Magazine*, March 1939, p. 151
4. St Rollox Drawing Register, NRS, BR/CAL/5/56
5. Caledonian Railway, Extracts from Board Minutes, NRS, BR/CAL/5/13, entries for 10th February and 6th April 1920
6. Caledonian Railway, Staff Emoluments (1920-1923), NRS, BR/CAL/15/15
7. *Master Builders of Steam*, H.A.V. Bulleid (Ian Allan, 1963), pp. 52ff
8. *Under 10 CMEs*, E.A. Langridge, Volume One (Oakwood Press, 2011), pp. 71ff
9. *J.G. Robinson, A Lifetimes Work*, David Jackson (Oakwood Press, 1996)
10. ILocoE, Paper No 97, 'Some Points in Connection with Lubrication and Lubricators', Irvine Kempt, 20th January 1921
11. *Forty Years of Caledonian Locomotives 1882-1922*, Campbell Cornwell (David & Charles, 1974), p. 15
12. 'The new CME of the L&SWR', in *The Railway Magazine*, January 1913, p. 77
13. J.F. McEwan papers, William Patrick Library, Kirkintilloch, ref. T25/1/26, etc
14. St Rollox Drg No. 19969, dated 22nd May 1919, Montague Smith Collection, NRS, GD456, RHP136355/9
15. *Locomotive Valves and Valve Gears*, J.H. Yoder and G.B. Wharen (Pennsylvania Railroad Co., 1917), pp. 20-34 and Fig 30, etc
16. 'Pickersgill, A Relative View', Ralph Needham, in *The Caledonian Journal*, No. 5, 1988, pp. 11ff
17. Caledonian Railway, St Rollox Staff, Rates of Pay, NRS, BR/Cal/15/21
18. 'My Own Memoirs by George Heppell, May 1925', published as *North Eastern Locomotives, a Draughtsman's Life*, George Heppell et al. (The North Eastern Railway Association, 2012)
19. *The Caledonian Railway*, OS Nock (Ian Allan, 1963), p. 143
20. Caledonian Railway, Staff Emoluments, NRS, BR/CAL/4/81
21. *Master Builders of Steam*, H.A.V. Bulleid, p. 50
22. 'Scottish Topics – Past and Present', O.S. Nock, in *The Railway Magazine*, January 1965, pp. 20ff
23. Private correspondence, E.S. Cox to A.G. Dunbar, 6th May 1968, NRS, GD 344/6/12/5
24. Unpublished autobiography, H.N. Marshall; extracts published in *British Railways Illustrated*, September 1996, p. 657
25. Private correspondence, Graeme Miller to David Newlands, 1st September 1966
26. *The Caledonian Dunalastairs*, O.S. Nock (Ian Allan, 1968), p. 101
27. *Trains Illustrated*, October 1953, Letter to the Editor, Montague Smith
28. *The True Line*, No 80, April 2003, Article by Jim MacIntosh, p. 18, quotes from E.S. Cox publications *Locomotive Panorama* (Ian Allan, 1965) and *Chronicles of Steam* (Ian Allan, 1967)

Plate 27
No. 956 passing Balornock shed with the 5.00 pm Buchanan Street to Aberdeen Pullman express on the 9th August 1922. James Grassie was seemingly at the regulator. It is very likely No. 956 would have been fitted with Stephenson's link motion for the centre cylinder drive at this time.
Ken Nunn, NRM/LCGB3371

CHAPTER 10

ANECDOTAL COMMENTS ON '956' CLASS PERFORMANCE

GENERAL COMMENTS

This section brings together anecdotal evidence on overall '956' Class performance, specifically from those who had first-hand knowledge of the class, or who were well acquainted with railway employees who themselves had operated the locomotives or been involved in their design.

From the introduction of the class in August 1921, the railway technical press has been favoured with articles and letters on the performance of the '956' Class engines, a common theme being comparison with the '49' and '903' classes on identical duties. With few exceptions, the conclusion offered by most commentators is that the '956' Class had difficulty in consistently handling duties performed relatively easily by the big McIntosh superheated 4-6-0s.[1,2,3,4] A.J. Powell[5] has suggested that drivers were almost afraid to allow the '956' Class to run at anything over 60 mph, this being due to serious rough riding at speed. Indeed, the large McIntosh 4-6-0s persisted unaided on the principal Glasgow to Carlisle and Glasgow to Aberdeen turns until the advent of the 'Royal Scot' Class in late 1927,[6] a series of duties from which the '956' Class locomotives were by-and-large prematurely retired around 1924, with the exception of the erstwhile No. 956.[7]

Whilst the general tenor of articles concludes that the '956' Class never lived up to anywhere near expectations, there is the recognition that good work was sometimes, by exception, done with 300 ton loads. Campbell Cornwell[8] draws attention to a number of workings where something approaching satisfactory performance was achieved. Additionally, C.J. Allen, writing under his pen-name of 'Voyager'[9] in the GER magazine and also in *The Railway Magazine*,[10] describes the detail of a run he had, hauled by No. 957, on the 10.00 am Carlisle to Glasgow working in September 1921.

Allen[9] recorded this train weight as 260 tons (gross) and Beattock station, at 39¾ miles from Carlisle, being passed in 46 minutes, the unaided climb to the summit being run in just short of a further 22 minutes, which was 2 minutes in excess of the scheduled time for the ascent. Allen introduced his remarks by noting, '*Truth to tell, it was a little disappointing – maximum speed touched at Lockerbie was 64½ mph*',[10] going on to note '*the comparatively subdued exhaust, suggesting the engine was being worked well below full forward gear; indeed, we passed Summit Box quite proudly with steam blowing off*'.[9] However, it is generally accepted that the '956' Class had all the defects of the '60' Class, and in greater measure, together with a few more, a position underwritten by trials.

On the question of SHS, Montague Smith, who was an objective observer, noted in 1953 that short return loop superheater elements were, at the time of the '956' Class design, '*very much in fashion*'.[11] It seems that reduction in element length, leading to weight and cost reduction, with limited impact in superheat temperature, was seen as a trade-off worthy of pursuit. The author, however, would suggest that for the trade-off to be cost-effective, the final SHS should not have been less than 20 per cent of the total evaporative surface and the flue gas regime should have arranged for 45 to 50 per cent of combustion gases to pass through the flues.

Coal consumption figures also seem to have been a matter of divergence for commentators. Montague Smith,[11] referring to his friendship with Hugh Minilly, an LM&SR Locomotive Inspector, who had fired to James Grassie on No. 956, quoted Minilly as saying that coal consumption was '*no heavier than would be expected*', though no actual figures were quoted. However, published data by

Philip Atkins,[12] for various LM&SR 4-6-0s, shows the '956' Class in a particularly poor light, with average coal consumption in 1931 of 74 lbs per mile, compared to a '60' Class average figure of 66 lbs per mile. Ostensibly, these figures, taken from LM&SR accountants' data, would be based on both locomotive types using Scottish bituminous coal of broadly similar calorific value.

David Newlands,[13,14] writing of his personal recollections of '956' Class operation, noted that they '*were rather a dismal failure as main line engines*', though, No. 956 herself, '*seemed to be the most successful performer and right up to the middle of 1927 was a regular member of the link which worked the 5.00 pm Aberdeen out of Buchanan Street – as far as Perth probably*'. He acknowledges, however, that other than No. 956, '*from about late 1922, the class seemed to be employed on goods trains*'. Plate 27 shows No. 956 passing Balornock with the 5.00 pm Buchanan Street to Aberdeen Pullman express on the 9th August 1922, the locomotive probably fitted with Stephenson's link motion.

Mr Newlands[14] also passes comment, from his many observations, on the '*accent and tempo*' of No. 956's exhaust, as it climbed out of Buchanan Street on the Aberdeen workings. He notes that '*alternate exhaust beats were heavy, then light, in a ONE-two-THREE-four-FIVE-six repeating sequence*'. Moreover, '*when running light, especially in back gear, some of the beats were apt to be missing altogether*'. (It should be noted that the missing exhaust beats could arise at higher cut-off conditions with Stephenson's gear, since excessive lead could result in much reduced MEP in the centre cylinder, or at earlier cut-off with the derived motion, when lost motion approached the associated valve port opening. Such problems as existed would not have been helped by the valve chest exhaust layout.) Mr Newlands observations on '*accent and tempo*' unfortunately do not have a related time marker, so it is not clear what form of valve gear was fitted when his observations were recorded; if they are taken as applicable to No. 956 just prior to the 1923 amalgamations, then it is most likely that Stephenson's link motion was in place at that time.

Uneven exhaust beats, contributing to reduced smokebox vacuum and adverse effects on steaming are noted by Newlands,[14] with the comment that two sets of connection points for manometers were mounted on the left side of the smokebox for vacuum measurement during trials. (It is not clear how any vacuum results from trials were used, since no draughting changes seem to have been implemented, so far as available records show.) Very limited smokebox vacuum data from trials is given in the Appendices.

Graeme Miller[15] made a number of observations on '956' Class performance in private correspondence dated 1966. Commenting on the first form of the derived motion, Miller noted that:

'*the need for multiplying levers and consequent increase in mass, together with the number of pin joints, unfortunately combined at certain cut-offs, to produce a disturbing effect throughout the whole of the gear.*'[15]

Additionally, he acknowledged that all derived motions had mechanical design problems, when he continued:

'*that reciprocating forces in the line of the centre valve spindle had to be designed for, both in regard to the point of their final reaction and the retarding influence of the outside rotating members.*'[15]

For the second form of the derived gear, Miller goes on to say, *'this revised gear was introduced on engines Nos. 957 and 958 in early 1923, and later stabilised by fitting a dashpot'.*[15] (As far as can now be determined, no written or photographic evidence has emerged to establish that engines No. 957 and No. 958 were ever fitted with the second form of the derived motion in CR days, though as LM&SR No. 14801, the former No. 957 was refitted with derived motion in late 1931. It is likely that Miller may have made a slip of the pen.) Miller concluded his remarks by taking issue with the suggestion *'that the CR 3-cylinder venture was a dismal failure ... had the "Caley" continued as an entity, the ultimate verdict may well have been different'.*[15]

Patrick Ramsome Wallis recorded No. 14802 languishing at Kingmoor on the 12th September 1924 and wrote in his notebook *'it is learned that these engines are absolute failures and are continually running hot. Great difficulty is experienced with the valve settings'.*[16]

David Newlands clearly recalls that *'No. 956 and No. 959 had a form of derived motion for the middle valve, while No. 957 and No. 958 had Stephenson's link motion inside, with launch links on account of the shortness of the eccentric rods'.*[13] Newlands also noted that No. 956's centre valve was converted to Stephenson's motion and then reverted to the second form of derived gear, going on to remark:

'The steam distribution achieved by this contraption [the second form of derived motion] did not appear to be of a very satisfactory character to judge by the exhaust beats from the two engines concerned, although I don't recall the two with Stephenson's gear were any better off.'[13]

Whilst it is generally accepted that No. 956 was fitted with a dashpot arrangement to dampen inertial effects, Newlands examined the between-the-frames arrangements on No. 959 in the autumn of 1922, commenting:

'I discovered a new piece of apparatus mounted inside the left-hand main frame and attached to the centre pin of the two-to-one lever. This I suppose was some sort of dashpot arrangement, intended to restrain the gear in its wilder oscillations.'[13]

Whilst his description of the levers and the dashpot connection is not exactly correct, David Newlands' comment confirms that No. 959 was fitted with a dashpot, thus corroborating the views of driver George Newlands, in whose custody No. 959 was placed at Perth.

O.S. Nock, usually a repository of objective comment and balanced judgement, referred to the '956' Class in 1966 as *'one of the worst monumental flops of all time'*,[2] a judgement which was not backed up by any substantive technical analyses on his own part and probably relied too heavily on engine No. 956 operating on one specific working.

LORD MONKSWELL'S FOOTPLATE TRIP ON ENGINE NO. 956

Nock's opinion[2] was perhaps mistakenly crystalized through his being custodian, *post mortem*, of Lord Monkwell's notebooks, diaries and related technical papers, which set out in some detail the noble lord's many footplate experiences. Monkswell (Robert Alfred Hardcastle Collier, 1875-1964) was an acknowledged and influential observer of UK railway matters, who succeeded as 3rd Baron in 1909, and whose views carried weight in parliament, through his membership of the House of Lords. Not being an engineer, however, Monkswell's footplate observations tend to be more concerned with train timings and speeds, rather than objective technical assessment of what was happening below the footplate, between the frames and in the boiler.

One specific footplate trip made by Monkswell with engine No. 956 on 8th September 1922 and his subsequent recorded observations certainly show the locomotive's performance to have been more than somewhat lacking. Nock wrote of the run in 1965,[2] details not having previously been published.

In opening his record of that September 1922 day, Monkswell noted: *'I found Mr Barr with the engine and the driver was James Grassie, who had driven No. 50 from Perth to Glasgow in 1913, when I was also with Mr Barr'.*[17] At the time, No. 956 had been altered to Stephenson's gear for the centre cylinder, Monkswell recording: *'this engine has ordinary shifting link valve gear for the inside cylinder, but the others (Nos. 957 to 959) have "floating lever" arrangements'.*[17] The latter part of Monkswell's note seems incorrect, since by May 1922 it is known that No's 957 and 958 had also been fitted with inside Stephenson's gear, though Monkswell's remarks do tie up with Graham Miller's observations.[15]

The Caledonian people made something of a special occasion for Monkswell's trip and the working did not accord with normal routine. No. 956 was put on the 1.30 pm Up 'Corridor', from Glasgow Central to Carlisle, and her regular driver James Grassie was imported from Balornock especially for the working. Moreover, as noted, John Barr, the CR Assistant Locomotive Superintendent (Running) rode on the footplate. Arrangements were made for the engine to return on the Down 'Corridor', so that the round trip was made exactly the same as *Cardean's* old duty.

The load on the Up train was 415 tons (gross) and the engine made what Lord Monkswell later described as a *'remarkably poor ascent to Craigenhill'.*[17] The 15 miles southbound, at an average gradient of 1 in 135, from milepost 93 (Uddingston Junction) to Craigenhall Summit (732 ft), took 33 minutes, with an average speed of only 27 mph. Boiler pressure was maintained at 160 psi, until passing Law Junction (milepost 84), at which point the regulator was opened from one-half to fully open and *'pressure dropped to 125 psi, even though the driver was using no more than 8 notches out of 23 on the reversing scale'.*[17] Monkswell recorded the pyrometer readings, noting, *'the temperature of the steam was usually 550 deg. F.'*[17] (An indicated boiler pressure of 125 psi infers 110 to 115 psi at the steam chests for a standard superheater arrangement at fully open regulator, but may only have been 100 to 105 psi in the case of No. 956, due to the fitting of small bore superheater elements. Also, with steam temperatures 100°F lower than an anticipated 650°F, steam consumption would be around 10 per cent higher for the same work output.) Monkswell went on to note: *'we passed Carstairs in 54 minutes, 6 minutes late'.*[17]

After Carstairs, the engine continued to make heavy weather of it, and when, at Monkswell's request,[17] the regulator was opened wide on the last stage of the climb to Beattock Summit, the Craigenhall experience was repeated and pressure progressively fell to 125 psi at the summit. The descent to Carlisle was sluggish, taking 54 minutes for the remaining 49¾ miles and arrival was 2½ minutes late for a total journey elapsed time of 140½ minutes. By comparison, in *Cardean's* day, the Up 'Corridor' was allowed 135 minutes with a total load of 400 tons (gross). Monkswell makes no reference to No. 956 riding on the downhill stretch from Beattock Summit, nor to whether the regulator was closed or cracked open at that time. The highest speed recorded was 65½ mph between MPs 19 and 17.[17]

On the return train, with a load of around 350 tons (gross) and timed to leave Carlisle at 7.00 pm, No. 956 put on a performance which Monkswell described as *'even poorer than that in the opposite direction'.*[17] The locomotive took 49 minutes to reach Beattock station, against the 45 minutes allowed, and from the restart, with banking assistance, took 31 minutes for the 10 mile climb to the summit, against the 20 minutes allowed. Nearing the Summit, No. 956 was recorded as being worked all-out, *'full regulator and full forward gear, with a boiler pressure of 130 psi'.*[17] Monkswell noted James Grassie's comment during the ascent that *'some of the brake blocks must be rubbing against the wheels'*, a sure sign that Grassie knew all was not well. Barr's remarks are not recorded.

More time was lost downhill and Glasgow was eventually reached 15 minutes late. Monkswell's recorded: *'the work was poor throughout: the trouble was principally that the engine would not steam'*.[17]

By way of contrast, on the next day, Monkswell recorded[17] his return to London on the 10.00 am Up from Glasgow, again with a load of 400 tons (gross) and with '903' Class engine No. 906 on the working, making easy work of it. The time for this run to Carlisle was 137 minutes, inclusive of an unplanned intermediate stop at Motherwell. Interestingly, Monkswell also recorded the detail of his onward journey from Carlisle to Euston, noting that with an L&NWR 4-6-0, the 2½ miles down Shap (milepost 31½ to milepost 34) were run in 1 minute 52 seconds (average speed in excess of 80 mph), Monkswell noting *'very smooth in the dining car at this speed'*.[17]

To support his notebook observations, Monkswell took several photographs related to his footplate run on No. 956, Plate 28 showing the engine prior to the 1.30 pm departure from Glasgow Central station.

Interestingly, the results of Lord Monkswell's trip on No. 956 and his observations from the footplate were not published until many years later, indeed not until after his death in 1964, leading to the suggestion they were suppressed by the CR. Writing of Caledonian company locomotive performance in the second edition of his own book *The Railways of Great Britain*, published in 1926, Monkswell states that *'the story of the decline of Caledonian locomotive speeds from highest levels of 1896 is as dismal a story as can be found in the annals of any British railway'*.[18] However,

Monkswell goes on to note *'there were runs on the Caledonian, which kept alive the remembrance of former brilliancy'*,[18] and then favourably records a 1913 footplate trip on a superheated 'Dunalastair IV' Class, in which the locomotive ran from Forfar to Perth (32½ miles) in even time, with 335 tons behind the tender – but that was a McIntosh locomotive and Monkswell was a great McIntosh fan!

McIntosh had provided Monkswell with many footplate passes, one early working which the noble lord recorded in detail being his riding on the engines of the Down 'West Coast Postal', from Stirling to Aberdeen on the 23rd September 1898,[19] when aged 24. Joining the working at Stirling, where he boarded 'Dunalastair II' Class No. 774, Monkswell recorded speeds of 60 mph at Crieff Junction (Gleneagles) and 76 mph running down into Perth, with about 150 tons behind the tender. An engine change at Perth produced 'Dunalastair I' Class No. 726, the load being reduced to around 100 tons. A number of signal checks impeded an exceptional run to Aberdeen, though, passing Glamis, 73 mph was recorded for several miles. Monkswell was most impressed by the 'Dunalastair II', observing: *'they are the most strikingly steady machines I have ever been on … their general behaviour is such that it would be hard to suggest an improvement'*.[19]

Monkswell's first footplate experience on a 'Dunalastair I' Class took place in July 1897, on the midnight Euston to Glasgow sleeper. Having stayed awake during the night logging the run, Monkswell boarded No. 735 at Carlisle and recorded: *'I was most delighted with the engine. She ran very smoothly indeed, and the ease with which she brought the train along was quite absurd'*.[20]

Plate 28
No. 956 just prior to departure from Central station for Carlisle on the occasion of Lord Monkswell's return footplate trip on the 8th September 1922.
The engine performed badly, Monkswell commenting that the *'work was poor throughout: the trouble was principally that the engine would not steam'*. It was only after Monkswell's death in 1964 that his log of the journey was made public, leading to the suggestion that the CR had suppressed publication.
Lord Monkswell, courtesy Ted Talbot

COMMENTS ON LORD MONKSWELL'S TRIP

So, what does one make of this working by No. 956, particularly the return to Glasgow? Firstly, for Nock[2] to make such an outright condemnation, based on a single journey, might suggest his objectivity was in question, Nock's article being written in a hyperbolistic style with the benefit of over-emphasised hindsight. Clearly, the engine would not steam and the steaming problems seemed to multiply exponentially as the day progressed, resulting in the calamitous ascent of Beattock and 15 minutes late into Glasgow Central.

Unfortunately, no data for smokebox vacuum or steam chest pressure conditions is available, neither is any record available for engine preparation at Polmadie. One would have thought that the lack of sparkle on the Up working would have ensured No. 956 was given a thorough and exhaustive inspection at Kingmoor, the ashpan completely emptied and the fire thoroughly cleaned. With Lord Monkswell on the footplate and John Barr in immediate attendance, anything less would have been completely unacceptable and suggestive of the company adopting a detached *laissez faire* attitude to the working.

There is no reference from Monkswell's notes[17] to servicing at Kingmoor, and if this was mismanaged, or insufficiently thorough, the responsibility must lie squarely with Barr. Conspiracy theorists might suggest it was in Barr's interests to 'remain neutral' in the 4-4-0 versus 4-6-0 debate, it having already been noted that Barr was *'virtually dismissive of the 4-6-0s as of little consequence in the working of the main line express traffic'*.[21]

Monkswell's notes do, however, record that he rode on the light engine to Kingmoor shed and, after a brief look round and taking some photographs, *'we walked into Carlisle and had a meal in a hotel'*.[17] This suggests, unfortunately, that Monkswell and Barr did not overly concern themselves with the detail of engine servicing at Kingmoor, which, had they done so, might have provided more data on No. 956's poor performance. The approach taken by Barr is surprising – almost one of indifference. Going off to lunch, whilst his company's reputation for locomotive running was clearly compromised, hardly speaks well of Barr, though he may have been under instruction to give Monkswell 'a good lunch'.

Whilst James Grassie was 'imported' for the driving, nothing is said of the fireman and his experience of firing '956' Class locomotives. With their shallow sloping grate and potential for poor burning conditions in the grate aft section, firing may have been a tricky operation, maintaining an even fire at high combustion rates requiring skill and experience. It is just possible that No. 956 was inadequately serviced at Kingmoor and a fireman with very limited '956' Class experience had the shovel. Some weeks after this working involving Monkswell, No. 956 was instrumented and worked a 500 ton special 'test train' from Polmadie to Kingmoor and return. The results are given in Appendix 3, and on this latter trip they are unfortunately just as poor, though Monkswell was not to know that.

POWER OUTPUT ON LORD MONKSWELL'S TRIP

For the Down working, between milepost 39¾ (Beattock station) and 49¾ (Beattock Summit), with a banking engine sharing the work and an overall average speed of 19 mph for the 31 minutes climb, and the summit being breasted at 21 mph, it is possible to calculate the average DBHP. The height differential between station and summit is 656 ft, the train gross weight being around 520 tons (including train engine and tender plus banking engine). Assuming an average rolling resistance of 4.8 lbs/ton, the DBHP is 810 HP, allowing for the train's kinetic energy at the summit. The banking engine probably accounted for around one third of the DBHP, with No. 956 contributing only around a feeble 550 DBHP.

From the restart at Beattock station, despite the apparent heavy working, No. 956 struggled to produce 550 DBHP, there being no mention of slipping to account for the slow climb. However, for the Stephenson's valve gear arrangement fitted to No. 956[22] and the related valve events,[23] equal leads for inside and outside gears were set at around 25 per cent cut-off. In full gear, at around 65 per cent cut-off, the lead for the outside Walschaert's motion would remain fixed at ¼ in., whereas the Stephenson's gear lead at 65 per cent cut-off could have exceeded ¾ in. (back port lead is ½ in. at 35 per cent cut-off[22] and with this arrangement of Stephenson's link motion, the lead increases on notch back). In these circumstances, centre cylinder port openings would be overly advanced, there being excessive cushioning and a not insignificant reduction in centre cylinder MEP. This would not, however, seem to be the major source of difficulty.

With the boiler steaming very inadequately, resulting in low steam chest pressure and inadequate superheat (recorded steam temperature of 550°F would require around 10 per cent additional steam flow to that with 650°F, for the same power output), a lower than normal efficiency would result; the Stephenson's link motion valve settings would compound the problem. Also, at long cut-offs, the influence of the exhaust steam chests inter-connections may have provided an additional increase in centre cylinder 'effective lead', but the main explanation for this lamentable performance, excluding mismanagement of the engine, must be incorrect draughting coupled with poor grate and ashpan layout.

Such output DBHP figures, 550 HP for No. 956, are very poor for an engine of this size; even the BR Standard Class '4' 4-6-0, a much smaller machine, some 13 tons lighter than No. 956, was pushed to a continuous output of just over 1,100 DBHP using Grade 2 Blidworth coal.[5]

REFERENCES

1. *The Scottish 4-6-0 Classes*, C.P. Atkins (Ian Allan, 1976), pp. 63ff
2. 'Scottish Topics-Past and Present', OS Nock, in *The Railway Magazine* January 1965, pp. 20ff
3. *Fifty Years with Scottish Steam*, A.G. Dunbar and I.A. Glen (Bradford Barton), pp. 40ff
4. *West Coast 4-6-0s at Work*, C.P. Atkins (Ian Allan, 1981), pp. 116ff
5. A.J. Powell, Sundry 956 Class papers, NRM, not catalogued
6. 'Pickersgill 4-6-0s of the "Caley"', W.J. Probet, in *Trains Illustrated*, July 1953, pp. 273ff
7. Private correspondence, David Newlands to Graeme Miller, July 1966
8. *Forty Years of Caledonian Locomotives 1882-1922*, Campbell Cornwell (David & Charles, 1974), pp. 183-4
9. Article by 'Voyager' (pen-name for C.J. Allen) in *Great Eastern Railway Magazine*, May 1922, p. 4,
10. 'British Locomotive Practice & Performance', C.J. Allen, in *The Railway Magazine*, January 1922, pp. 102ff
11. *Trains Illustrated*, October 1953, Letter to the Editor, Montague Smith
12. 'Heavenly Blue Enigmas, the CR 956 Class', C.P. Atkins, in *BackTrack*, February 2009, Pendragon Publications, pp. 104ff
13. Private correspondence, David Newlands to Graeme Miller, July 1966
14. The Pickersgill 4-6-0s of the Caledonian Railway, David Newlands, in *The True Line*, No. 47, Autumn 1994, pp. 21ff
15. Private correspondence, Graeme Miller to David Newlands, September 1966
16. P. Ransome-Wallis personal notebook No. 2, entry for 12th September 1924, NRM
17. From Lord Monkswell's original notebooks, courtesy Ted Talbot
18. *The Railways of Great Britain*, Lord Monkswell (Geoffrey Bles & Co., London, 1926), p. 146
19. 'Lord Monkswell's Notebooks', ed. Edward Talbot, Books 1 and 2, 1898, in *Railway Archive*, No. 38, Lightmoor Press, p. 51
20. *The Caledonian Dunalastairs*, O.S. Nock (David & Charles, 1968), p. 27
21. *The Caledonian Dunalastairs*, O.S. Nock, p. 101
22. St Rollox Drg No. 21396, dated 24th December 1921, Campbell Cornwell Collection, (Figure 44)
23. St Rollox Drg No. 19947, dated 23rd September 1919, Montague Smith Collection, NRS, GD456, RHP136355/7, (Figure 27)

CHAPTER 11

RATIONALE FOR A REBUILD

GENERAL

In unpublished papers held at the NRM, the late A.J. Powell,[1] one time technical assistant to E.S. Cox, made a number of handwritten and typed notes on what might have been attempted by way of a rebuild of the '956' Class, though he accepted that the LM&SR did very little rebuilding to 'improve their breeds'. Such rebuilds as were carried out (L&NWR 'Claughton', 'Royal Scot' and 'Patriot' classes with 2A boiler, Stanier '3P' Class 2-6-2T) were invariably brought about by boiler life expiry or, in the case of the Stanier 2-6-2Ts, for boilers which were manifestly inadequate.

The LM&SR preference, maintained from its inception, was to eliminate non-standard classes when the boilers were life expired, without any major improvements to unsatisfactory mechanical parts in the meantime. This position is clearly set out in a July 1928 memo from D.C. Urie,[2] LM&SR Mechanical Engineer at St Rollox, to Sir Henry Fowler, the CME at Derby. In an appendix to the memo, covering Northern Division 4-6-0s, Urie notes that, *inter alia*, only the boilers of ex CR '944', '908' and '60' classes are to be perpetuated. Additionally, it is noted that boilers for ex CR '55', '918', '600', '938', '179', '191', '49', '903' and '956' classes were not to be perpetuated, though the '938' Class were later provided with new fireboxes.

In the LM&SR publication 'Particulars and Classification of Engines on Northern Division', dated the 30th September 1931,[3] i.e., very shortly after No. 14800 had been withdrawn (No. 14800 officially withdrawn on the 20th August 1931), it notes against No's 14801-3: '*Set aside when next in need of heavy repairs*'. At the time, it was considered the Horwich 2-6-0 would be a potential replacement. In the same publication, against the ex G&SWR Whitelegg 4-6-4Ts, it states: '*These are very heavy engines for the work on which they are employed. As they are only nine years old, they should remain in service, but be set aside when in need of new boilers*'. Interestingly, two of these 4-6-4Ts accumulated life mileages of 422,034 and 423,913 miles, seemingly without firebox replacements.[4]

Powell[1] suggested that as only four '956' Class engines were built, with no spare boilers, only three would have been rebuilt, the fourth boiler being kept as a spare. When these rebuilt boilers reached life expiry, he suggested an option of a further modest rebuild using a standard boiler, the 'Patriot' Class 'G9½S' appearing to be suitable.

There is, however, the recognition in Powell's papers that the Stanier regime from 1932 onwards would have precluded any rebuild, though Powell's analysis is helpful in pointing up his own solutions to the various known '956' Class deficiencies. His suggestions are noted below.

BOILER AND ASSOCIATED EQUIPMENT

The existing boiler would be shortened by about 1 ft 6 ins, the precise figure depending on the pitch of the rivets in the longitudinal butt joint straps. The front tubeplate and smokebox attachment would be retained, with a number of tubes being plugged to reduce the tube bank to between 180 and 190 tubes. The superheater flue holes would be opened out to take larger flues, the detail shown on the modified '956' Class boiler drawings[5,6] being acceptable. The hole for the main internal steam pipe would be opened out to take a 6 ins I/D pipe and a standard regulator head to suit the larger steam pipe provided.

A new inner firebox complete would be provided, with the crown lowered by 3 to 4 ins from the existing shoulders. A new grate would be provided, deeper at the front and with greater slope from the centre hump, with a deepened and restructured ashpan. A new superheater header would be necessary, taking 1¼ ins I/D elements, full return loops being provided, similar to the initial fit on the '938' Class,[7] ex HR 'River' Class.

CHASSIS AND WHEELS

The existing frames would be cut at a point about 1 ft 8 ins in front of the leading coupled axle and new 1¼ ins straight front sections welded on, reducing the trailing bogie/leading coupled axle centres distance from 6 ft 8 ins to 6 ft 0 ins, the same dimension as the '60' Class.[8] New hornstays of the type used on the trailing axlebox guides would be required to suit laminated springs. A new fabricated smokebox saddle with blastpipe base insert would be complemented by continuous horizontal stretchers and a vertical stretcher between the new motion plates.

The existing bogie centre pin casting would be set approximately 2½ ins lower, to suite the reduced diameter bogie wheels. New laminated springs would be fitted throughout, with more powerful side control spring arrangements, to reduce the potential for 'nozing', recognising the reduced front-end length and weight. New fabricated motion plates, motion girders and rear motion girder brackets would be provided.

Replacement bogie wheels, 3 ft 0 ins diameter, salvaged from withdrawn L&Y 'Dreadnought' Class 4-6-0s would be used with existing axles, with collars turned off to provide clearance from cylinder flanges. The existing bogie would be used, the smaller wheels necessitating machining a little off the bottom of the side frames and the flange of the centre stretcher to retain rail clearance.

Intermediate coupled wheel bosses would be reduced in thickness on the outside by about ⅝ in. to suit new driving crankpins, giving longer coupling rod journals. A new leading axle would be required and collars turned off all coupled axles. New cast steel coupled axleboxes with pressed-in brasses having continuous white-metal bearing surfaces would be fitted. Coupled wheels would need to be rebalanced, perhaps for 50 per cent of the reciprocating masses.

CYLINDERS AND MOTION

Powell's papers[1] contain a series of hand written estimates of cylinder and frame dimensions, from which he concludes that using the Horwich 2-6-0 cylinders and the '956' Class modified frames would provide a feasible solution. A distance of 6 ft 8 ins between cylinder centres would be obtained, which compares favourably with the 6 ft 9¾ ins for the '60' Class. The cylinders would be mounted at a reduced angle to those on the Horwich 2-6-0, though driving crank pin loadings would need attention due to increased thrust from the larger diameter cylinders.

Accordingly, standard 21 in. x 26 in. cylinders as fitted to the Horwich 2-6-0s, with 11 ins piston valves and 1¾ ins liner ports would be fitted with new steam and exhaust pipes within the saddle. New rear valve chest covers, incorporating valve spindle crosshead guides would be used. The existing coupling and connecting rods would be retained, with longer bushes at the coupling rod crankpins. Existing crossheads and crosshead arms would be re-used, with new slidebars to fit both crossheads and the standard 2-6-0 rear cylinder cover.

New long-lap Walschaert's valve gear would be provided, with a lap plus lead of 1¾ ins. The gear would generally follow Midland/LM&SR practice in using a 2-piece box-type expansion link, radius rod, reversing die-block and 4-stud crank fixing. The existing '956' Class lever reverse and steam servo would be replaced by a suitable direct-drive reversing screw recovered from withdrawn locomotives. To accommodate this, the cab would need to be widened, the existing sides being retained and a new spectacle plate plus roof provided.

THE END PRODUCT

Mr Powell[1] concluded the rebuilt engines would constitute a useful mixed traffic class, speedy and with ample boiler power to sustain heavy working, whilst possessing the simplicity of maintenance of a robust 2-cylinder machine. Nominal tractive effort

would be around 24,000 lbs. Engines would expect to remain in traffic with the modified boilers until after World War II. No data is given in Mr Powell's papers for costs related to the rebuilds.

REFERENCES
1. A.J. Powell papers, NRM, 956 Class Material, Uncatalogued
2. D.C. Urie memo to Sir Henry Fowler, 23rd July 1928, NRS, BR/LMS/5/176
3. 'Particulars and Classification of Engines on Northern Division', LMS September 1931, C.P. Atkins Collection
4. Correspondence to author from C.P. Atkins 2013
5. St Rollox Drg No. 19915, Smokebox Tubeplate, Campbell Cornwell Collection, 956 Class Drgs, CRA 6/1/3/2, Arch. Gp. 48
6. St Rollox Drg No. 19912, Firebox Tubeplate, Campbell Cornwell Collection 956 Class Drgs, CRA6/1/3/2, Archive Group 48
7. NBR Co., Cowlairs, Drg 'Highland Railway No. 1', NRS, Montague Smith Collection, NRS, GD456/3
8. St Rollox Drg No. 18940, dated 24th January 1917, in A.J. Powell papers

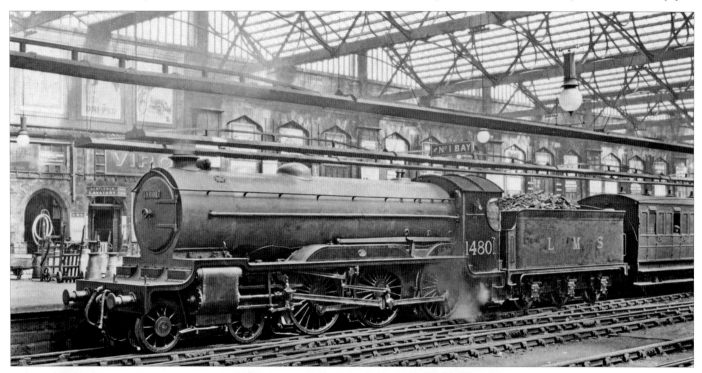

ABOVE: Plate 29
LM&SR No. 14801, the former CR No. 957, is illustrated on a local passenger train working at Carlisle circa 1930, prior to the refitting in 1931 of the second type of derived motion, which is assumed to have been recovered from the withdrawn No. 14800. At this time, No. 14801 carries Stephenson's link motion for the centre cylinder, there being no rocking shaft bearing on the upper slidebar and no yoke on the valve rod between the combination lever input and the rear valve chest cover.

CRA460168a

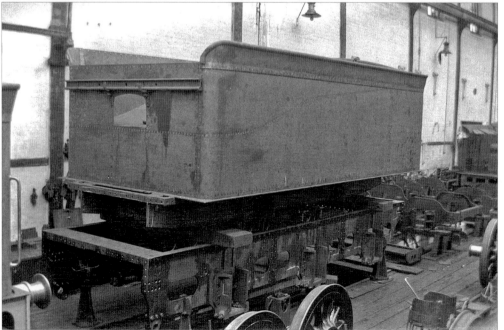

LEFT: Plate 30
A '956' Class tender tank assembly, supported on an un-wheeled tender frame is shown in St Rollox works erecting shop. The tenders for the '956' Class were based on the '60' Class framing and were recognisable by their being slightly wider and having a less pronounced flair to their coping.

A.E. Glen

CHAPTER 12

LOCOMOTIVE WITHDRAWALS AND USE OF SURVIVING TENDERS

GENERAL

Withdrawal of the '956' Class locomotives commenced in the early 1930s, the first to be condemned being LM&SR No. 14800, the former CR No. 956, in August 1931, followed by No. 14803, the former No. 959, in July 1933, both engines being fitted with the second form of the derived motion. No. 14801, the former No. 957, by then refitted with the second derived motion, was removed from stock in March 1934, being followed by No. 14802, the former No. 958, in January 1935. On withdrawal, No. 14802 retained Stephenson's link motion.

For almost the last ten years of their lives, with the apparent exception of No. 14800,[1] the engines were, by and large, confined to freight workings, though the occasional passenger turn did arise. Plate 29 illustrates No. 14801, then fitted with Stephenson's link motion, on a passenger working at Carlisle. In this photograph, the absence of the transverse rocking shaft bearing mounted on the upper slidebar denotes Stephenson's motion being fitted for the inner cylinder.

The four special '956' Class tenders were based on the '60' Class framing, with visibly wider tanks which increased the water capacity to 4,500 gallons. They could be identified through having a less pronounced flare to their coping and remained in service for many years post '956' Class withdrawals. Ernest Glen photographed these larger tenders during their build,[2] Plate 30 showing the tank positioned above a yet un-wheeled frame in the erecting shop in St Rollox, whilst Plate 31 illustrates the finished product in the works yard prior to painting.

The tenders had been numbered No's 6238-6241 by the LM&SR and were used firstly to replace the McIntosh 8-wheeled bogie tenders on 'Dunalastair IV' Class locomotives, Plate 32 showing non-superheated No. 14357 at Kingmoor coupled to a '956' Class tender. They were also paired with superheated 'Dunalastair IV' Class engines, Plate 33 illustrating No. 14438, paired with tender

Plate 31
A completed '956' Class tender illustrated in St Rollox Works yard, undercoated, prior to final painting and varnishing.
A.E. Glen

Plate 32
Former CR '140' Class engine No. 148, as LM&SR No. 14357, at Kingmoor shed, coupled to a '956' Class tender. Whilst No. 14357 was withdrawn in 1938, the tender saw further use. The tender illustrated is probably No. 6239, which was ultimately paired with former '60' Class engine No. 14652. On the withdrawal of No. 14652 in 1948, the tender was almost certainly scrapped with the locomotive. *CRA440153*

No. 6241, at Balornock coaling stage on the 27th June 1936. Further McIntosh engines running with these tenders in LM&SR days included No's 14439, 14451 and 14458, with No. 14451 remaining paired with tender No. 6241 from December 1938 until withdrawal in 1955. Plate 34 shows BR liveried No. 54451, paired with tender No. 6241 at Dalry Road, whilst Plate 35 illustrates No. 54456, paired with tender No. 6240 at Greenock in 1956.

Pickersgill 4-6-0 and 4-4-0 locomotives known to have been paired with former '956' Class tenders include No's 14652, 14463 and 14505 in LM&SR days plus No. 54463 in BR days. The longest and last pairing is that related to engine No. 14463/54463, this pairing with tender No. 6238 having commenced under LM&SR auspices, from at least 1946. Plate 36 depicts No. 54463 at Tain on the 11th September 1958, heading the 3.50 pm working to Inverness, the tender carrying the final form of the BR Totem.

The actual tender record cards for three of the four tenders have survived, their respective details being noted as follows.

TENDER DATA

TENDER NO. 6238[3]
The building date for this tender is given on the card as June 1921, constructed at St Rollox to order Y125, though no other CR data is recorded, apart from weights plus fuel and water carrying capacities. The earliest entry on the record card is the 7th June 1946, when the tender was paired with Pickersgill 4-4-0 No. 14463, with which it remained until the 22nd October 1959. On that day the tender was transferred to 4-4-0 No. 54496, and on the same day withdrawn from traffic with No. 54496, the tender having a residual value of £234 4s 4d. Tender repairs were noted as having been undertaken at various times in the 1950s, locations being St Rollox, Inverness and Inverurie.

TENDER NO. 6239
No record card data survives for this tender and it is assumed it was latterly paired with Pickersgill 4-6-0 No. 14652, which was withdrawn by BR in November 1948. In the absence of any further data, it is assumed this tender was withdrawn with the associated locomotive.

TENDER NO. 6240[4]
The building date for this tender is given on the card as August 1921, constructed at St Rollox to order Y125. The earliest entry on the card is the 21st February 1944, when the tender was paired with McIntosh 4-4-0 No. 14439, with which it remained until the 23rd April 1954, when it was transferred to No. 54456. On the withdrawal

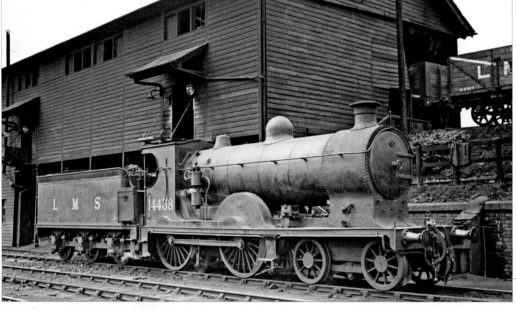

LEFT: Plate 33
Former CR locomotive No. 923, was built at St Rollox in 1907 and rebuilt in 1917 with new 20¼ ins x 26 ins cylinders and a new boiler with a Schmidt superheater. As LM&SR No. 14438, the engine is illustrated at Balornock shed coaling stage on the 27th June 1936, and is coupled to '956' Class tender No. 6241. The locomotive was withdrawn in 1955 as BR No. 54438.
Fred A. Plant, CRA7/1/3/26, 43

BELOW: Plate 34
Former CR '43' Class engine No. 44 is illustrated as BR No. 54451 at Dalry Road shed, Edinburgh, circa 1950, when coupled to '956' Class tender No. 6241. No. 54451 was withdrawn in 1955. *CRA*

Plate 35
Former CR '43' Class locomotive No. 39 is shown as BR No. 54456 at Greenock in 1956, when coupled to '956' Class tender No. 6240. The engine was withdrawn in 1957.
Author's collection

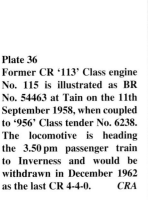

Plate 36
Former CR '113' Class engine No. 115 is illustrated as BR No. 54463 at Tain on the 11th September 1958, when coupled to '956' Class tender No. 6238. The locomotive is heading the 3.50 pm passenger train to Inverness and would be withdrawn in December 1962 as the last CR 4-4-0. *CRA*

of No. 54456 in February 1957, the tender was taken out of traffic on the 14th February 1957, with a residual value of £292 14s 8d and scrapped on the 29th March at St Rollox. The record card notes only St Rollox as having undertaken repairs.

TENDER NO. 6241[5]
The surviving card for this tender contains the most information, the tender being built at St Rollox in August 1921, and paired with the undernoted locomotives:

DATE	PAIRED WITH LOCOMOTIVE NUMBER
August 1921	CR No. 959
10th February 1928	LM&SR No. 14802
Undated	LM&SR No. 14803
15th December 1933	LM&SR No. 14438
23rd December 1938	LM&SR No. 14451

The tender remained with 4-4-0 No. 54451 until the locomotive was withdrawn from traffic in September 1955 from Dalry Road, the tender being taken out of traffic on the 14th September, with a residual value of £221 4s 9d.

FINALE

It seems the last former '956' Class tender was condemned in late 1959, almost twenty-five years after the last of the locomotives, and, with that, the Caledonian Railway '956' Class hardware story concludes, somewhat later than might have been imagined in 1935. The penultimate survivor of the locomotives, No. 14801 was withdrawn in March 1934, Plate 37 showing the locomotive in the scrap line at St Rollox works around that time. As can be seen, at this time No. 14801 was fitted with the derived motion rocking shaft bearing mounted on the upper slidebar. Whilst juxtaposed with a McIntosh bogie tender in Plate 37, it is fairly certain none of the '956' Class locomotives was ever paired with such a tender in service, though for a trials working in October 1922, with a 500 ton 'test train', an 8-wheeled 5,000 gallon capacity tender may have been used.

REFERENCES:
1. 'Pickersgill 4-6-0s of the Caledonian Railway', David Newlands, in *The True Line*, No 47, Autumn 1994, p. 21
2. A.E. Glen Collection, private collection, courtesy Dr Ann Glen
3. Tender Record Card, Tender No. 6238, NRS, GD 344/4/22/67
4. Tender Record Card, Tender No. 6240, NRS, GD344/4/22//68
5. Tender Record Card, Tender No. 6241, NRM, ID685, ALS3/7/4/G

Plate 37
Former CR No. 957, as LM&SR No. 14801, at St Rollox works yard in March 1934 following withdrawal. This engine had been refitted, in late 1931, with the second type of derived motion, which was recovered from the withdrawn No. 14800. The rocking shaft link and its bearing on the upper slidebar are visible.   *Author*

BELOW: Figure 14
Some Caledonian Railway Locomotive Parameters. Of particular note are the ratios of SHS to Total Heating Surface used by McIntosh, which averaged around 24 per cent for new construction. Equivalent parameters for Pickersgill engines varied from around 15 per cent in the case of '113' and '60' Classes, through 13.2 per cent in the '944' Class, to 11.4 per cent in the case of the '956' Class. In similar fashion, the Flues to total Free-gas areas used by McIntosh averaged around 45 per cent, whilst Pickersgill engines regressed from 48 per cent in the '113' Class, to only 34.8 per cent for the '956' Class. Comparative data for the Gresley 'K3' and CR '938' Classes demonstrate a consistency with McIntosh locomotive parameters.   *Author*

CR LOCOMOTIVES – BOILER RATIOS

CLASS	WHEEL ARRANGEMENT	THS SQ. FT	FBHS SQ. FT	TOTAL HS SQ. FT	SHS SQ. FT	SHS PER CENT OF TOTAL HS	L/D	FREE GAS /GRATE, PER CENT	FLUES /FREE GAS, PER CENT	GRATE SQ. FT	ASHPAN CU. FT	DEPTH INCHES
McIntosh												
766	4-4-0	1,094	119	1,213	214	17.6	91	15.9	41.0*	20.6	21.4	17
900	4-4-0	1,094	138	1,232	214	17.4	91	14.3	41.0*	23.0	25.0	17
903	4-6-0	1,666	148	1,814	515	28.4	114	15.5	44.5	26.0	35.0	18
139	4-4-0	1,220	145	1,365	330	24.2	92	18.0	47.0	21.0	23.0	17
34	2-6-0	1,071	119	1,190	267	22.4	85	17.1	45.0	20.6	21.0	12
179	4-6-0	1,439	128	1,567	403	25.7	102	18.9	45.0	21.0	24.0	17
Pickersgill												
113	4-4-0	1,185	144	1,329	200	15.0	92	18.0	48.0	20.7	24.0	17
60	4-6-0	1,530	147	1,677	258	15.4	105	15.5	45.0	25.5	28.3	18
944	4-6-2T	1,395	121	1,516	200	13.2	116	15.3	40.5	21.5	24.0	17
956	4-6-0	2,200	170	2,370	270	11.4	110	18.6	34.8	28.0	36.0	20
External												
938	4-6-0	1,460	140	1,600	350	21.8**	101	15.5	45.2	25.3	39.0	30
K3***	2-6-0	1,719	182	1,901	407	21.4	96	19.2	49.2	28.0	–	–

NOTES:
*   Rebuilt '766' Class had 50 per cent return loop superheater elements.
**   As modified by Pickersgill when CR acquired the locomotives. As built, SHS was 448 sq. ft, being 28 per cent of Total Heating Surface.
***   Gresley GNR 'K3' Class

CHAPTER 13

BOILER DESIGN

GENERAL

In attempting some assessment of the 'as-built' '956' Class boiler, the following commentary is made to illustrate what might have been possible at St Rollox if a slightly different design approach had been adopted, recognising previous St Rollox experience and established practice of the time. Clearly, more detailed technical analyses would have been needed to confirm the exact detail of what is set out below, and perhaps some of these points may well have figured in St Rollox thinking.

The boiler designer, as with most things, was faced with a series of trade-offs and compromises. Up to around 1900 many locomotive engineers used plain tube length/diameter proportions in the ratio 80:1 to 85:1,[1] this ratio seemingly giving an acceptable performance both for combustion and evaporation. Trials at PRC Altoona, reported in 1913,[2] suggested that optimised proportions for the tubes was a L/D ratio of slightly more than 100:1, i.e. up to 120:1,[3] though in his compendium, Phillipson[3] suggests (based on pre-1918 data) lower ratios than those recommended by Altoona are more appropriate to British practice, the higher ratios being related to inferior grades of coal. As such, a ratio of around 100:1 was seen as ideal in UK conditions, it having been pointed out by PRC[3] that ratios much above this gave no advantage, as any further increase beyond this limit demanded more steam for draught than is provided by any small incremental increase in boiler efficiency arising from increased tube length.

In a 1909 IMechE paper, Professor Dalby[4] showed that of the total temperature gradient between the hot gasses in the tubes and the water surrounding them, 97 per cent is utilised to overcome the resistance of the gas film, 1 per cent that of the metal and 2 per cent that of the water film. It follows that tube thickness and the tube material are relatively unimportant as regards heat transmission efficiency and the basic problem resolves into destroying, as far as possible, the inert non-conducting gas adhering to the tube inner surface. This is best done by increasing the gas flow velocity in the tubes to around 300 to 400 ft per second[5] and using the smallest diameter of tube possible, commensurate with established L/D criteria and flue gas flow ratios (flue gas area to total free-gas area) round 45 to 50 per cent.[6,7]

The ratio of free-gas area through the tube bank to the grate area had usually been set at around 15 per cent, a ratio recognised by McIntosh,[8] though it was considered that with this ratio above 17 per cent, coal consumption could rise noticeably and heat transfer could be detrimentally affected through incomplete combustion. Additionally, the ratio of free-gas area for the superheater flues to the total free-gas area should be selected to ensure sufficient gas was passed through the flues so achieving final steam temperatures around 650-675 °F, or slightly more. As noted, a ratio around 45 to 50 per cent was seen as satisfactory,[6,7] coupled to an SHS of around 20 to 25 per cent of the evaporative surface totals,[8] figures which were in line with Dr Schmidt's recommendations,[9,10] and as used by McIntosh.

In summary, the boiler designer of that time had a number of parameters to meet to ensure effective and efficient steam raising, the process of design being an iterative one:

– select L/D ratio around 100
– set tubeplate free-gas area/grate area ratio at around 15 to 17 per cent, recognising fuel consumption economy

– set free-gas area for flues/total free-gas area at 45 to 50 per cent
– select SHS to obtain 650/675 °F, usually 20 to 25 per cent of evaporative surface totals
– check superheater elements pressure loss against known criteria.

By way of comparison, Figure 14 sets out a number of these boiler related parameters for various classes of Caledonian company locomotive.[11,12]

Additionally, in selecting boiler parameters, the practicalities of firing the locomotive had to be considered, one school of thought suggesting that a firebox internal length of 8 to 9 ft was near the upper limit for effective firing with a narrow firebox, giving a maximum grate area in the range 26 to 30 sq. ft. Other designers have, however, supported the longer grates position, suggesting 30 to 32 sq. ft as being nearer the maximum.

It was shown earlier that an evaporative heating surface of around 2,200 to 2,300 sq. ft is needed to meet the hill climbing requirement of 30 mph on a 1 in 100 grade with a 550 ton all-up train weight. Having chosen the '956' Class internal firebox length in the 8 to 9 ft range, with a corresponding grate area of, say, 28 sq. ft, the FHS area is very broadly determined in the 155 to 180 sq. ft range.[13] In British practice, a FHS to grate area ratio of around 5.5 to 6.5 was taken as standard for a narrow firebox locomotive,[13] the limit being loading gauge dependent. If the FHS is set at a mid-range value of 170 sq. ft (as was the case for the '956' Class, and which would have been around 180 sq. ft for 30 sq. ft grate), then, the tube heating surface (THS) should be around 2,000 to 2,100 sq. ft, noting that the '956' class THS was 2,200 sq. ft.

It would seem, *prima facie*, that St Rollox selected appropriate evaporative surfaces and grate area to meet accepted criteria for these parameters, though other factors may suggest modifications. Moreover, in arranging all three cylinders in line, under the smokebox, even with a short centre cylinder connecting rod of 6 ft 6 ins, Pickersgill had to accept an elongated front end for the '956' Class. The distance between the rear bogie axle and the first coupled axle on the '956' Class, at 6 ft 8 ins, was 1 ft greater than that on the '938' Class,[14] and 1 ft 6 ins greater than on the HR 'Clan' Class,[14] as a result of which the '956' Class boiler was at least 1 foot longer than it otherwise needed to be. Using a vertical firebox throatplate, the '956' Class tube bundle was unusually long at 16 ft 0 ins between tubeplates. There is no indication from the drawing register that a recessed smokebox tubeplate or sloping firebox front throatplate were considered by St Rollox.

In estimating boiler steam raising capacity, it is generally accepted that a locomotive should meet its peak demand for steam at a firing rate of around 100 to 110 lbs of coal per hour per sq. ft of grate area.[15,16,17] Also, assuming fuel of calorific value around 13,000 to 13,500 BTU/lb, numerous trials have determined the equivalent steam production rate to be 7.0 to 7.5 lbs of steam per lb of coal fired.[18,19] Amalgamating these parameters, and based on a 28 sq. ft grate, the '956' Class boiler should have produced steam in the range 19,600 to 23,000 lbs per hour at near maximum working conditions, assuming adequate draughting. A maximum steam rate of 20,000 to 21,000 lbs per hour would be a reasonable working assumption.

The following series of iterations on the 'as-built' '956' Class boiler are given to illustrate what might have been possible if outline boiler ratios approaching best practice in the immediate post 1918 period

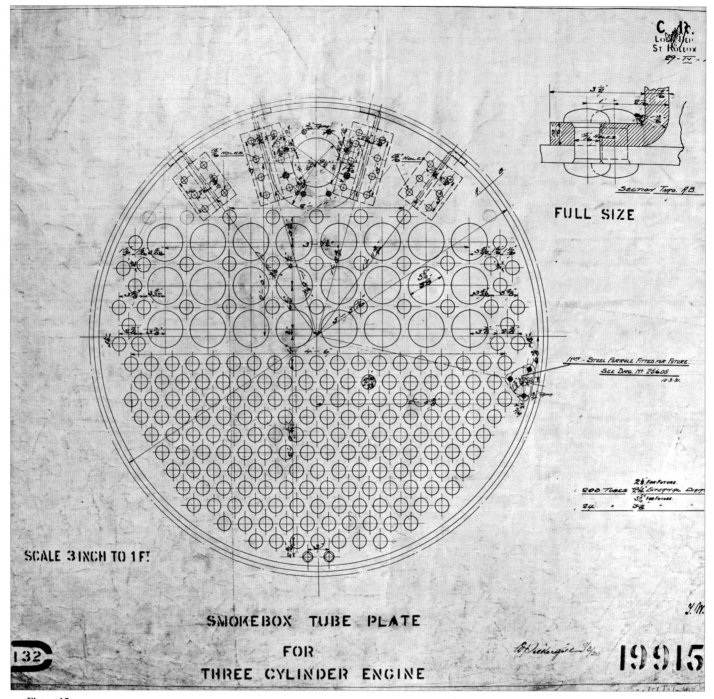

Figure 15
'956' Class. Smokebox Tubeplate. Drg No. 19915, dated the 28th April 1919. This drawing lays out the flue and tube arrangements for the 'as-built' '956' Class and it is also annotated to increase the respective diameters of both. Whilst there is no date associated with this annotation, it is likely the changes were made post the 1921 trials on No. 956. It is not clear if these changes were ever implemented on a locomotive.   *CRA: CRA6/1/3/2/48/2/1*

had been applied, these ratios being very similar to those in use at St Rollox in the McIntosh era.

TUBE SELECTION

For the '956' Class, the tubeplates and superheater element drawings have survived. The smokebox tubeplate drawing No. 19915,[12] dated the 8th April 1919, shown as Figure 15, indicates that 203 tubes of 2 1/16 ins O/D were used, the I/D being 1 3/4 ins (the drawing is annotated, without date, to specify 2 1/8 ins O/D tubes for future locomotives construction). The twenty-four superheater elements were housed in flues of 5 1/8 ins O/D (again the drawing is

annotated, without date, to specify 5 5/16 ins O/D flues for future class construction, these annotations ostensibly being a result of 1921 trials on No. 956). Drawing No. 19912,[12] dated the 18th April 1919, depicted as Figure 16, gives the firebox tubeplate arrangement. An additional June 1931 note on this drawing indicates that for future construction the tubes should be reduced to 1 7/8 ins O/D.

This 1931 annotation might well be associated with the LM&SR policy of the period through which tube and superheat arrangements were changed on Pickersgill locomotives to restore the McIntosh era parameters and to reflect Dr Schmidt's criteria.[9,10]

The superheater elements arrangement is shown as Figure 17, drawing No. 20118,[12] dated the 22nd August 1919. The internal

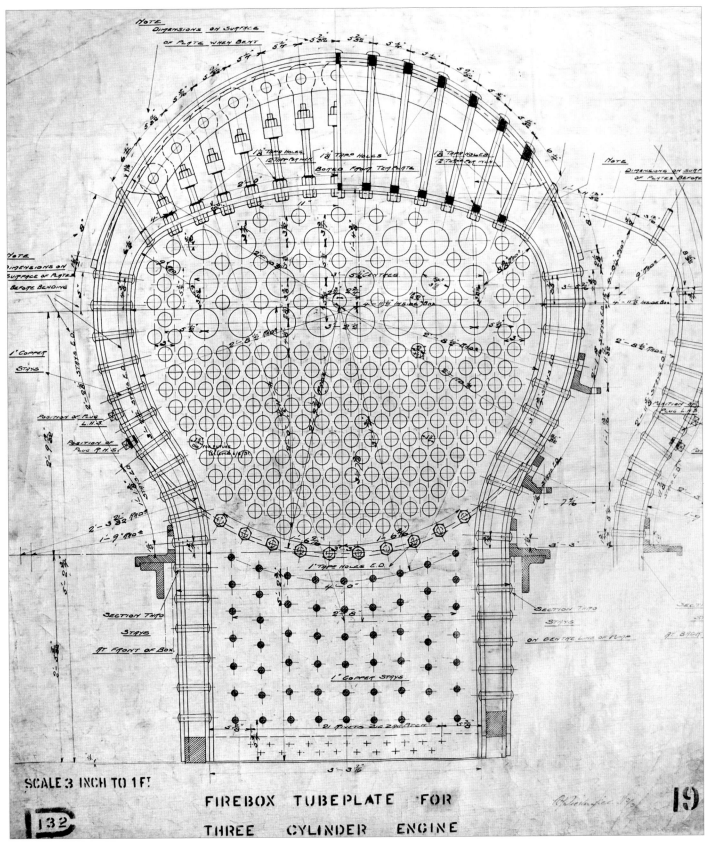

SCALE 3 INCH TO 1 FT.

FIREBOX TUBEPLATE FOR THREE CYLINDER ENGINE

Figure 16
'956' Class. Firebox Tubeplate. Drg No. 19912, dated the 18th April 1919. As with the smokebox tubeplate drawing, similar modifications were made for the firebox tubeplate post the 1921 locomotive trials. Further modifications were also made in 1931, a specific annotation stating that the nominal 2 ins diameter tubes were to be reduced to 1⅞ ins *'for new construction'*, this being dated the 6th June of that year. As far as available records show, no new tubeplates were manufactured for the '956' Class, though the increase in flue diameter and the corresponding reduction in tube diameter would have significantly improved the basic boiler ratios and steaming capacity. Sling stays used to connect the boiler outer wrapper plate to the firebox crown sheet are laid out in some detail.
CRA: CRA6/1/3/2/48/2/2

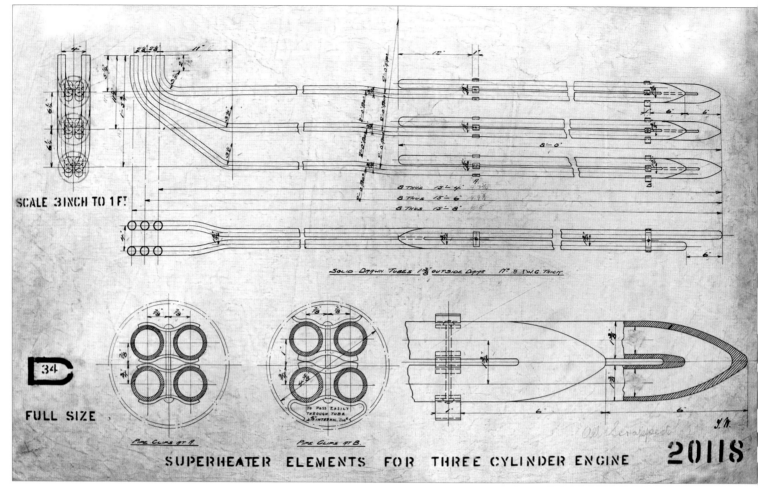

Figure 17
'956' Class. Superheater Elements. Drg No. 20118, dated the 25th August 1919. The '956' Class were provided with short return loop elements which had a reduced bore compared to the McIntosh era equivalent components. The result was a significant reduction in the percentage of SHS to total heating surface, from around 24 per cent for McIntosh locomotives to 11.4 per cent for the '956' Class, plus an unhelpful increase in superheater pressure loss. By restoring the McIntosh era element bore of 1¼ ins I/D in place of the Pickersgill I/D of just over 1 in., the superheater pressure loss is almost halved for the same steam flow.
CRA: CRA6/1/3/2/48/4/9

diameter of the flues is given as 4⅝ ins, there being four element runs per flue: each element being 1⅜ ins O/D, with a wall thickness of No. 9 IWG, giving an approximate I/D of 1¹⁄₁₆ ins. Return bends at 50 per cent of full length were provided.

For the 'as-built' '956' Class boiler the free-gas area for the 203 tubes is 3.39 sq. ft, and for the flues, taking account of the superheater elements, is 1.81 sq. ft, giving a total of 5.2 sq ft; this gives a flue-to-total free-gas ratio of 34.8 per cent, which would be most unlikely to provide the required final superheated steam temperatures.

Moreover, the L/D has also to be considered, Figure 14 showing L/D parameters for various CR locomotive classes.[11,12] At 110, the L/D figure for the '956' Class boiler could be considered marginally on the high side using the accepted guidelines, the tube bundle being too long. Also, the total free-gas area, at 18.6 per cent of the grate area, is marginally too high, leading, potentially, to higher than anticipated coal consumption.

As a first iteration, a 10 per cent reduction in tube bundle length to reduce the L/D would assist, recognising St Rollox increased the flue diameter to 5⁵⁄₁₆ ins O/D, which would also be of benefit. Additionally, a reduction in tube diameter would assist in diverting tube gasses to the flues and also reduce the free-gas to grate area from the rather high 18.6 per cent. A 10 per cent reduction in tube bundle length would also sit well with the recognition that the length between tubeplates was already perhaps artificially long due to the selected cylinder and front end layout.

Various options to achieve this potential reduced tube bundle length are possible, including recessing the front tubeplate into the boiler barrel, fitting a firebox combustion chamber, increasing the firebox length, or using a sloping front firebox throatplate. The choice is not straightforward. Moreover, fitting a combustion chamber has the disadvantage of a more expensive and technically complex boiler in addition to potentially adding to boiler weight, though water weight would be reduced, but the centre of gravity potentially moved forward. Increasing the FHS by increasing the firebox length has definite merit, but unfortunately the '956' Class 'as-built' layout gives limited scope for this, as the GA shows the firebox foundation ring being near its forward limit, though a forward sloping lower front throatplate would be possible and desirable.

Experiments undertaken pre-1900 on tube bundle heat transfer,[20] indicated that the forward 10 per cent of the tube stack contributed less than 3 per cent of total heat transfer capability, so the '956' Class tube bundle length can be reduced by 1 ft 6 ins, from 16 ft to 14 ft 6 ins (around a 10 per cent reduction), with no appreciable loss in steam production.

Additionally, a reduction in tube O/D to around 1⅞ ins (from the 2¹⁄₁₆ ins shown on drawing No. 19915[12]), with an I/D of 1⅝ ins, would give a tubes free-gas area of 2.9 sq. ft, resulting in a total free-gas area of approximately 4.7 sq. ft.

From this, a free-gas to grate area ratio of 16.8 per cent with a 28 sq. ft grate pertains, and 15.7 per cent with a 30 sq. ft grate, the latter ratio being almost ideal. The L/D ratio, with the reduced tube diameter of 1⅞ ins O/D and reduced tube length of 14 ft 6 ins, is 107, which is moving in the right direction. However, the ratio of free-gas area through the flues to the total free-gas area, at 38.5 per cent, is still not sufficiently high to meet superheat requirements.

A further iteration on the boiler parameters is therefore needed to increase the proportionate share of gas flow through the flues and a simple way to achieve this is to reduce the number of tubes, to, say, 175, recognising that whilst there will be some loss in heating surface, the addition of 16 sq. ft to the FHS, by fitting a sloping firebox front throatplate, should more than compensate, this utilising the space vacated in reducing the length between tubeplates by 1 ft 6 ins.

The reduction in tube numbers from 203 to 175, with the smaller diameter tube, results in a 2.52 sq. ft free-gas area through the tubes and, taking account of the proposed increase in flue O/D to 5⁵⁄₁₆ ins, with an increased superheater fit, gives 2.09 sq. ft through the flues, providing a 4.61 sq. ft total free-gas area and a 45.3 per cent ratio for the flue free-gas area, which is just acceptable.

The output in this exercise results in a boiler having the following parameters:

Length between tubeplates	14 ft 6 ins
Tubes	175 x 1⅞ ins O/D (1⅝ ins I/D)
Flues	24 x 5⁵⁄₁₆ ins O/D (5.0 ins I/D)
Free-gas area	
– tubes	2.52 sq. ft
– flues	2.09 sq. ft
Total	4.61 sq. ft
Tubeplate Free-gas/grate area ratio	
– with 28 sq. ft grate	16.5 per cent
– with 30 sq. ft grate	15.4 per cent
Free-gas flues area/total area	45.3 per cent
Main internal steam pipe diameter	5.0 ins
Heating surfaces	
– tubes	1,246 sq. ft
– flues	484 sq. ft
– firebox	186 sq. ft
Total	1,916 sq. ft

To a first order, the weight of this marginally modified boiler could be accommodated within the weight of the operational 'as-built' boiler, though detailed checks on increased boiler and water weight would be needed.

Having reduced the length between tubeplates to 14 ft 6 ins, then changed the THS by reducing the tube diameter plus number of tubes, and increased the flue diameter, a check on boiler steaming capacity is needed. Advantage can, of course, be taken of introducing the sloping front throatplate to the inner firebox – utilising all of the reduced tube bundle length – gaining approximately an extra 16 sq. ft of FHS. Taking account of these potential modifications gives a maximum steam generating capacity of around 20,500 lbs per hour,[21] assuming adequate draughting.

Whilst accepting this reduction in length between tubeplates, a very different boiler arrangement might have been obtained if Pickersgill had taken a more aggressive approach to the design, which of course would have required a higher superheat solution. If the number of superheater flues had been increased to 32 x 5⁵⁄₁₆ ins by fitting an additional row of flues in the boiler, and 203 x 1⅞ ins tubes retained, the boiler parameters would, including the additional 16 sq. ft of FHS, have been as follows:

Length between tubeplates	14 ft 6 ins
Tubes	203 x 1⅞ ins O/D (1⅝ ins I/D)
Flues	32 x 5⁵⁄₁₆ ins O/D (4⅞ ins I/D)
Free-gas area	
– tubes	2.92 sq. ft
– flues	2.56 sq. ft
Total	5.48 sq. ft
Tubeplate Free-gas/grate area ratio	
– with 28 sq. ft grate	19.6 per cent
– with 30 sq. ft grate	18.3 per cent
– with 32 sq. ft grate	17.1 per cent
Free-gas flues area/total area	46.7 per cent
Main internal steam pipe diameter	5.0 ins
Heating surfaces	
– tubes	1,445 sq. ft
– flues	645 sq. ft
– firebox	186 sq. ft
Total	2,276 sq. ft

This further iteration, with a 28 sq. ft grate and sloping front firebox throatplate may have required a small increase in boiler diameter and perhaps been marginally too heavy. However, if the locomotive structure had been lightened, this alternative boiler arrangement may have fitted within the 20 ton axle loading limit. High superheat conditions would have prevailed, much akin to the Gresley 'K3' Class boiler.[6] The maximum steam production rate, for this 'more aggressive approach', assuming adequate draughting, would have been around 22,000 lbs per hour,[21] which again would be considered satisfactory.

One further area would require detailed checking, that being the firebox tubeplate's ability to accommodate this proposed high superheat proposal, both in physical and heat transfer terms. CR practice on their larger engines was to use a firebox crown sheet having a radius of around 5 ft between shoulders, the influence of which will be considered when reviewing firebox crown sheet geometry.

As previously noted, a tube bundle length at around 14 ft 6 ins is broadly in line with tests undertaken at PRC Altoona,[2,3] from which it was shown that little heat transfer advantage is obtained by allowing the tube length to exceed around 100 to 120 times the internal diameter (1⅝ ins x 110 = 178 ins = 14 ft 10 ins).

As built, the '956' Class boiler free-gas to grate ratio of 18.6 per cent would point to higher than normal coal consumption; this indeed being the case, with '956' Class average coal consumption being recorded at around 74 lbs per mile in 1931, as previously noted.[22]

SUPERHEATER

In reviewing the superheater surface (SHS) requirements, Figure 14[11,12] is again instructive and points to a CR regime, under Pickersgill, in which SHS was low compared to contemporary designs, to previous Caledonian company practice, as well as to Dr Schmidt's proposals.[9,10] By comparison, when new superheated boilers were provided for NBR 'Atlantic' Class locomotives in 1921, the SHS at 385 sq. ft[23] was 21.5 per cent of the evaporative surface total, a representative figure in British practice being between 20 and 25 per cent of the total evaporative surface.[24] As built, the '956' Class SHS was only 11.4 per cent of the evaporative surfaces. By using full extension loops, and arranging the SHS to be around 20 to 25 per cent of the evaporative surfaces, the SHS area would be enhanced to a proportion not dissimilar to the McIntosh era.

The cross sectional area for steam flow through the superheater elements must now be considered, and should be larger than that of the internal main steam pipe, not only to allow for the volumetric increase, but also to allow for the effects of flow friction. Steam entering a superheater is far from dry, Dr Schmidt showing that at least the first quarter of the SHS area is needed to remove all water droplets and ensure the steam is 100 per cent dry[9,10] prior to superheating. Once superheated to 150-200°F,[25] steam behaves almost as a perfect gas and the standard Boyles' and Charles' laws apply.[9,10] The corollary is the superheater cross section is usually set in the range 1.1 to 1.4 times the main steam pipe cross section, depending on the degree of superheat applied, though the ratio can be as high as 1.5[9,10,26] for higher superheat conditions. Accepting the '956' Class 'as-built' main internal steam pipe at 5 ins diameter, the 'as-built' superheater elements area ratio is too low at 1.085 (based on super-heater elements of 1$\frac{1}{16}$ ins I/D), and should be at least 1.4, recognising the intended 650-675°F average superheat conditions.

This low ratio at 1.085 provides additional explanation why, for further '956' Class construction, the flues were to be increased to 5$\frac{5}{16}$ ins diameter, thus accommodating a greater superheater cross section and reduction in superheater pressure loss, as well as increasing the flue gas flow regime. Moreover, if this area ratio was to be increased from 1.08 to 1.40, the superheater elements I/D, which have been worked into the modified boiler design, would be around 1$\frac{1}{4}$ ins (just over 1$\frac{1}{2}$ ins O/D), as opposed to the 1$\frac{1}{16}$ ins I/D 'as-built'. For the '956' Class, this increase to 1$\frac{1}{4}$ ins I/D elements raises the element cross section by around 40 per cent, and almost halves the superheater pressure loss for identical steam flows. The LM&SR 1930 boiler book records the '938' Class superheater elements having an I/D of 1$\frac{1}{4}$ ins.[27]

The 'as-built' superheater area restriction would have reduced the steam chest pressure at maximum working, by perhaps a further 10 to 15 psi over that which might normally apply. Whilst the author would support the St Rollox proposed increase in flue diameters, he would not support the initially proposed increase in tube diameters which would have adversely affected the flue gas flow regime and further prejudiced final superheated steam temperature, a position belatedly appreciated by St Rollox in 1931,[12] when the tubeplate drawings were further annotated to reduce the tube diameter to 1$\frac{7}{8}$ ins O/D.

The fitting of full extension superheater elements having 1$\frac{1}{2}$ ins O/D in 5$\frac{5}{16}$ ins O/D flues, with 14 ft 6 ins between tubeplates (allowing for elements terminating 3 ft from the firebox tubeplate), provides an SHS of 434 sq. ft, i.e. 22.6 per cent of the 1,916 sq. ft evaporative surface for the modified boiler, which would seem satisfactory. Fitting 50 per cent return loop lengths in these circumstances would reduce the SHS to around 16.9 per cent, which the author would not support.

Normal practice of the day suggested that the superheater elements terminate at around 3 ft from the fireside of the firebox tubeplate, and with boilers of average dimensions, the element return bends at the smokebox end extended almost to the tubeplate itself, since the minimum prevailing flue gas temperature is sufficiently high to benefit the superheat. When, however, the length between tubeplates exceeds approximately 16 ft, the final temperature of the superheated steam in the elements may exceed that of the surrounding gases,[28,29] To prevent this condition arising, the length of the return loops was at times considerably reduced, in some cases by 50 per cent, with some sacrifice to superheat transfer energy.

Over the years, a difference of opinion has emerged as to the benefits related to longer or shorter return loops for superheater elements; also, it has been suggested that a reduced superheater element loop length is of little consequence for heat transfer, but the experience of Schmidt[9,10] and others suggests otherwise. So long as the smokebox exhaust gas temperature exceeds the steam temperature in the superheater, the superheat will be enhanced. This author would, however, suggest a 50 per cent return loop length can be tolerated, with advantage to superheater pressure loss, and overall weight, only so long as the final SHS does not fall below 20 per cent of the evaporative surfaces area, a position exemplified for the reduction in SHS on the '938' Class. Additionally, it should be recognised that the higher the degree of superheat, the higher will be the cylinder mean effective pressure (MEP), the power output and the thermal efficiency of the engine.[30] Moreover steam consumption will be proportionally reduced.

By way of comparison, the superheating stance taken by various CMEs for representative locomotives is given in the table below, showing THS plus FHS and SHS data, it being clear that the Pickersgill's policy diverged significantly from mainstream progressive thinking.

STEAM CIRCUIT

Whilst the largest steam system pressure loss will normally be in the superheater elements at maximum working, there remain other parts of the circuit which compel attention, to ensure overall pressure loss between boiler and steam chests is 8-10 per cent of boiler pressure in these circumstances. Contemporary GWR trials on their 4-cylinder locomotives showed an approximate 8 per cent pressure loss near maximum working,[36] despite relatively low superheat.

Further, when one notes that the piston valve diameters for both '34' Class and '956' Class engines were identical, yet the potential steam raising capacity of the respective boilers was hugely different, this can hardly be seen as assisting the performance of the larger locomotive.

Additionally, there seems to have been a CR company engineering

SUPERHEATER SURFACE RATIOS – COMPARABLE LOCOMOTIVES							
DATE	COMPANY	WHEEL ARRANGEMENT	CLASS	CME	THS + FHS*	SHS*	SHS AS PERCENT OF (THS + FHS)
1911	G&SWR	4-6-0	128	Manson	1,560	445	28.5[31]
1913	L&NWR	4-6-0	Claughton	B-Cooke	1,818	413	22.7[32]
1920	L&YR	4-6-0	Class 8	Hughes	1,686	552	32.7[33]
1920	MR	4-4-0	4P Compound	Fowler	1,317	291	22.1[34]
1920	GCR	4-6-0	9P	Robinson	2,044	343	16.8[35]
1921	GNR	2-6-0	K3	Gresley	1,901	407	21.4[6]
1916	CR	4-6-0	60	Pickersgill	1,676	258	15.4[11]
1921	CR	4-6-0	956	Pickersgill	2,370	270	11.4[11]

NOTE:
* all values in square feet.

standard in the application of steam pipe diameters in both the boiler internals and the smokebox, which was universally applied, irrespective of the boiler steaming capacity. All the McIntosh designed larger classes had 5 ins diameter boiler internal steam pipes, the same size being used in the 956 Class. Smokebox steam pipes in the corresponding McIntosh classes were 4 ins diameter as against 4.5 ins for the '956' Class.[11]

For the boiler internal steam pipe, the accepted design criteria of the day was to provide as generous a diameter as could be accommodated. For superheated locomotives, a 'rule of thumb' laid down that, for two cylinder engines, the boiler internal steam pipe should have 1 sq. in. of cross section for every 21 sq. ins of total piston area,[37] and, for cases involving more than two cylinders, around 1 sq. in. of cross section for every 30 sq. ins of total piston area.[37] This leads to the need for a boiler internal steam pipe diameter greater than the 5 ins I/D fitted to the '956' Class. Rounding up to 6 ins would have been beneficial.

In his L&NWR 'Claughton' Class,[38] Bowen-Cooke used a 6 ins I/D steam pipe for the boiler internals and a 5 ins I/D pipe for smokebox steam distribution, the 'Claughton' and '956' classes having almost identical total cylinder volumes. In similar fashion, the total cross sectional area of the subsidiary smokebox branch pipes taking steam to each cylinder, subsequent to superheating, should be about 2.4 times as great as that of the main steam pipe.[37] For the 956 Class, this leads to the selection of 5 ins diameter for each of these three pipes. These suggested pipe sizes and layout could have been accommodated in the boiler and smokebox design, but for some unknown reason were not.

Not only do the '956' Class smokebox superheated steam pipes seem to have been marginally under-sized, but the actual layout contained a further peculiarity. Whilst the right-hand cylinder was supplied individually by a single 4½ ins I/D pipe, a pipe of the same diameter supplied both the centre and left-hand cylinders via a branch at the smokebox floor just above the centre cylinder steam chest, as shown in Figure 3. Moreover, the steam pipe lengths were not of the shortest and most direct, which would have been achieved if external pipes had been fitted, though this was not normal UK practice until the middle 1920s, but standard in the USA pre 1914.

Interestingly, the G&SWR '128' Class superheated 4-6-0s, built by the North British Locomotive Co. in 1911,[39] had short outside steam pipes, suggesting the builder and James Manson were well aware of the advantages to be gained in following US practice. Additionally, these engines had 5⅞ ins I/D internal boiler steam pipes[39] and 4⅞ ins I/D pipes from the superheater header to the steam chests.[39]

As noted, the selection of 8 in. piston valves can be questioned, notwithstanding the fact that other companies used this as standard at similar power levels to the '956' Class. It is believed that Pickersgill may have considered 9 ins diameter valves, but this was ultimately rejected. Dugald Drummond,[40] writing in 1912, declared that piston valve diameter should be 60 per cent of the corresponding cylinder diameter, though this ratio was eventually reduced to the 50 to 55 per cent range. Indeed, Churchward,[41] in setting out the cardinal points of his cylinder design criteria, noted that the diameter of piston valves, whenever possible, should not be less than half the cylinder bore.

Whilst the '956' Class was a 3-cylinder machine, it would nevertheless have been very desirable to use 9 in. or even 10 in. valves, with almost no additional construction cost. The advantage of doing so is two-fold: first, with the same ratio of support bridges, the steam and exhaust port areas would have been increased by 12 per cent (for the 9 ins diameter option), reducing the steam circuit pressure losses further and diminishing any tendency to 'wire drawing' at short cut-offs; second, by giving the same added clearance to the exhaust ports, the back pressure would also have been reduced. It is unclear why, in selecting 11 ins diameter piston valves for the 20 ins

diameter cylinders on his proposed 1918 outside-cylindered 4-4-0,[42] Pickersgill reverted to 8 ins diameter on the '956' Class.

Compared with contemporary GWR practice,[36] equivalent data from indicator trials on CR engine No. 60 in May 1917[43] suggests the equivalent CR steam circuit pressure loss position was higher. When working at 74 per cent cut-off, climbing out of Buchanan Street station, on a Perth express, with 357 tons (gross) behind the tender, the regulator fully open, and boiler pressure at 170 psi, the steam chest pressure was recorded at 150 psi – that is, steam circuit losses were around 12 per cent.

BOILER PRESSURE

In selecting a boiler pressure of 180 psi, Pickersgill was being both conventional and conservative. The advantages in using 200 psi, over 180 psi, are significant, including an 11 per cent increase in power and a reduction in steam specific volume. The usual reason given for remaining with a reduced pressure solution was increased boiler maintenance costs, which should not in fact be the case. Writing on this subject, E.S. Cox[44] noted that high pressure, up to about 300 psi, does not of itself cause higher maintenance costs per mile; integrity of design plus water quality and chemistry are the determining factors, a point well appreciated by Churchward, who was using 225 psi boilers pre-1914.[45]

Surviving '956' Class firebox staying and dome interface drawings give some indication of the design criteria used for the boiler. The boiler shell, details of which are given on drawing No. 19874,[12] dated the 19th March 1919 and shown as Figure 18, was manufactured from 21/32 in. steel plate and had an external diameter of 5 ft 7¹¹/₁₆ ins for the middle ring, the rear ring having an external diameter of 5 ft 9 ins. The material characteristics of this boiler plating would have had an Ultimate Tensile Strength (UTS) of around 28 tons per sq. in.[46] In hoop stress, at 180 psi and allowing a riveting efficiency of 0.8, the factor of safety (FoS) for the shell would have been 5.3 in UTS terms. Raising the pressure to 200 psi would have reduced the factor of safety to 4.77, again allowing 0.80 for riveting efficiency. An increase in plate thickness to ¹¹/₁₆ ins would have raised the factor of safety to 5.0, which was the standard used in the UK,[47] but excludes a corrosion allowance.

American practice of the day suggested a factor of safety of not less than 4.5, or even 4.0, with a riveting joint efficiency of 0.85.[47,48] Applying this to a 200 psi boiler, using 21/32 in. plate for the barrel, gives a boiler shell FoS of 5.07 in UTS terms; for ¹¹/₁₆ in. plates the factor of safety is 5.3. With a 5 per cent corrosion allowance, the shell FoS exceeds 5.0. For the use of a 200 psi boiler, it would have been prudent to use ¹¹/₁₆ in. plate, any additional weight which might have breached the axle loading limit being compensated by reduction in the 'massive construction' of the frames and engines. The outer firebox wrapper to which the firebox sling stays were attached was manufactured from ¾ in. plate, the detail being given on drawing No. 19948[49] and illustrated in Figure 19.

The '956' Class staying arrangement, using 1 in. diameter screwed stays at 4 in. centres for the inner firebox,[12] itself manufactured from ⅝ in. copper sheet, is a very standard arrangement, though marginal adjustments may have been needed to allow operation with satisfactory safety margins at 200 psi. Whilst St Rollox had not designed and built a boiler with a sloping front throatplate, the process would not have been beyond their boiler makers' skills, many of whom may have worked with other locomotive builders in Glasgow, and suitable flanging blocks could be hired as needed. The layout arrangements for gussets and the related riveting were well established for the production of boilers with combustion chambers and sloping front throatplates.[50] Moreover, St Rollox had previous experience in the design, build and operation of 200 psi boilers, these being used by Drummond on engines No. 76 and No. 79 in 1889[51] and by McIntosh[52] on the initial building of the '49' and '903' Classes.

There seems no reason why these marginally enhanced stress levels arising from the use of 200 psi could not have been accommodated equally satisfactorily elsewhere in the boiler shell plus firebox[50], and the material characteristics outlined should have been acceptable in the prevailing operating temperature conditions and taking account of a ten year pressure and temperature cycling regime, with due allowance for corrosion. As noted, some detailed checks would have been needed to ensure plate, riveting and staying stresses were acceptable, especially around the firebox, and on the tubeplates, but these were not a particularly high technology matter.

FIREBOX CROWN SHEET GEOMETRY

The '956' Class round-topped firebox was 9 ft 3 ins long, with generous water legs, giving a 28 sq. ft grate. The firebox was relatively shallow at the tubeplate end, being only 5 ft 3 ins deep from the boiler centre-line, compared to the Horwich 2-6-0,[53] which was 5 ft 9 ins. The firebox crown[12] sheet was given a radius of about 5 ft, a feature of the larger Caledonian company boilers: this raised the crown higher in the centre and gave only about 1 ft 5 ins below the outer wrapper plate, a very low figure for a boiler of '956' Class size. Both the McIntosh and Pickersgill 4-4-0s had horizontal crown sheets, the '139' Class height to the outer wrapper being 1 ft 4 ins. Comparable crown sheet to outer wrapper data[54] for

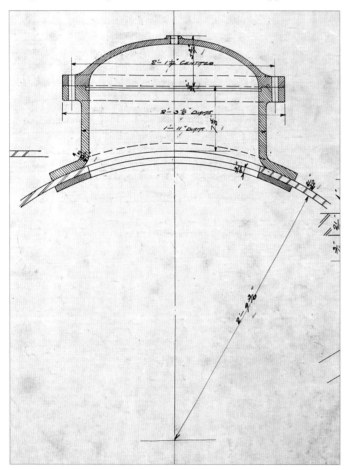

Figure 18
'956' Class. Boiler Section at Steam Dome. Drg No. 19874, dated the 19th March 1919. This drawing illustrates the sections of plate used in the boiler barrel and allows assessment of factors of safety for the 180 psi boiler built using $^{21}/_{32}$ in. steel plate. Structural enhancement in the way of the dome is provided. There would seem no obstacle to a working pressure of 200 psi, though steel sections would require a marginal increase if factors of safety of 5.0, inclusive of a 5 per cent corrosion allowance, were to be met. *CRA: CRA6/1/3/2/48/1/8*

similar large parallel boilers (each with the advantage of a Belpaire firebox) are:

L&YR	'Dreadnought' (8 Class)	1 ft 9 in.
LM&SR	'Royal Scot'	1 ft 10 in.
LM&SR	'Patriot'	1 ft 8 in.

As a result, the volume of steam in the '956' Class boiler at 'half-glass' was smaller than would be expected for a boiler of this size, the approximate equivalent steam volume and surface area figures at 'half-glass' for the '956' and 'Patriot' Classes being:[54]

		'956'	'PATRIOT'
Steam volume	cu. ft	65	103
Water Surface Area	sq. ft	100	106

In thermal inertia terms, assuming respective steady-state steam raising rates, the '956' Class boiler would have had a lesser short-term overload capacity than that of the 'Patriot'. Moreover, a higher water level than that normally needed on the L&YR and LM&SR engines would be necessary on the '956' Class to protect the firebox crown. Additionally, the number of summits on CR main lines with direct transition from rising to falling gradients, and involving not insignificant water level changes, could have encouraged water carryover, priming and further loss of superheat.

Figure 20 (see page 79) sets out the comparative positions for 'half-glass' water conditions on the L&YR 'Dreadnought' and the '956' Class boilers, the L&YR locomotive data being on the right side of the diagram. Looking at the L&YR boiler, illustrated as Section 'X', a distance 'a-a¹' has been chosen as representative of the set minimum water level to protect the crown sheet, the gauge glass being shown with distance 'b-b¹' representing the working coverage of the glass. With the water level at the gauge glass 'bottom nut' the boiler crown sheet is protected, the 'half-glass' condition being at level 'c' and the distance from the crown sheet to 'half-glass' being 'a-c'.

For a curved crown sheet boiler, as shown as Section 'Y', the same distance 'a-a¹' is used to give the minimum water level to protect the crown sheet, distance 'b-b¹' again representing the working coverage of the gauge glass. The 'half-glass' water level now being at level 'd', and the distance from the crown sheet to 'half-glass' being 'a-d'. Additionally, the water level at 'half-glass' at Section 'Y' has reduced the available steam volume and the surface area for steam disengagement, compared to that available for a horizontal crown sheet.

Scaling the '956' Class general arrangement drawing suggests the '956' Class 'as-built' gauge glasses were set in the backhead to give the position shown as Section 'Z', on the extreme left of Figure 20. Whilst the 'half-glass' water level is now at 'e' and the steam volume and disengagement area are both increased, the margin of safety available for crown sheet protection is reduced.

It is unclear why a radiused crown sheet was specified. One possibility may have been to ensure that thermal plasticity (ensuring the firebox energy could be conducted to the water without localised firebox overheating) and resultant mechanical stressing in the upper area of the firebox tubeplate were both within acceptable limits. However, recognising that St Rollox altered the tubeplate drawings post the No. 956 trials in 1921 and 1922 to increase the flue and tube areas, it is unlikely that plasticity and stressing values were approaching limiting conditions.

Dugald Drummond[55] set out some guidance for crown sheet protection, noting that the distance from the top of the gauge glass 'bottom nut' to the firebox crown sheet top should be 1½ ins, this being seen as a minimum safe value. In these circumstances, the gauge glasses should be set into the boiler backhead such that at 'half-glass'

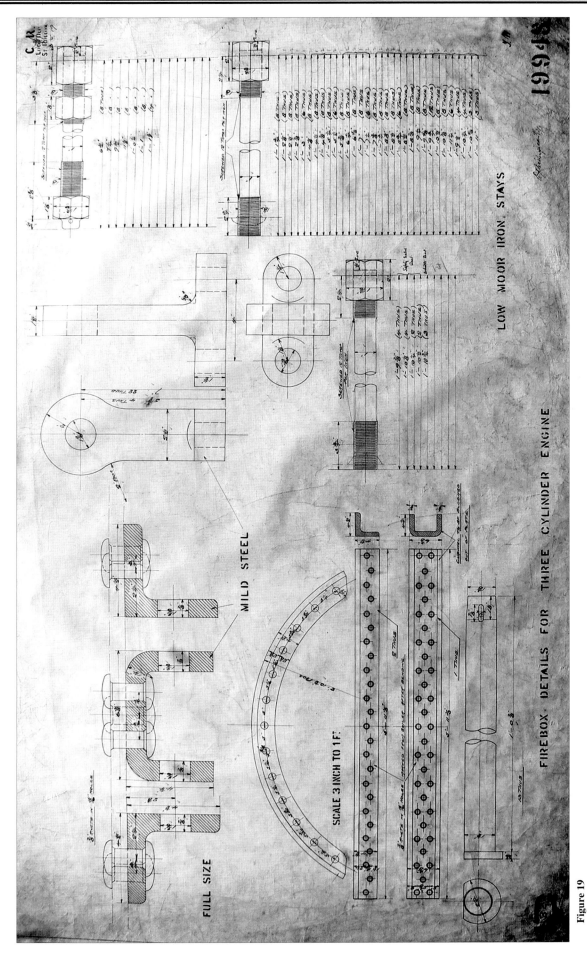

Figure 19
'956' Class. Firebox Details. Drg No. 19948, dated the 9th May 1919. The design and dimensions of the sling stays and their attachment to the wrapper plate is laid out in detail, from which all the components could be manufactured. Two rows of sling stays were fitted, the remaining crown sheet staying being of the screwed variety. The arrangement is very standard, as is the use of Low Moor ductile iron for the stays.

NRS: GD456, RHP136355/8

conditions, the water coverage on the crown sheet should be 5 ins as a minimum. Drummond noted that operation of the locomotive by the crew must ensure boiler water was maintained at 'half glass' in all working conditions, this being sufficient to cater for water level fluctuation arising from gradient changes.

OBSERVATIONS

A number of observations on the 'as-built' 956 Class boiler, its superheater, the steam circuit, the working pressure regime and water levels can be made:

1. The overall boiler proportions were not engineered to the best criteria of the day, and coal consumption would have been higher than it might have otherwise been. Part of the difficulties lay with the selection of the cylinder layout resulting in a longer than necessary frame and boiler tube-bundle. Two alternatives seemed available to Pickersgill, the larger having a 32-element superheater, the smaller having 28 elements, each with sloping front throatplate. Recognising that post the August 1921 trials, boiler modifications were needed, it would have been difficult to change the 'as-built' tube-bundle length, and fitting new tubeplates would have been expensive and probably out of the question in the prevailing financial circumstances, though the flues could have been bored out and larger flues and superheater elements fitted. A proportion of the tubes could have been plugged to advantage, as noted by A.J. Powell, though again finance constraints and available labour may have denied these options.

2. The '956' Class L/D ratio was marginally too high, again as a direct result of the cylinder layout, and the proportion of gases passing through the flues was much too low. For the smaller boiler option, a reduction in small tubes to 175 with 1⅛ ins O/D, plus the fitting of 5⁵⁄₁₆ ins flues, would have improved the heat transfer performance and reduced coal consumption. The retrospective fitting of a sloping front firebox throatplate would have required a major boiler rebuild and would have been virtually impossible in the prevailing conditions. For the larger boiler option with a 32-element superheater, the original number of small tubes could have been retained. Advantage to steaming could have been achieved by deepening the firebox at the tubeplate end and utilising a greater grate slope, but in the prevailing financial climate this option, requiring major boiler surgery, was again potentially a non-starter. The provision of a 30 sq. ft grate should have been seriously considered at the design stage.

3. The superheater design contained a number of shortfalls, and should have been improved in three respects. First, the SHS was too low and should have been raised to around 20 to 25 per cent of the evaporative surface. Second, the cross section of the superheater elements was too small leading to higher than necessary pressure loss in the superheater. Third, the flue gas ratio was too low, with insufficient gases being carried by the flues, again prejudicing the degree of superheat. Whilst these points were belatedly recognised at St Rollox, significant expenditure would have been unavoidable on the four original boilers to overcome the superheater difficulties. Trials results on No. 956 indicated steam temperatures averaging 525 to 550°F, whilst trials on No. 139 in August 1910 achieved just over 650°F. This 100°F shortfall in steam temperature would have increased the steam consumption for No. 956 by 10 to 15 per cent over that pertaining to the same engine operating in similar loaded conditions with 650°F steam temperature. For a boiler which

would not steam well, this additional handicap may well have been the 'straw which broke the camel's back'. Coal consumption would have been proportionately lower in the 650°F superheat conditions.

4. The boiler should have been designed and rated for a working pressure of 200 psi, there being no real obstacle to this. If necessary, consideration should have been given to a slight increase in boiler plate thickness, or using a chrome-alloy steel, any consequential excess on axle loading being removed by reduction in frame and structure. This increase in pressure could have been achieved at minimal cost increase at the design stage and, *prima facie*, would have required no adjustment to staying centres. A sloping front throatplate would have been of immense assistance. The benefits in using the higher boiler pressure and other related matters had been well laid out by Churchward in 1906.[56]

5. The steam circuit design could have been improved, reducing pressure losses in all the main steam pipes and on the valve ports by adopting 9 ins or even 10 ins diameter piston valves. Additionally, the provision of more direct steam passages from the piston valves would have been of benefit. The feeding of two cylinders from one steam pipe is inexplicable.

6. The fitting of a radiused firebox crown sheet, with the need for higher boiler water levels and reduction in steam space plus steam disengagement area, was perhaps not appreciated by St Rollox during the design process. A horizontal crown sheet and greater clear height to the outer wrapper plate, with consequent opportunity to operate the locomotive with lower water levels, would have been of significant benefit. The increase in available steam volume, and greater steam disengagement area, would have improved the ability of the '956' Class to sustain higher transient outputs, with minimised reduction in boiler pressure. In these circumstances, the probabilities of water carry-over, inhibiting superheat temperatures would have been minimised. Interestingly, whilst the '903' Class also had a similarly radiused firebox crown sheet, the much higher superheat conditions in that class may well have ensured that the probabilities of water carry-over could be discounted.

It is unclear if Thomas Weir's examination of the 'Claughton' design in early 1919 provided any guidance on boiler or superheater design matters, the St Rollox drawing register making no reference to such issues. Weir would, of course, have been very familiar with St Rollox superheating policy from the McIntosh era.

SOME BOILER COMPARISONS

The table below gives an indication of what CMEs on the L&NWR and GNR were achieving with contemporary designs, and what, in an operational and performance sense, should have been achievable by St Rollox. The table includes the 'as-built' '956' Class and final columns give the parameters of the two suggested boilers, both using contemporary knowledge, which might have been considered by St Rollox.

'956' CLASS BOILERS – BUILDING AT ST ROLLOX

Ernest Glen[58] captured the '956' Class boilers during their build phases, Plate 38 depicting the completed shell, with back-head bosses in place, prior to the fitting of the inner firebox – the shallowness of the sloping grate is evident. The firebox outer wrapper plate is of the 'tri-partite' form, which was previously found only on CR '903', '908', '918', '179' and '60' classes.[59] It has been suggested this feature may have been copied from contemporary Belgian practice.[59]

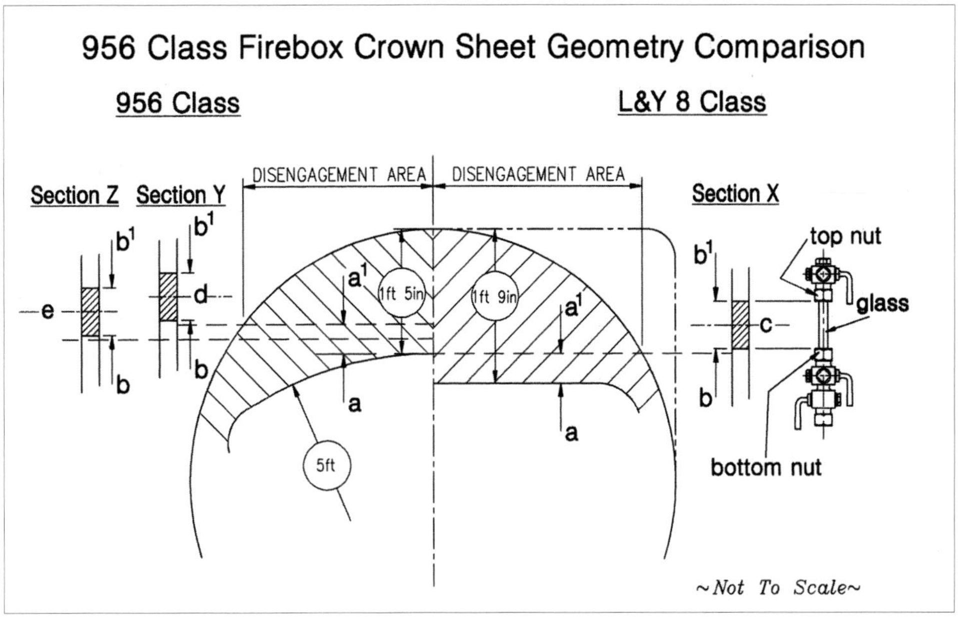

Figure 20
'956' Class. Firebox Crown Sheet Geometry Comparison. It is not clear what advantages the Caledonian company expected in using a curved crown sheet on their larger passenger engines. Its use, however, raised difficulties, principally in relation to ensuring a defined minimum allowable water depth over the crown sheet. This in turn led to a reduction of steam volume above the water level and the increased probability of water carry over. Further, the area for steam disengagement was lowered and the reduction in available steam volume would further prejudice the boiler's short term overload capacity. In both McIntosh and Pickersgill 4-4-0 classes a flat crown sheet was used. ***Author***

The upper backhead area, showing partial completion with backhead fittings, is illustrated in Plate 39, by which time the inner firebox was in place. Hydraulic testing of the complete boiler and fittings assembly at 150 per cent of normal working pressure was a 'proving' requirement, Plate 40 showing one of the '956' Class boilers ostensibly in such circumstances, the calibrated pressure gauge being connected to the boiler top and positioned to the right of the firehole opening. The St Rollox build order Y125 is clearly identified in chalk on the boiler barrel to the right of the encircling chain.

The superheater header and elements arrangements integrated with the completed boiler are shown in Plate 41, whilst that assembly, as fitted to a locomotive prior to adding the smokebox, is illustrated in Plate 42. This latter illustration shows clearly the smokebox construction, with what appears to be a lower saddle, yet not using a circular one-piece cylindrical drum arrangement. It would seem that a rolled partial cylinder was attached to the lower outer faces of the saddle and then riveted to the smokebox front plate and an angled section attached at the rear to facilitate connection to the boiler barrel.

Boiler Ratio Comparisons

		L&NWR Claughton	GNR K3	CR 956 As Built	CR Options 956 Mod. 1	956 Mod. 2
Small Tubes	– Quantity	149	217	203	175	203
	– O/D, inches	1⅞	1¾	2 1/16	1⅞	1⅞
Superheater Flues	– Quantity	24	32	24	24	32
	– O/D, inches	5¼	5¼	5⅛	5 5/16	5 5/16
Elements	– Quantity	24	32	24	24	32
	– Diameter, O/D, inches	1½	1½	1⅜	1½	1½
	– Bore, I/D, inches	1¼	1¼	1 1/16	1¼	1¼
Heating Surfaces	– Tubes, square feet	1,574	1,719	2,200	1,730	2,090
	– Firebox, square feet	171	182	170	186	186
	– Total (Tubes and Firebox), square feet	1,745	1,901	2,370	1,916	2,276
	– Superheat, square feet	413	407	270	434	434
	– Superheat, per cent of Total HS	23.7	21.4	11.8	22.6	19.1
	– THS, square feet	2,158	2,308	2,640	2,350	2,710
Grate Area, sq. ft		30.5	28.0	28.0	30.0	30.0
Free-gas/Grate ratio, per cent		14.0	19.3	18.6	14.8	18.3
Boiler Diameter		5 ft 2 ins	6 ft 0 ins[57]	5 ft 7½ ins*	5 ft 7½ ins*	5 ft 7½ ins**
L/D Tubes		110	96	110	107	107
Length between TPs		14 ft 10 ins	12 ft 0 ins	16 ft 0 ins	14 ft 6 ins	14 ft 6 ins
Boiler Pressure, psi		175	180	180	200	200
Steam Generation as per cent of '956' Class 'as-built' boiler		81.0	87.5	100	88.2	100

Notes:
* Centre boiler barrel ring.
** Assessment of boiler diameter and weight to take extra row of superheater flues not undertaken in detail.

Plate 38
An almost complete '956' Class boiler shell in the boiler shop at St Rollox works, the inner firebox and tubes having yet to be fitted. The firebox outer wrapper plate is of the tri-partite form, which may have been copied from Belgian practice.   *A.E. Glen*

Plate 39
In a more advanced stage of completion, this '956' Class boiler has the firebox fitted and the backhead fittings in place. The two lifting injectors are to the right and left sides of the boiler. Gauge glasses and related protectors remain to be fitted.   *A.E. Glen*

Plate 40
Boiler 'proving' by hydraulic test at 150 per cent of working pressure was an essential element of the construction process, the illustration showing one of the '956' Class boilers apparently being prepared for testing. What is assumed to be the calibrated test gauge is connected to the top of the boiler and mounted to the right of the firehole aperture. The order number Y125 is clearly chalked on the boiler barrel to the right of the encircling chain.   *A.E. Glen*

Plate 41
The superheater elements and header fitted to a '956' Class boiler prior to its fitting to the frames is illustrated. Note, there are only two take-off points on the header for steam supply to the three cylinders, the connection on the right of the header supplying the left and centre cylinders, as depicted in Figure 3.

A.E. Glen

BELOW: **Plate 42**
With the boiler fitted to the frames, the smokebox construction is clearly illustrated. This arrangement, whilst not using a completely cylindrical smokebox and perhaps being more complex to install, does provide unhindered access to the smokebox during its fit-out.

A.E. Glen

BOILER RECORD CARDS

Boiler record cards for three of the '956' Class locomotive boilers have survived,[60] the engines to which they were fitted being LM&SR No's 14801 to 14803 inclusive, the boilers being classed '89-N70' by the LM&SR. The cost of manufacture of each boiler at St Rollox is given as £2,367, this comprising £805 for the boiler shell, £804 for the copper fire-box and £758 for boiler mountings. The table below gives the recorded disposal details

Unfortunately, the LM&SR engine record cards have not survived, it having been LM&SR policy to dispose of the associated card when the locomotive was scrapped. It seems that some repairs were

'956' CLASS BOILER DISPOSALS

ENGINE NO.	BOILER NO. SCRAPPING	DATE OF SCRAPPING*	MILEAGE RECORDED	REPAIRS VALUE	RESIDUAL VALUE
14801	1691	24th March 1934	281,252	none	£75 5s 2d
14802	1692	26th January 1935	281,589	none	£89 2s 3d
14803	1693	15th July 1933	275,893	none	£63 13s 3d

Note:
* Record cards annotated as *'Date taken off and Scrapped'*.

undertaken to the boilers at St Rollox, the cards noting references for repairs, but unfortunately no detail is given.[60] Whilst it is assumed, through lack of evidence to the contrary, that individual boilers remained paired with specific locomotives throughout their respective lives, the fact that engine and boiler numbers run in sequence tends to support this position.

Interestingly, the record card for engine No. 14801[60] notes the boiler was reunited with the engine's frame on the 25th December 1931 (not a public holiday in Scotland in those days). If this were so, it would seem that No. 14801 was refitted with the second type of derived motion between August and December 1931, the former being the withdrawal date for No. 14800, from which the derived motion for refit to No. 14801 was recovered. These dates tie in with photographic evidence of No. 14801 carrying Stephenson's motion then derived motion for the centre cylinder in its latter years. It is very likely the decision to refit derived motion to No. 14801 would have been endorsed by John Barr, who may even have initiated it.

REFERENCES

1. *Modern Locomotive Practice*, C.E. Wolff (Manchester Scientific Publishing Co., 1907), pp. 69-71
2. 'E6s Locomotive', PRC, Locomotive Test Plant, Altoona, Bulletin No. 21, 1913, pp. 60ff
3. *Steam Locomotive Design: Data and Formulae*, E.A. Phillipson (The Locomotive Publishing Co.), p. 93, Altoona data
4. Prof. W.E. Dalby FRS, IMechE paper, 1909
5. *Steam Locomotive Design: Data and Formulae*, E.A. Phillipson, pp. 93-4
6. *The LNER 2-6-0 Classes*, John F. Clay and J. Cliffe (Ian Allan, 1978), K3 data, Appendices pp. 64-76
7. As CR '60' Class ratio and McIntosh locomotives
8. As McIntosh Dunalastair I-IV locomotives
9. *The Use of Superheated Steam in Locomotives*, Dr W. Schmidt, 1908
10. *The Application of Highly Superheated Steam to Locomotives*, Dr W. Schmidt (1911)
11. *Forty Years of Caledonian Locomotives*, Campbell Cornwell (David & Charles, 1974), Appendices 2-5
12. Campbell Cornwell Collection of CR 956 Class drawings, CRA6/1/3/2, Archive Group 48
13. *Steam Locomotive Design: Data and Formulae*, E.A. Phillipson, pp. 59-62, Tables XV, XVI
14. *Highland Railway Locomotives, Book 2*, J.R.H. Cormack and J.L. Stevenson (RCTS, 1990), pp. 96ff and pp. 129ff
15. 'Results of Testing E2A Locomotive', PRC, Locomotive Test Plant, Altoona, 1910, figs 902, 903 (pp. 16, 17)
16. *Locomotive Engineers' Pocket Book 1935* (The Locomotive Publishing Co), pp. 36, 41
17. *Steam Locomotive Design: Data and Formulae*, E.A. Phillipson, pp. 45-50
18. *Locomotive Engineers' Pocket Book 1935*, table XIII, p. 56, Prof Goss, pre 1914
19. *Steam Locomotive Design: Data and Formulae*, E.A. Phillipson, p. 51
20. *Locomotive Engineers' Pocket Book 1935*, p. 58 table XVII
21. *Locomotive Engineers' Pocket Book 1935*, p. 50
22. 'Heavenly Blue Enigmas', C.P. Atkins, in *BackTrack*, February 2009, pp. 104ff
23. *The North British Railway*, C. Hamilton Ellis (Ian Allan, 1955), p. 206, (also *Railway Magazine*, January 1922)
24. *Steam Locomotive Design: Data and Formulae*, E.A. Phillipson, p. 67, Tables XV, XVI
25. *Superheating on Locomotives*, J.F. Gairns (The Locomotive Publishing Co., 1914), p. 13
26. *Steam Locomotive Design: Data and Formulae*, E.A. Phillipson, pp. 155ff
27. LMS Engine Boiler Book 1930, NRS, BR/LMS/5/131A, Drg No 19493, N79 boilers
28. *Steam Locomotive Design: Data and Formulae*, E.A. Phillipson, p. 63
29. PRC, Locomotive Test Plant, Altoona, Volume 28, June 1915, pp. 5
30. *Steam Locomotive Design: Data and Formulae*, E.A. Phillipson, p. 156
31. *Locomotives of the G&SWR*, David L. Smith (David & Charles, 1976), p. 111, and NB Loco Drg L440 for 128 Class
32. *The British Steam Railway Locomotive, 1825 to 1925*, E.L. Ahrons (The Locomotive Publiahing Co.), p. 354, Table XV
33. *The British Steam Railway Locomotive, 1825 to 1925*, E.L. Ahrons, p. 359, Table XVII
34. *The Midland Compounds*, O.S. Nock (David & Charles, 1964), p. 80
35. *Robinson Locomotives*, Brian Haresnape and Peter Rowledge (Ian Allan, 1982), pp. 110ff
36. *Steam Locomotive Design: Data and Formulae*, E.A. Phillipson, p. 14
37. *Steam Locomotive Design: Data and Formulae*, E.A. Phillipson, pp. 108-9
38. *An Illustrated History of LNWR Locomotives*, Edward Talbot (OPC, 1984), p. 297
39. NB Loco Co., G&SWR 128 Class GA Drg, L440, courtesy of G&SWR Association
40. Address to LSWR Engineering Society, Dugald Drummond, 27th June 1911
41. *Railway Progress 1909-1959, Vol. 1, The Churchward Era*, (SLS, 1959), pp. 1ff
42. St Rollox Drg No. 19346, dated 30th January 1918, NRS, RHP132352
43. Indicator Trials, Engine No. 60, 18th May 1917, Montague Smith collection, NRS, GD456, RHP136352/49
44. Contribution by E.S. Cox in *Royal Scots of the LMS*, ed. Douglas Doherty (Ian Allan, 1970), p. 15
45. *The GWR Stars, Castles and Kings*, O.S. Nock (David & Charles, 1967), p. 16
46. *Locomotive Engineers' Pocket Book 1935*, Strength of Materials, p. 310
47. *Steam Locomotive Design: Data and Formulae*, E.A. Phillipson, pp. 74ff
48. *Locomotive Boilers and Engines*, L.V. Ludy (American Technical Society, Chicago, 1918), p. 72
49. St Rollox drg No. 19948, dated 9th May 1919, Montague Smith Collection, NRS, GD456, RHP136355/8
50. *Locomotive Boiler Construction, A Practical Treatise for Boilermakers*, Frank Brasil (NW Henley Publications, 1912)
51. *Forty Years of Caledonian Locomotives, 1882-1922*, Campbell Cornwell, pp. 45ff
52. *The McIntosh Locomotives of the Caledonian Railway*, A.B. MacLeod (Ian Allan, 1948), pp. 20, 21
53. *The Hughes and Stanier 2-6-0s* (RCTS, 2009), pp. 4-13
54. A.J. Powell papers, NRM, 956 Class Material, uncatalogued
55. *Lectures to L&SWR Enginemen*, Dugald Drummond (The Locomotive Publishing Co., 1921 reprint), pp. 24ff
56. 'Large Locomotive Boilers', IMechE paper, 2nd February 1906, G.J. Churchward (noted in O.S. Nock, *Stars, Castles and Kings*)
57. Gresley once said he would rather carry an extra ton of hot water than an extra ton of frame and engine to gain adhesion, cited in *The LNER 2-6-0 Classes*, John F. Clay and J. Cliffe (Ian Allan, 1978), p. 24
58. A.E. Glen Collection, private collection, courtesy Dr Ann Glen
59. Correspondence between author and C.P. Atkins, 2014
60. 956 Class Boiler Record Cards, NRS, GD344/4/32/1-3

CHAPTER 14

DRAUGHTING, GRATE AND ASHPAN ARRANGEMENTS

DRAUGHTING

One area having very significant effect on locomotive performance is the design of blast pipe and chimney liner, and in the early 1920s, few appreciated how large an effect small changes in blast pipe diameter and height setting, plus chimney choke diameter could have on steam generating capacity. As noted previously, it was suggested that even the GWR had encountered this problem with their second purchase of de Glehn compound 'Atlantics'. However, through testing at PRC Altoona and trials by Professors Goss and Ludy at Purdue in the 1910 to 1915 period, a number of key blast pipe and chimney parameters were set down, which, when followed, seemed to give acceptable results,[1,2,3]

The key to success, appreciated by several UK CMEs, was to ensure adequate smokebox vacuum under maximum working conditions. The normally expected smokebox vacuum at firing rates of around 100 lbs per hour per sq. ft of grate area, was shown to be around 8 to 11 ins water gauge (WG) in the smokebox main body,[2] with the chimney entry vacuum being around 12 to 13 ins WG, this latter figure being quoted for an express locomotive with a grate area in the 25 to 30 sq. ft range, running at 50 to 60 mph.[4] Contemporary tests reported by Gresley[5] for GNR locomotives give broadly similar values, it being noted that closing the dampers increased the smokebox vacuum by 2 ins WG.

There were certainly steaming problems with the '956' Class, Alan Dunbar[6] noting that No. 956 itself had the blast pipe reset twice in September 1922 and that on three other occasions the orifice was changed, the latter change incorporating an insert to reduce the blast orifice diameter. No information has come to light on any specific '956' Class blast pipe height changes, nor any diagrams showing the blast cone's impact on the chimney liner structure. The only surviving '956' Class smokebox vacuum data[7] is the minimal information recorded during the 1921 and 1922 trials on No. 956, when vacuum was found to be in the range 4 to 7 ins WG, a figure lower than might have been anticipated.

The results from the Altoona and Purdue University trials,[1,2,3] reported in various test bulletins, set out graphs of the relationship between steam generation, smokebox vacuum and coal firing rate. Additionally, for optimised vacuum conditions, chimney liner arrangements were noted as having a continuous taper of around 1/12, with a throat diameter of around 17 ins and a well-radiused lower bell-mouth chimney liner entry arrangement. The sighting of the blast nozzle height with relation to the chimney choke point was seen as of prime importance and was reported on in detail.

Professor Ludy[3] demonstrated by trials that the bell-mouthed chimney entry and tapered liner was essential. Additionally, and most importantly, the height of the blast nozzle should be set such that the divergent blast cone impacted on the chimney liner between the choke point and the chimney exit lip. This arrangement was shown to maximise exhaust gas entrainment, giving highest smokebox vacuum conditions. Comparative testing with various tapers and parallel chimney liners showed distinct disadvantage to smokebox vacuum and steam generation if parallel liners were used. Phillipson[8] also sets out the related pre-1918 US data in his text on the subject.

Professor Dalby[9] noted, and endorsed, the work of the US Railway Master Mechanics Association (RMMA), reported in their Proceedings for 1906, in which smokebox layout parameters for maximised steam production and efficient combustion were detailed. Dalby also refers to an Adams & Pettigrew[10] series of trials carried out by the L&SWR between Exeter and Waterloo in 1895, and gives details of related vacuum measurements from an Institution of Civil Engineers paper on the trials. Adams and Pettigrew found that with a mean speed for the journey of 45 mph, mean smokebox vacuum varied between 4.7 and 7.3 ins WG, with a peak level at the middle row of tubes being above 9 ins WG. Tests conducted by the L&NWR[11] in 1908, using an 'Experiment' Class locomotive between Preston and Carlisle, and reported to the IMechE by Dr F.J. Brislee, showed smokebox vacuum over the series of trials to have a mean value between 5 and 9 ins WG.

A few notable UK locomotive superintendents and private builders followed the US inspired work, one being Bowen-Cooke, whose initial blast pipe arrangement in the 1913 L&NWR 'Claughton' Class[12] followed the PRC guidance and is depicted in Figure 21. In similar fashion, the drafting arrangement for the superheated GWR 'Star' Class[13] is shown in Figure 22. The tapered chimney liner and bell-mouth are obvious in both schematics, as it was for the '938' Class arrangement previously noted and illustrated in Figure 9. Mention has also been made of the 1917 ILocoE paper[14] in which the layout of chimney liner and petticoat pipe to achieve optimised steam production were discussed, the contribution of the SE&C company staff endorsing the layout suggested by Professor Goss.

As part of the publication in 1919, giving details of his 3-cylinder coal engine No. 461 which carried the first multi-pinned derived motion, Gresley[15] revealed details of his smokebox layout and these are illustrated in Figure 23. The divergent blast cone form is specifically laid out on the drawing, giving the desired effect in obtaining maximum exhaust gas entrainment. Commentary on the working of GNR No 461 paid specific attention to steam raising capacity,[15] it being noted that *on no occasion was any difficulty experienced in maintaining a full head of steam, the fireman maintaining a fairly light but even fire over the whole of the grate*.

Based on these available and clear understandings of the time, a distinct disadvantage can be immediately noted in the '956' Class petticoat and blast pipe layout, which are shown in Figure 24,[16] though Pickersgill was broadly following the layout fitted to the superheated McIntosh '139' Class.[17] The subtle difference for the '956' Class compared with the '139' Class arrangement was the former's stack height being significantly shorter, potentially compromising the '956' Class flue gas entrainment capability, a position not unlike that experienced by the GWR with the second type of French 'Atlantic'.

As indifferent steaming, probably related to poor drafting, was a serious ongoing problem, it is most surprising that the St Rollox team did not immediately investigate the position and instigate a series of trials, using simple smokebox manometers. It should have been relatively straightforward to arrange the '956' Class smokebox to accord with the '938' Class, or the Altoona layout. Anecdotal evidence suggests smokebox manometer connections were actually fitted to engine No. 956,[18] although no detailed trials data in this area has come to hand.

A relatively simple series of tests to demonstrate the correct operational interrelation of blast nozzle height and diameter with the chimney choke and liner taper is set out in detail in PRC Bulletin No. 19,[19] concerning the draughting of a K29 4-6-2 locomotive, the report being dated 1912. Indeed, the first smokebox vacuum trials of this type were conducted by PRC and published in 1910.[1] By measurement of the differential pressure across the chimney exit lip, the blast nozzle height could then be set to ensure this differential pressure was almost constant across the lip at maximum steaming

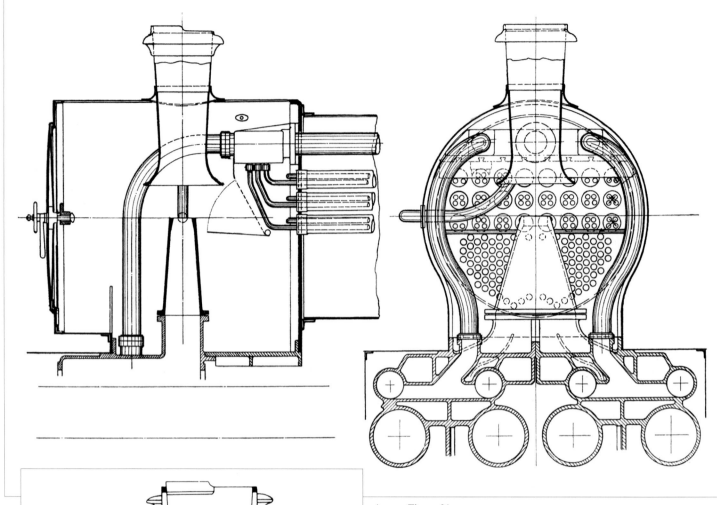

ABOVE: Figure 21

Smokebox layout. L&NWR 'Claughton' Class. In illustrating his views on smokebox layout to achieve optimal vacuum conditions, Professor Dalby approached various UK railway companies for technical material, the data provided by the L&NWR showing that they followed the scheme laid out by Professor Ludy, which ensured maximum exhaust gas entrainment. It was crucial to ensure that the exhaust cone impinged on the chimney liner around halfway between the choke point and the chimney exit lip. The 'Claughton' Class had almost exactly the same cylinder volume as the '956' Class.

W.A. Dalby, Steam Power *(Arnold, 1915), p. 278 (L&NWR)*

LEFT: Figure 22

Smokebox layout. GWR 'Star' Class. Churchward, a keen follower of US best practice, laid out the 'Star' Class smokebox broadly on the model developed experimentally by Professors Goss and Ludy. The bell-mouth entrance and the tapered chimney liner, essential to obtain correct smokebox vacuum conditions, are self-evident. However, even the GWR could at times be misled on steaming matters, as seemingly occurred on the acquisition of the second type of 'Atlantic' Class locomotive from France.

Griffiths and Stephens, Locomotive Engineers of the GWR *(1987), p. 70*

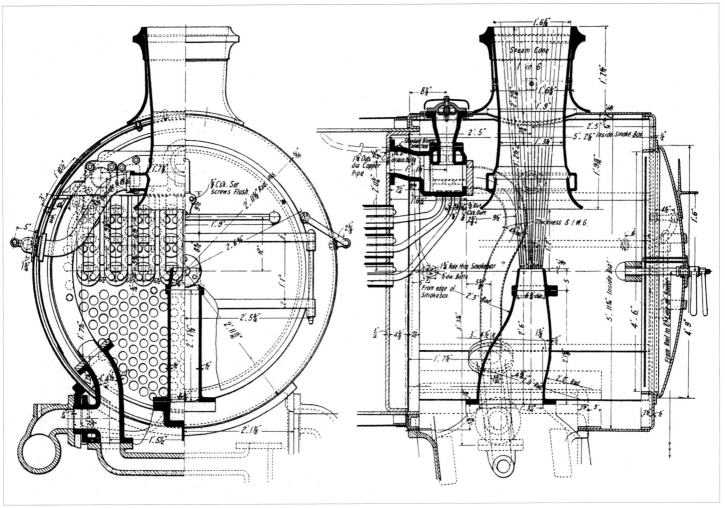

ABOVE: Figure 23

Smokebox layout. GNR No. 461, Gresley 2-8-0 3-cylinder Coal Engine. Gresley published much material on his locomotive developments and in 1919 revealed the smokebox and draughting arrangements on his 3-cylinder coal engine No. 461. The exhaust cone, detailed on the Gresley drawing, seems to impinge on the upper level of the chimney liner, so it may have been necessary to marginally adjust the blast nozzle to lower the impingement point. By all accounts, the steaming of No. 461 was most satisfactory.

The Railway Magazine, March 1919, p. 148

RIGHT: Figure 24

'956' Class. Smokebox Layout. This view is taken from the General Arrangement drawing shown as Figure 1. Straight away one can see that the scheme laid out by Professor Ludy has not been followed, the chimney liner being parallel and a truncated cone forming the entry arrangement. The '956' Class arrangement was, however, copied from the CR '139' Class, but the major difference is the shortness of the chimney stack on the former. From this '956' Class arrangement, it would seem that the blast cone might not touch the chimney liner at all, in which case exhaust gas entrainment might be far from being maximised. From available records, no effort seems to have been made by St Rollox to alter the original '956' Class draughting to accord with acknowledged best practice.   *The Railway Engineer, October 1921*

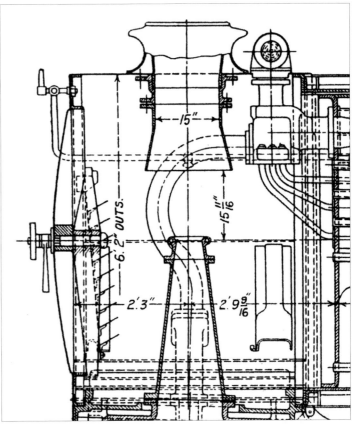

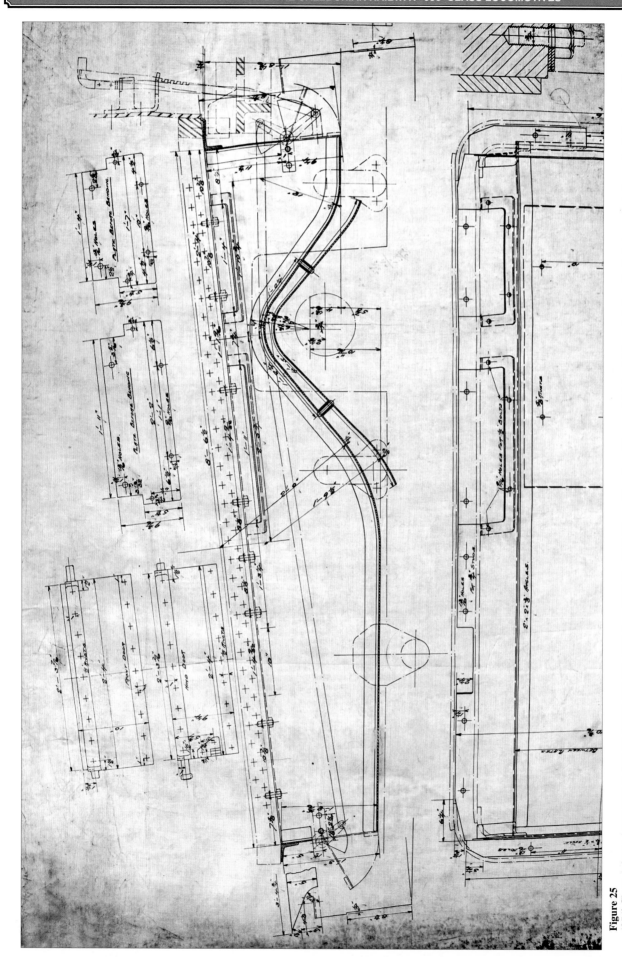

Figure 25
'956' Class. Ashpan Arrangement, Drg No. 20000, dated the 10th June 1919. The '956' Class suffered, as did several 4-6-0s of this period, from limited clearance between the boiler foundation ring and the rear coupled axle, a point well made in this illustration. Choked ashpan conditions were reported on trials, and one suspects poor combustion conditions prevailed on the grate rear section. The grate, having a gentle slope, may have required significant firing experience to generate a brightly burning fire across the whole grate area. Ashpan and grate modifications would have been essential to improve steaming.

CRA: CRA6/11/3/2/48/3/6

conditions. The blast cone would then impinge at the most effective point on the chimney liner, ensuring maximised exhaust gas entrainment and resulting in higher smokebox vacuum and the most effective draughting conditions.

A much simpler expedient, and one which should have assisted reasonable steaming, would have been to follow the published Gresley arrangement[15] and set the blast cone to impinge on the chimney liner half way between the chimney choke and the exist lip. Unfortunately, no work in this area seems to have been attempted by St Rollox; it would have needed no more than a few weeks of effort to implement this approach, with minimal investment and significant potential gain for locomotive operation. The St Rollox drawing register[20] has no entries for any drawings or drawing modifications related to chimney or blastpipe.

Of course, any gain in steaming capability by providing more effective draughting would require that ashpan and grate layout also be improved to meet recognised criteria.

GRATE AND ASHPAN ARRANGEMENTS

Unfortunately, the 956 Class grate and ashpan arrangements were not ideal. Whilst the ashpan layout appears adequate, the maximum ashpan depth, at only 20 ins, is significantly short of the 30 ins available in the '938' Class, this latter depth also being used on 4-6-0 LM&S Class '5' locomotives. From Figure 14, the ashpan depths on many CR locomotives seem unnecessarily restricted.

The weight of ash produced in burning coal in a locomotive firebox is dependent on the fuel calorific value, the type of coal, the related chemical composition and the firing rate. Ash production varies from 6 to 11 per cent by weight of fired coal, a representative figure being 8 per cent for bituminous coal of 13,500 BTU/lb.[21]

On a Buchanan Street to Aberdeen express working of 3½ running hours, and assuming a fuel calorific value of 13,500 BTU/lb, a '956' Class loco would anticipate burning 3 to 3½ tons of coal and producing around 6 cwt of ash. Using coal of 12,000 BTU/lb, for the same journey, around 9 cwt of ash would be produced. Alan Dunbar[6] recorded that in 1921, with a Buchanan Street to Aberdeen trials working, operating to the usual express train timetable, engine No. 956 started to become very short of steam at Forfar, the fireman maintaining the ashpan had become progressively choked due to its shallowness. On the occasion of another test train worked by No. 956, Dunbar[6] quotes James Grassie, in the same context, as commenting there was '*mair trouble in an oor than I thoct possible*'. It is likely that firing the uniformly sloping, 1-in-8 gently graded grate would require a degree of skill uncalled for normally. The coal would hardly vibrate forwards on such a slender slope and precise positioning of coal might have been needed to keep an even fire.

The '956' Class ashpan layout drawing No. 20000[22] has fortunately survived and this is shown as Figure 25. Two dampers were provided, annotated as 'front' and 'hind', each having a cross section, when fully open, of around 3½ sq. ft. Surprisingly, only one control rod was provided, there being no independent control on 'front' or 'hind' apertures, which, with the restricted layout, must have been unhelpful.

Several criteria were available to assist determining the primary air apertures, initially being seen as 'rules of thumb', but broadly confirmed by a series of Altoona trials reported in the 1910 to 1915 period.[23,24] Accepting that under heavy working conditions the vacuum in the ash pan should be no greater than ¾ to 1 in. WG, it was shown, that with dampers fully open, the ashpan air inlet apertures should be set at 90 to 100 per cent of the tubeplate free-gas area, or approximately 20 per cent – and certainly not less than 15 per cent – of the grate area. These values gave reasonably optimised combustion conditions, and seem self-evident.

Based on the tubeplate free-gas area criteria, the inlet apertures should total around 5.0 sq. ft, and on the grate area criteria should be 5.6 sq. ft. The individual '956' Class 'as-built' apertures, each of 3½ sq. ft, and 7 sq. ft in total, would suggest an adequate primary air supply as being available, though the balance of air supply could have been improved. As the severely restricted area above the rear coupled axle could act as a choke point, the forward three-quarters of the grate would then potentially be fed by a disproportionately smaller volume of air.

Moreover, with a comparatively shallow ashpan, and front damper even partially open, accumulated ash could be pushed against the axle guard area, potentially reducing the available grate area for combustion, with the maintenance of an evenly burning fire becoming progressively more difficult. If this position arose after a period of hard steaming, a modest further opening of the dampers could compound the problem.

There is also the suggestion that when running at speed, the air inlet conditions on the rear section of the grate might be severely constrained, owing to partial vacuum conditions arising, since almost no air flow from the front section was available. Philip Aktins[25] has pointed out that many of the early 4-6-0s suffered a common failing in that the close proximity of the firebox foundation ring to the trailing coupled axle severely restricted the access of air to the rear section of the grate, where combustion became poor. Indeed, for the L&YR '8' Class 4-6-0s,[26] introduced in 1908, the fire burned badly in the rear section of the grate until an adequate air supply was ducted to the rear area, the ducting passing under the rear axle from the ashpan front section. The grate air supply position was less severely constrained on the L&NWR 'Claughton' Class,[27] introduced in 1913, as the trailing coupled axle to foundation ring clearance dimension was greater and the trailing axle was much nearer the boiler backhead. Additionally the L&NWR engine had a much more inclined grate and a larger ashpan depth.

It is noticeable in ashpan drawing layouts for the Caledonian '60'[28] and '191'[29] 4-6-0 classes, the trailing coupled axle to foundation ring distances are very restricted, with gently sloping grates being used. Indeed, the '956' Class arrangement is potentially the most restricted of the three, with maintenance of a brightly burning fire in the rear section of the grate perhaps being problematic. By comparison, the steeply sloped grate arrangement on the '938' Class, shown in Figure 26,[30] is completely unrestricted with a deep high-capacity ashpan. Figure 26 is taken from the original NBR Co. general arrangement drawing for the HR 'River' Class, prepared at Cowlairs in 1915, which also shows the initially provided drop grate and its operating mechanism, these being removed when the CR acquired the engines.

If the '956' Class ashpan had been deepened by, say, an additional 8 ins, a further 4 sq. ft of aperture would be created, thus raising the primary air input areas to 11 sq. ft in total. Moreover, the axle guard clearance to the grate could have been reduced a little and vertical faces provided to the ashpan in way of the rear coupled axle. The provision of a large area fore-to-aft ashpan duct connection below the rear axle should have been considered, as provided on the L&YR '8' Class, allowing a much better primary air flow to the grate rear section.

As bituminous coal would have been in use on the '956' Class, a lighter fire than that necessary with Welsh Steam coal or Anthracite would have been needed, since the former type forms a caking arrangement, whereas the latter types split when burning and if the fire is insufficiently thick, it can be lifted in conditions of heavy working. Maintaining an evenly burning bright fire using bituminous coal in the '956' Class grate would have been greatly assisted with these suggested modifications.

One further small point relates to the brick arch. From Figure 1, the horizontal component of the brick arch length is only around 50 per cent of the firebox length and this could have been usefully increased to 60 or even 65 per cent with positive effect for the introduction of secondary air, yet maintaining the same final terminal height. There seems no reason why a more pronounced slope should not have been provided to the front half of the grate at the design stage, which would have assisted combustion by increasing the prospects for coal forward vibration.

OBSERVATIONS

One has to record that in drafting arrangements and grate design, the '956' Class seemed to suffer from a poorer treatment than was merited, recognising the accepted design criteria of the time and acknowledging the potential power output intended. Any potential restrictions on primary air supply, plus the shallow ashpan depth and the rear grate air supply difficulties could have been dealt with relatively simply, and at virtually no cost, though the boiler would require lifting to fit any modified ashpan arrangements. The extent to which St Rollox expenditure constraints prevented this is not

known, but the ordering of material may have been thwarted by the Chairman's edict.

Drafting could have been significantly assisted by noting and then implementing the layout on the' 938' Class, or the conclusions from Altoona, or referring to several UK CME's published work. Running a series of relatively simple smokebox vacuum trials, to investigate blast nozzle height alterations leading to a maximised smokebox vacuum condition should have been a priority.

All the more puzzling, in the face of much published and compelling evidence, both in the UK and elsewhere, is Pickersgill's stance in ostensibly making no serious efforts to investigate and improve performance in these areas. No evidence has been noted from the St Rollox drawing register[20] to indicate any proposed changes to the original smokebox or ashpan layouts. Again, unfortunately, one has to record that the '938' Class precepts in drafting and in grate plus ashpan layout seemed to have been ignored or overlooked.

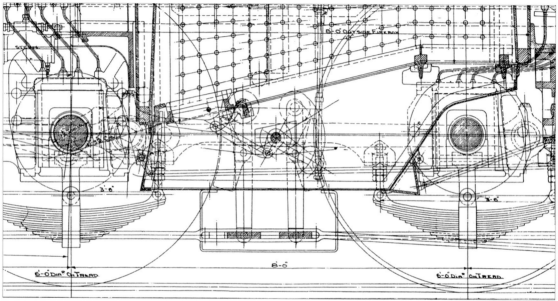

Figure 26
Grate & Ashpan Layout, '938' Class, as built by Hawthorn, Lesley & Co. Compared to the gently sloping grates and restricted distances between foundation ring and trailing coupled axles on the CR '60', '191' and '956' Classes, the steeply sloping unrestricted grate arrangement of the '938' Class has much to commend it. This illustration is taken from the original drawing prepared by the NBR at Cowlairs and shows the initially provided drop grate mechanism, this being removed when the CR acquired the locomotives.   *NRS: GD456/3*

REFERENCES

1. 'Report on Tests on E2A Locomotive', PRC, Altoona (1910), Fig 902, pp. 16ff
2. PRC, Altoona, Bulletin No. 21, 1913, pp. 60ff
3. *Locomotive Boilers and Engines*, L.V. Ludy (American Technical Society, 1918), Fig. 56, pp. 55ff
4. *Locomotive Engineers' Pocket Book* (The locomotive Publishing Co.), p. 298
5. IMechE paper, 1925, H.N. Gresley, 'Smoke-box Vacuum Conditions' (noted by Phillipson, p. 189)
6. *Fifty Years with Scottish Steam*, Alan G. Dunbar and I.A. Glen (Bradford Barton), p. 40
7. See Appendices in this publication
8. *Steam Locomotive Design: Data and Formulae*, E.A. Phillipson (The Locomotive Publishing Co.), Chapter VIII, etc
9. *Steam Power*, Prof. W.E. Dalby FRS (Arnold, London, 1915), pp. 83ff; Proc. Amer. RMMA, 1906
10. 'Trials of an Express Locomotive', W. Adams and W.F. Pettigrew, Proc. ICE, Vol. 125, January 1896
11. LNWR Data to IMechE, 1908; *Steam Power*, W.E. Dalby, p. 94
12. Claughton Class Smokebox Arrangement, *Steam Power*, W.E. Dalby, p. 278
13. *Locomotive Engineers of the GWR*, Denis Griffiths (Patrick Stephens, 1987), p. 70
14. 'Locomotive Blast Pipes and Chimneys', J. Maxwell Dunn, ILocoE paper No. 56, 24th November 1917

15. Article on GNR 3-cylinder Engine No 461, in *The Railway Magazine*, March 1919, pp. 148ff
16. 'New Three-Cylinder 4-6-0 Type Locomotive, Caledonian Railway', *The Railway Engineer*, October 1921, p. 365
17. *The Application of Highly Superheated Steam To Locomotives* (Schmidt Superheater Co., 1910), Fig. 4 in Supplement
18. 'The Pickersgill 4-6-0s of the Caledonian Railway', David Newlands, *The True Line*, No. 47, pp. 21ff
19. 'Report on Tests of K29 Locomotive', PRC, Altoona, Bulletin No. 19, 1912, Fig 34, pp. 64ff
20. St Rollox Drawing Register, NRS BR/CAL/5/56
21. *Locomotive Engineers' Pocket Book 1935*, 1904 data, Table VI, p. 39
22. Campbell Cornwell Collection of CR 956 Class drawings, CRA6/1/3/2, Archive Group 48
23. 'Report on Tests on E2A Locomotive', PRC, Altoona, 1910, pp. 4-6ff
24. *Steam Locomotive Design: Data and Formulae*, E.A. Phillipson, pp. 91-2
25. *West Coast 4-6-0s at Work*, C.P. Atkins (Ian Allan, 1981), pp. 90ff
26. *Lancashire & Yorkshire Railway Locomotives*, Barry C. Lane (Pendragon, 2010), pp. 142ff
27. *An Illustrated History of LNWR Locomotives*, Edward Talbot (Oxford Publishing Co., 1984), pp. 297ff
28. '60' Class GA, St Rollox Drg No. 18940, dated 24th July 1917, Author's collection
29. NB Loco. Co. GA, '191' Class, Drg No. G 27219, NRS, BR/CAL/LOCO/43
30. NBR Co., Cowlairs, Drg 'Highland Railway No 1', 1915, NRS, Montague Smith Collection, GD456/3

CHAPTER 15

CYLINDER ARRANGEMENTS, DIMENSIONS AND VALVE GEAR

Be not the first by whom the new is tried,
nor yet the last to cast the old aside
Alexander Pope (1688-1744)

CYLINDER ARRANGEMENTS AND DIMENSIONS

Accepting the need to develop 1,500 IHP at 65 mph on level track, Pickersgill faced a choice in the number of cylinders to be provided. A 2-cylinder solution was probably seen as potentially difficult due to lateral loading gauge constraints, the cylinder diameter being in the 21 to 22 ins range. Moreover, further complications were possibly seen in accommodating piston thrust as it would impact on crank pin and other motion component stresses, a point made by A.J. Powell[1] in his '956' Class outline rebuild considerations. Having considered a four cylinder solution,[2] Pickersgill opted for three cylinders, as did Gresley in producing his 'K3' Class design around the same period.

The necessary 1,500 IHP at 300 rpm (65 mph with 6 ft 1 in. diameter wheels) can be obtained from a 180 psi boiler, 3-cylinder engine, using 18½ ins diameter cylinders, when operating at a cut-off giving a mean effective pressure (MEP) of around 20 to 25 per cent of boiler pressure, assuming a piston stroke of 26 ins.[3] Pickersgill's choice of cylinder numbers, stroke and diameter meet the accepted criteria in use at the time and should have given perfectly satisfactory performance, presupposing the provision of short, direct, large area, steam and exhaust passages plus a free steaming boiler.

During his St Rollox apprenticeship, Ernest Glen[4] photographed the '956' Class cylinder assemblies, Plate 43 illustrating a fully machined '956' Class centre cylinder block, prior to fitting between the engine frames, all studding to accept associated covers being in place. The bar attached to the machined cylinder face and seemingly giving a 'centre' for piston stroke at the forward end of the casting may have been used to assist line-up of the cylinder block to the crank axle.

With regard to steam and exhaust passages, those on the '956' Class could have been more direct. As shown in Figure 1, the portways from valves to cylinders were severely S-shaped, accentuated by deeply dished piston heads and covers, resulting in several directional changes for the steam. It was possible for these bends on the cylinder steam inputs to have been designed out by increasing the valve length and using slightly extended steam chests, which could have been achieved at negligible cost increase and would have reduced steam circuit pressure loss, in addition to reducing clearance volumes. Pre-1914 L&NWR practice used extended steam chests and much more direct steam passages.[5]

The exhaust passages were generous in area, but unconventional in layout. Front and rear exhaust passages stretched straight across from the left cylinder through the ends of the inside valve chest, as shown in Figure 1, then to the blast-pipe base via some right-angled bends. Exhaust flow was far from streamlined, indeed this exhaust layout could have contributed to performance limitations.

The chosen '956' Class layout arranged all three cylinders in line, with divided drive, the centre cylinder powering the leading axle. It is not known if Pickersgill considered moving the centre cylinder

Plate 43
A fully machined centre cylinder, complete with studs for covers and forward bore centre identified to facilitate line-up awaits installation between the frames. *A.E. Glen*

forward, which, with the same length of connecting rod, could have shortened the locomotive. Such a move, however, may have prevented the use of centre cylinder derived motion. Gresley, in arranging his 'K3' Class design,[6] concentrated the drives on the centre coupled axle and raised the inside cylinder to clear the leading axle, the three valve chests being in the same horizontal plane.

Having selected the cylinder dimensions and knowing the approximate boiler steam raising capability, the approximate steam consumption of the '956' Class locomotive operating under intended working conditions can now be estimated. Each cylinder has a volume of 4.04 cu. ft, and if 55 per cent cut-off is taken as that necessary to achieve 30 mph hauling the stipulated 555 ton train on a 1 in 100 grade, then with 150 degrees of superheat, the steam requirement is approximately 22,900 lbs per hour.[7] With 200 degrees of superheat, the requirement is 21,600 lbs per hour, and with 250 degrees of superheat, the requirement is 20,500 lbs per hour.[7] These simple approximate calculations show the effect of increasing the superheat provision.

These steam consumption figures are broadly compatible with the boiler steam generating capacities derived earlier.

Valve Gear – Background Information

There is some confusion with regard to which arrangement of valve gear was fitted to which of the four '956' Class locomotives at particular times in their early careers and what subsequent changes were made to specific engine fits by way of valve bobbin dimensional modifications, centre valve events resetting and the fitting of dash-pots, as well as major motion type changes. The position is further complicated by St Rollox drawings with annotated manuscript notes indicating a specific modification for an individual locomotive or locomotives. At times, there is no clear evidence as to whether all such specific modifications were actually implemented. Moreover, various '956' Class arrangement drawings show changes to the structural support for certain valve gear bearings and motion parts, suggesting that, in some areas, initial structural stiffness was inadequate. These structural modifications, adding rigidity for minimum weight increase, would undoubtedly have influenced the valve events on the centre cylinder for the better.

It seems clear that the four locomotives were initially provided with Pickergill's original derived motion using fourteen pin/slide joints per side, with the following initial shed allocations:[8] No. 956 went to Balornock, in the charge of driver James Grassie; driver Joe Cooper (who was killed in the Dinwoodie smash in 1928) had No. 957 at Kingmoor; No. 958 also went to Kingmoor in the charge of driver Will Little; No. 959 went to Perth in the custody of George Newlands. From Balornock, No. 956 initially ran in workshop grey.

Alan Dunbar,[8,9] a St Rollox apprentice of the time, who worked on the valve gear templates for the class, noted that through repeated failures of valve spindle guides and other components, engines No. 957 and No. 958 at Carlisle saw little work through unreliability, while other sources[10] refer to fracturing of slidebars due to stresses set up in the outside valve spindle supports. As a result of this continuing unsatisfactory performance, No. 957 and No. 958 were fitted, in April 1922, with Stephenson's link motion for the inner cylinder, though just prior to that, No. 959 had been fitted with a modified version of the first derived motion. Around April 1922, No. 956 was also thought to have been fitted with a further modified form of the first derived motion,[8,9] though by the summer of 1922, No. 956 was again at St Rollox to have Stephenson's link motion fitted to the centre cylinder.[8,9]

Further confusion unfortunately arises, since there are conflicting observations from former St Rollox employees and other commentators of the day, regarding specific locomotive valve gear arrangements. After being fitted with Stephenson's motion in 1922, engine No. 956 was thereafter fitted with the second version

of derived motion, then with an inertial damping arrangement (this scheme is detailed on drawing No. 22376, dated the 22nd November 1923, and discussed later). Recognising one cannot be absolutely definitive on these matters, comment is made on valve motion for each member of the class using extant data, photographic evidence and various entries from the St Rollox drawing register.[11]

In laying out this commentary on the specific types of motion, the author, for continuity, has chosen to place the details on the Stephenson's gear at the end, though the order of valve gear fitting for certain members of the class may have been different.

Plate 26 shows No. 956 at Buchanan Street station on the 2nd August 1921, as originally built, with the first form of derived motion. Photographs of No. 957 with original motion have proved elusive, though No. 958 was captured at Dalry Road, Edinburgh in 1921, by Alan Dunbar, when thus fitted, as shown in Plate 44, whilst Plate 45 depicts No. 958, normally a Carlisle based engine, at Perth, when fitted with Stephenson's motion. Plate 45 suggests the engine is on a running-in turn, with non-corridor stock, No. 958 perhaps being newly fitted with Stephenson's motion, which would date the image as April or May 1922. No. 959, with original derived motion, is illustrated in Plate 46 at Perth in 1922.

The Initial Derived Motion

The outside cylinders were operated using conventional Walschaert's valve gear, the maximum valve travel being just under 6 ins at around 75 per cent cut-off, with a lap of 1½ ins (not stated on any drawings, but inferred from combination lever dimensions and piston stroke). This arrangement cannot be faulted, and indeed, with 1½ ins lap, should be applauded as being in advance of its time. This was the first and only occasion when Walschaert's gear was designed and manufactured at St Rollox, though experience of its operation was available from the successful ex HR '938' Class engines.

The intended valve events for the class are shown on CR drawing No. 19947,[12] signed personally by Pickersgill in April 1920, which is depicted as Figure 27. The gear was designed with ¼ in. lead and, whilst the tabulated results show cut-off figures up to 70 per cent or greater, a restriction at 65 per cent cut-off was apparently applied. Gresley also applied a 65 per cent cut-off restriction to his 'K3' Class,[6] in an attempt to prevent inertial effects causing centre valve over-run with consequent potential fracture of valve chest covers.

The method of operating the centre cylinder valve from the outside valve gears of a 3-cylinder locomotive, having cranks set at 120 degrees, originated with David Joy's patent of 1884 for triple expansion marine engines, for which Joy, who was then manager of The Barrow Shipbuilding Co., was awarded a Gold Medal at the 1885 London Inventions Exhibition. This was followed by Holcroft's 1909 patent (which had lapsed by 1915) and Gresley's 1915 patents.

Deriving the valve events for multi-cylindered engines from just two valves was in fashion at this time, with Churchward, Gresley, Hughes and Bowen-Cooke being acknowledged practitioners. Pickersgill, recognising some tangible technical and financial benefits from the use of derived valve motion, would, in preparing his designs, have been concerned not to infringe any extant Gresley/ Holcroft patent arrangements. It is believed the '956' Class derived motion detail was worked up by George Kerr, with Pickersgill[13] being involved in the process and advice being taken from Professor Alexander Mallenby,[13] then Professor of Mechanism and Mechanical Engineering at The Royal Technical College.

There are several St Rollox drawings laying out the detail of the original derived motion, the earliest being No. 19968,[14] dated the 22nd May 1919, the side elevation being shown as Figure 28. From this early drawing, it is noticeable that the driving wheel splashers are drawn as individual items, whereas, 'as-built', the leading and

Plate 44
Engine No. 958, fitted with the first type of derived motion, at Dalry Road shed, Edinburgh in 1921. This is the only image of No. 958 fitted with the first derived motion which, to date, has come to hand. *A.G. Dunbar courtesy Mitchell Library*

Plate 45
No. 958, normally a Carlisle engine, is illustrated at Perth, seemingly on a local passenger working, possibly a running in turn after the fitting of Stephenson's link motion to the centre cylinder. This would date the illustration as April or May 1922. *Courtesy C.P. Atkins*

Plate 46
Engine No. 959 at Perth shed in 1922, with original derived motion arrangements and looking quite majestic. *R.D. Stephen, NRM/RDS C23*

NOTCH		TRAVEL	LEADS		OPENING		CUT OFF		RELEASE		ANGLE OF CRANK	
			F.P.	B.P.	F.P.	B.P.	F.P.	B.P.	F.P.	B.P.	F.P.	B.P.
FULL FORWARD	10	5 15/16"	1/4	1/4	1 3/8	1 1/2	72	70	91	90	37°	36°
FORWARD	9	5 9/16"	1/4	1/4	1 7/32	1 5/16	68	66	90	88½	40°	39°
	8	5 3/16"	1/4	1/4	1 1/16 B	1 1/8	64	61	88	87	43°	42°
	7	4 7/8"	1/4	1/4	7/8	15/16	59	56	86½	84½	47°	46°
	6	4 9/16"	1/4	1/4	3/4	25/32	53	51	84	82	50°	49°
	5	4 9/32"	1/4	1/4	19/32	5/8	45½	43½	81	79½	55°	53°
	4	4"	1/4	1/4	15/32	1/2	37	36½	78	79	59½°	59°
	3	3 13/16"	1/4	1/4	3/8	3/8 F	27½	27	72	70	68°	65°
	2	3 5/8"	1/4	1/4	5/16	5/16	19	19	66	65	75°	71°
	1	3 17/32"	1/4	1/4	1/4	1/4	13	13	59½	59	83°	78°
MID	0											
BACKWARD	1	3 9/16"	1/4	1/4	1/4	1/4	10	12	55	56½	86°	79°
	2	3 5/8"	1/4	1/4	5/16	5/16	15	17	61	64	79°	70°
	3	3 13/16"	1/4	1/4	3/8	3/8 F	21	26	68	70	70°	64°
	4	4"	1/4	1/4	7/16	1/2	30	35	73	75	63°	58°
	5	4 3/16"	1/4	1/4	9/16 B	5/8 F	39	45	78	79	57°	52°
	6	4 1/2"	1/4	1/4	11/16	13/16	47	52	82	82	51°	47½°
	7	4 27/32"	1/4	1/4	13/16	1"	55½	59	85	84½	46°	44°
	8	5 1/8"	1/4	1/4	15/16	1 1/16	62	63½	87	86½	43°	41°
	9	5 9/16"	1/4	1/4	1 1/8	1 3/8	68	68	89	88	39°	38½°
FULL BACKWARD	10	6"	1/4	1/4	1 3/8	1 21/32	74	71½	91	89½	36°	36°

VALVE SETTING FOR 3 CYL ENGINE

Figure 27
'956' Class. Valve Setting Details, Drg No. 19947, dated the 8th May 1919. This valve events drawing, signed by Pickersgill on the 22nd April 1920, indicates the Walschaerts' motion was designed with ¼ in. lead. Coupled with valve lap of 1½ ins, this arrangement should be applauded as being in advance of its time. Valve travel in full gear cut-off of 75 per cent was just short of 6 ins, though a restriction to 65 per cent was apparently applied in an attempt to prevent inertial effects causing centre valve over-run with attendant potential fracture of valve chest covers. Gresley also applied a 65 per cent cut-off restriction to his 2-6-0 'K3' Class engines.
NRS: GD456, RHP136355/7

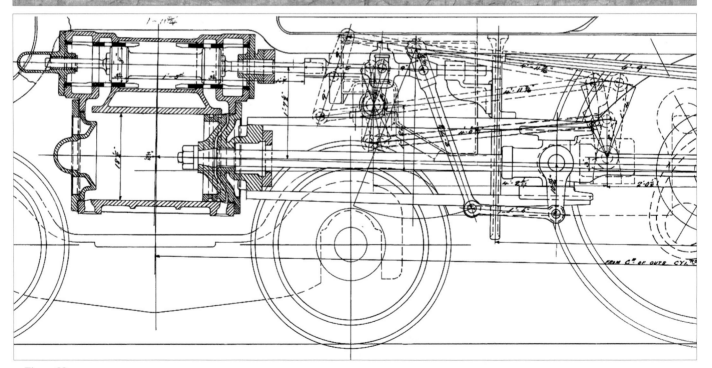

Figure 28
'956' Class. First Derived Motion Arrangement, Side Elevation, Drg No. 19968, dated the 22nd May 1919. This is the earliest dated drawing setting out the '956' Class derived motion, which is rather complicated to follow in detail. It does, however, show the deeply dished pistons and valve covers, and the 'S' shaped steam passages from the piston valves which could have been avoided by lengthening the piston valve assembly to give direct short steam passages. The drawing also shows individual splashers were initially intended above the running plate. *NRS: RHP132397*

driving coupled wheel splashers were combined, in a similar way to the '938' Class arrangement.

Drawing No. 19968, is somewhat complex in layout terms and most difficult to follow for centre cylinder valve gear detail. To assist the reader, it has been decomposed into three parts:

1. Figure 28(a), showing the standard external Walschaert's motion for the left-hand cylinder, together with the related upper slidebar bearing carrying the transverse rocking shaft driven from the yoke on the associated valve rod;

2. Figure 28(b), showing the internal drive from the left-hand rocking shaft, via associated motion rods to the related 1:2 multiplying lever and hence to the lower connection with the 'floating lever', the centre of which drove the inside cylinder valve rod;

3. Figure 28(c), showing the internal drive from the right-hand rocking shaft, via associated motion rods to the related 1:2 multiplying lever and hence to the upper connection with the 'floating lever'.

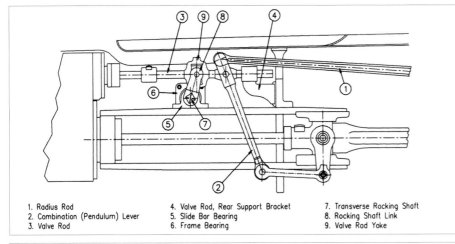

1. Radius Rod
2. Combination (Pendulum) Lever
3. Valve Rod
4. Valve Rod, Rear Support Bracket
5. Slide Bar Bearing
6. Frame Bearing
7. Transverse Rocking Shaft
8. Rocking Shaft Link
9. Valve Rod Yoke

Figure 28(a)
'956' Class. First Derived Motion Arrangement, Side Elevation, Outside Left-Hand Motion. To assist identification of motion parts, Figure 28 has been decomposed into three separate elements, this first element showing the outside, left-side, Walschaerts' valve gear together with the drive arrangement from the valve rod yoke which drives the associated rocking shaft. The outside rocking shaft bearing is mounted on the top slidebar. Major design change to some motion parts was necessary in the early months of service since component fracture and distortion occurred. *Author*

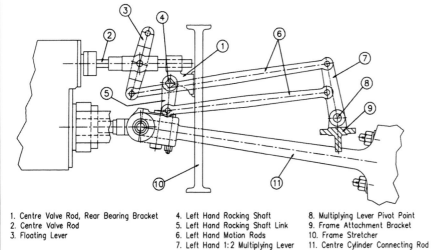

1. Centre Valve Rod, Rear Bearing Bracket
2. Centre Valve Rod
3. Floating Lever
4. Left Hand Rocking Shaft
5. Left Hand Rocking Shaft Link
6. Left Hand Motion Rods
7. Left Hand 1:2 Multiplying Lever
8. Multiplying Lever Pivot Point
9. Frame Attachment Bracket
10. Frame Stretcher
11. Centre Cylinder Connecting Rod

Figure 28(b)
'956' Class. First Derived Motion Arrangement, Side Elevation, Between-frames Levers, Left-Hand Drive. This, the second decomposed element, illustrates the between-frames levers driven from the left-hand external motion, which connect to the bottom pivot point on the 'floating lever', which in turn operates the centre cylinder valve spindle. The motion path can be traced from the rocking shaft, the rocking shaft link, the motion rods and the 1:2 multiplying lever to the 'floating lever'. Again there were problems with this arrangement though lack of structural rigidity in the frame attachment bracket and failures in the valve spindle guide bearing. *Author*

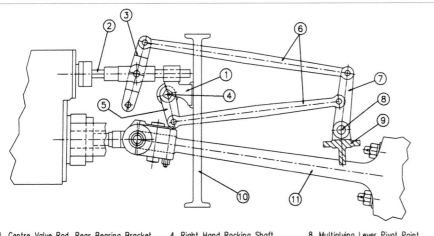

1. Centre Valve Rod, Rear Bearing Bracket
2. Centre Valve Rod
3. Floating Lever
4. Right Hand Rocking Shaft
5. Right Hand Rocking Shaft Link
6. Right Hand Motion Rods
7. Right Hand 1:2 Multiplying Lever
8. Multiplying Lever Pivot Point
9. Frame Attachment Bracket
10. Frame Stretcher
11. Centre Cylinder Connecting Rod

Figure 28(c)
'956' Class. First Derived Motion Arrangement, Side Elevation, Between-frames Levers, Right-Hand Drive. A further decomposition, the third element, shows the between-frames levers driven from the right-hand external motion, which connects to the top pivot point on the 'floating lever'. The motion path can again be traced from the right-side rocking shaft to the centre valve spindle. Through failures of the centre valve spindle bearing, major redesign was required in this area. *Author*

Figure 29
'956' Class. Composite Arrangement of Multiplying Levers between Frames for First Derived Motion. The first known occasion in which the '956' Class derived motion was discussed and subject to external professional review was in 1943, some eight years after the last of the class was withdrawn. In an ILocoE paper of that year, the author, T.H. Shields, prepared this diagram, which is again a little difficult to follow, as combination lever action is included and only the between-frames levers are shown. In the discussion following this paper, E.S. Cox, noting the number of pin joints in the motion, declared the design *'not to be a practical proposition at all'*.

ILocoE: T.H. Shields, Paper 443, Volume 33 (1943)

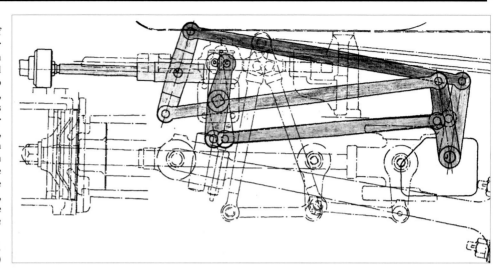

Superimposing Figures 28(a), 28(b) and 28(c) gives the original drawing, and indeed, in a 1943 ILoCoE paper on valve gear evolution,[15] the author, T.H. Shields, superimposed the equivalent of Figures 28(b) and 28(c) in an attempt to convey the '956' Class between frames layout, Mr Shields' drawing being shown as Figure 29. This drawing is again somewhat confusing in that right and left side combination levers and crossheads, plus valve rods, are juxtaposed with centre valve drive components.

The associated plan view from drawing No. 19968[14] is shown in Figure 30, in which the arrangement of the transverse rocking shafts is clearly identified, as are the mounting arrangements for the various bearings supporting the shafts and rocking levers. A key element contributing to successful derived gear operation is the design of the multiplying levers pivot point anchor bracket, which, as shown in Figure 30, is mounted from the in-board left-hand frame, just in front of the crank axle. It is vital that this pivot point support

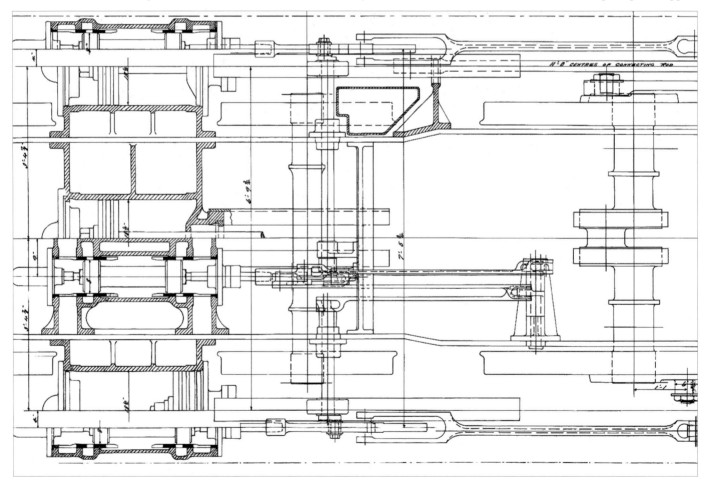

Figure 30
'956' Class. First Derived Motion Arrangement, Plan, Drg No. 19968, dated the 22nd May 1919. A plan view of the motion layout is illustrated in which the transverse rocking shafts and related support bearings can be identified, as can the motion plate/stretcher. Structural rigidity of the pivot point anchor bracket, mounted on the left frame just in front of the crank axle, is vital to ensuring precision in valve events. This anchor point was redesigned at least once in the 1921 to 1922 period, to provide increasing stiffness.

NRS: RHP132397

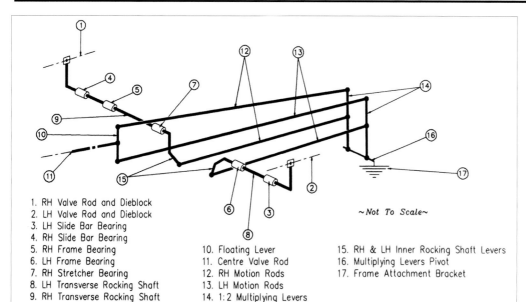

Figure 31
'956' Class. Perspective, First Derived Motion, based on Drg No. 20179, 3rd October 1919. With all major components identified, this illustrates the overall motion layout as initially installed. Whilst the sketch is not to scale, the gain and phase margins of the arrangement are correct. *Author*

1. RH Valve Rod and Dieblock
2. LH Valve Rod and Dieblock
3. LH Slide Bar Bearing
4. RH Slide Bar Bearing
5. RH Frame Bearing
6. LH Frame Bearing
7. RH Stretcher Bearing
8. LH Transverse Rocking Shaft
9. RH Transverse Rocking Shaft

10. Floating Lever
11. Centre Valve Rod
12. RH Motion Rods
13. LH Motion Rods
14. 1:2 Multiplying Levers

15. RH & LH Inner Rocking Shaft Levers
16. Multiplying Levers Pivot
17. Frame Attachment Bracket

~Not To Scale~

structure is made as rigid as possible, otherwise, it can further amplify lost motion or modify the phasing of centre valve events. This bracket was subsequently modified at least once to provide a more rigid structure.

To further assist understanding of the original derived motion as an integrated whole, Figure 31 shows the motion arrangement in a perspective form, as a sketch, with major components identified. Whilst this sketch is not to scale, the gain and phase margins of the arrangements employed on the '956' Class are theoretically correct.

The original layout of this motion arrangement was prepared in May 1919, the final version, to drawing No. 20179,[11] in October 1919. No data has come to hand on the detail of any external advice received on the design and operation of this derived valve gear, nor any calculations relating to system and component inertias or natural frequencies, if they ever existed. Of more immediate concern is the straightforward question of why St Rollox failed to appreciate, early in the design stage, the centre valve events would suffer from lost motion, compounded by inertial and structural deflection effects.

Gresley recognised these amalgamated lost motion difficulties from his earlier 1915 derived motion design, which on GNR engine No. 461,[16] employed transverse rocking shafts giving eight equivalent pin joints per side. After review of these matters, the much simpler Holcroft arrangements[16] were eventually adopted by Gresley. The basic reasoning for St Rollox selection of their specific derived motion solution, as opposed to a more conventional approach to 3-cylinder propulsion, using a third set of Walschaert's gear, will probably never come to light. By all accounts, however, Pickersgill was initially proud of this derived motion concept, referring to it as *'a wee contr-r-raption of my own'*, according to O.S. Nock.[17] The external physical layout of this original derived motion is well illustrated in Plate 47, showing the right-hand motion layout on No. 956 'as built'.

The valve rod arrangement drawing, No. 22063,[18] dated the 2nd January 1923, shown as Figure 32, lays out the integration of rocking shaft output and combination lever input functions, again visible from Plate 47. Drawing No. 22063 superseded drawing No. 19957,

Plate 47
Right-side motion on No. 956 as built, from the official photograph. The yoke on the valve rod and the rocking shaft link, together with the outboard rocking shaft bearing on the upper slidebar are clearly visible, as is the valve rod rear bearing, the source of much trouble through fractures.
NRM/SRX37

dated the 16th May 1919, a major difference being the specification of hardened cast steel bearing surfaces on the latter issue. No doubt the hardening of bearing surfaces was an attempt to reduce in-service wear and possibly to tighten 'as-built' limits and fits, drawing No. 22063 having been prepared for the second form of the derived motion. The outboard ends of the right-hand and left-hand valve rods were supported by a bearing bracket shown on drawing No. 20141, dated the 2nd September 1919, the right-hand bracket again being clearly identified in Plate 47. These cast iron brackets, with gunmetal bushes, were supported on a plate attached to respective right-hand and left-hand motion framework: they gave much trouble in service through repeated fractures,[8,9,10] which could have led to the failure of other associated components. These fracture issues are considered in more detail under Component Mechanical Design.

The 3 ins diameter transverse rocking shafts, which ran through the main locomotive frames, were supported in cast iron carriers with gunmetal bushes, being shown on drawing No. 20032,[19] Figure 33. The final connections to the 'floating lever' were made by links from the tops of the respective 1:2 multiplying levers, the lower ends being pivoted on the bracket secured to the left-hand inside frame. This

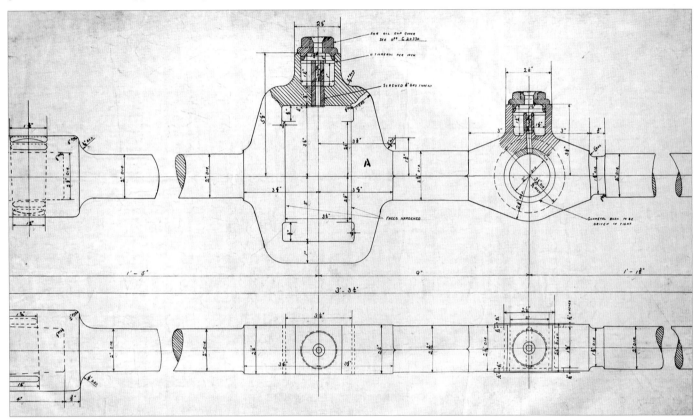

ABOVE: Figure 32
'956' Class. Valve Connecting Rod Arrangement, Drg No. 22063, dated the 2nd January 1923. This drawing illustrates the layout of rocking shaft output and combination lever input on the valve rod, the initial May 1919 drawing having been re-issued to incorporate changes including hardened cast steel bearing surfaces. The valve rod seems to have been the subject of repeated in-service failures, the undercut adjacent to the combination lever input being a significant weak point.
CRA: CRA6/1/3/2/48/10/3

RIGHT: Figure 33
'956' Class. Rocking Shaft Carrier, Through Frame Bearing, Drg No. 20032, dated the 26th June 1919. The 3 ins diameter transverse rocking shafts, which ran through the main frames, were supported in cast iron carriers with gunmetal bushes. For the second form of derived motion the rocking shafts were increased to 3½ ins diameter, suggesting that torsional effects were leading to valve events phasing mismatch.
CRA: CRA6/1/3/2/48/4/3

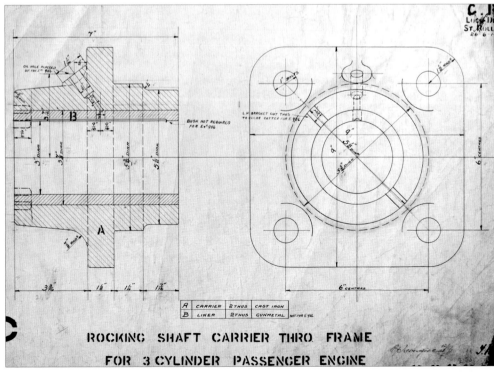

ROCKING SHAFT CARRIER THRO FRAME
FOR 3 CYLINDER PASSENGER ENGINE

'floating lever' for the first form of the derived motion is illustrated on drawing No. 20030,[20] dated the 25th June 1919, shown as Figure 34.

The centre valve crosshead arrangement was detailed in drawing No. 20037,[21] which is shown in Figure 35, the 'floating lever' central pivot being contained within the valve crosshead centre slot, the actual valve spindle being cottered to the forward end of this crosshead. The rear end of the crosshead was carried via an integral rod supported in a bearing bracket identical to those used on the outside valve rods. This inner valve crosshead rear bearing arrangement also appears to have been the subject of failures,[8,9,10] in similar fashion to the external valve rods' rear bearings. With the exception of the centre valve stuffing box and the rear support bearing on the crosshead rod, no intermediate direct support was provided for the 'floating lever' and crosshead assembly. As a result of in-service failures, this area was subject to major redesign for the second form of derived motion.

To support the inner right-hand and left-hand rocking shaft bearings, as detailed in Figures 30 and 31, a substantial motion plate/stretcher, was provided, the detail being given on drawing No. 20091,[22] a forward looking elevation being shown as Figure 36. The apertures on the upper left side of Figure 36 allow transit of motion parts, those on the right-hand side probably being provided to balance and lighten the structure. The centre aperture allows passage of the centre cylinder connecting rod, the shaded parts being the horizontally mounted centre cylinder slidebars. This first motion plate was, as with other components, the subject of significant re-engineering as valve gear redesign was progressed.

Ernest Glen[4] captured a number of unique images of the '956' Class valve gear build process, Plate 48 showing the partial assembly of a right-hand cylinder and associated motion. In this plate, the cross head assembly is in place, cottered to the piston rod. Directly above the crosshead, and mounted on the upper slidebar, is the right-hand rocking shaft bearing, with the shaft passing through the frame to the centre valve motion. The outboard forked end of the rocking shaft is clearly visible, as is the rear mounted valve rod bearing bracket. The right-hand valve rod (drawing No. 22063,[18] Figure 32), which will be cottered to the valve spindle, secured in the rocking shaft forked end and supported by the rear bearing, has yet to be fitted. The combination lever input to the valve rod will be fitted between the rear bearing and the rocking shaft output.

A more advanced stage of right-hand motion assembly is depicted in Plate 49, the valve rod, rocking shaft assembly and rear bearing arrangement being clearly illustrated. The combination lever has yet to be fitted. A main journal bearing, possibly for the left-hand first coupled axle lies on the erecting shop floor below the slidebars.

A record of the internal valve motion build process between the frames was also captured by Glen,[4] Plate 50 showing a forward looking view, towards the motion plate/stretcher (drawing No. 20091,[22] Figure 36), from just behind the centre coupled axle, the hornblocks of which are to the immediate right and left. To the fore of the left-hand leading axle hornblock, and mounted on the left frame, is the anchor point for the fixed end

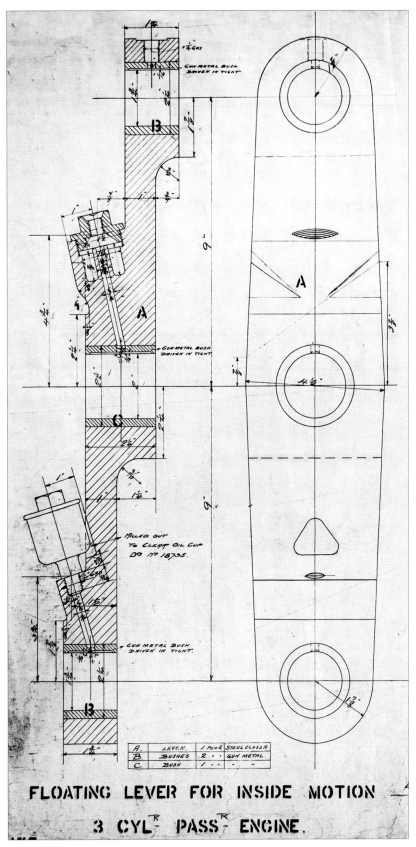

Figure 34
'956' Class, 'Floating Lever' for Centre Valve, First Derived Motion, Drg No. 20030, dated the 25th June 1919. Motion rods, driven from the right and left-side valve rods, were connected to respective top and bottom pivots of the 'floating lever', the centre pivot being directly connected to the valve rod. This arrangement was completely changed in the second form of derived motion as a result of related component failures.

CRA: CRA6/1/3/2/48/4/2

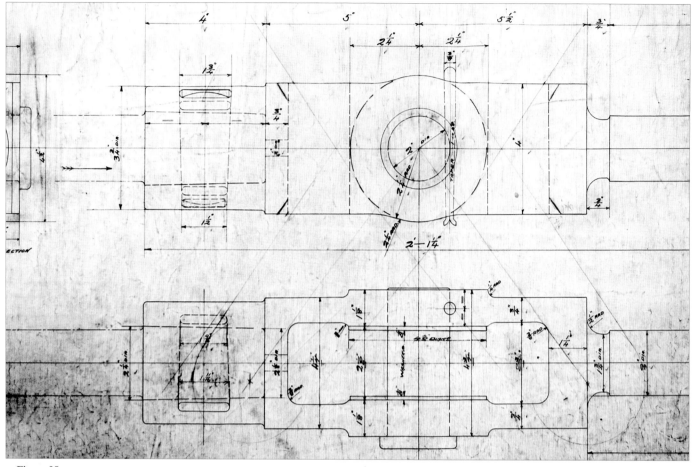

Figure 35
'956' Class. Centre Valve Spindle Crosshead, First Derived Motion, Drg No. 20037, dated the 28th June 1919. This component supported the 'floating lever' in its centre slot and acted as the drive rod for the centre valve spindle. A plane bearing, mounted on the motion stretcher, supported the rear bearing spindle of this crosshead. The crosshead spindle rear support bearing seems to have failed on a number of occasions and it is likely such failures resulted in serious damage to it and connected items. As a consequence, the locomotive could well have been completely immobilised.

CRA: CRA6/1/3/2/48/4/4

LEFT: Plate 48
Partial assembly of a '956' Class right-side motion is illustrated. Directly above the crosshead is the forked end of the rocking shaft, which will engage with the valve rod yoke. The rear valve rod bearing sits behind the rocking shaft.

A.E. Glen

FACING PAGE: Plate 49
An almost completed '956' Class right-side valve motion assembly is shown. The valve rod is cottered to the valve spindle, the yoke being engaged with the transverse rocking shaft. The support bearing on the upper slidebar and the frame penetration bearing, plus the rear valve rod bearing, are all in place. The combination lever and union link are yet to be fitted.

A.E. Glen

of the two multiplying levers. In the centre, the horizontal slidebars for the centre cylinder are visible, and to their upper left are the bolts in the motion plate securing the rear bearing bracket for the centre valve spindle, the bracket itself being mounted on the motion plate front face. The top of the 'floating lever' can just be seen above the top of the motion plate, being in line with the two left-hand bolts

securing the valve rod rear bearing bracket. On the erecting shop floor, to right and left are the respective engine crossheads.

Centre cylinder motion construction[4] at a more advanced stage is depicted in Plate 51, which again illustrates the motion plate and the centre cylinder slidebars. To the left, the multiplying levers are in place, their fixed bottom connection to the left frame anchor

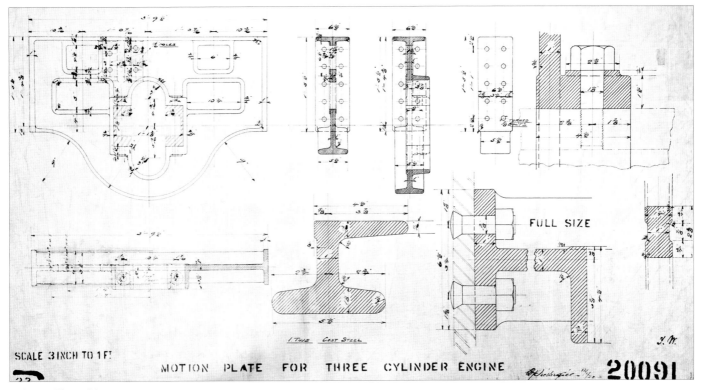

ABOVE: Figure 36
'956' Class. Motion Plate/Stretcher, First Derived Motion, Drg No. 20091, dated the 12th August 1919. To support the rocking shaft bearings and the centre valve rod bearing, plus other components, a substantial motion plate/stretcher was provided. The shaded areas in the centre aperture are the middle cylinder slidebars. This motion plate, as with other components, was the subject of significant redesign as valve gear changes were introduced.

CRA: CRA6/1/3/2/48/4/7

Plate 50
A forward view between the '956' Class frames looking towards the motion plate/stretcher and centre cylinder slidebars. Just to the front of the leading left-side hornblock is the frame-mounted anchor point for the multiplying levers. Above and in front of the motion plate/stretcher is the centre cylinder valve rod to which the 'floating lever' is attached. The large horizontal frame stretcher secured above the first coupled axle hornblocks is noticeable. *A.E. Glen*

Plate 51
The '956' Class multiplying levers assembly is shown partially completed, with the two output levers fitted. The top of the right-hand multiplying lever output is connected to the top of the 'floating lever', whilst the left-hand multiplying lever output is connected, through a frame aperture, to the bottom of the 'floating lever'. The drive arrangement to the centre of the left hand multiplying lever appears to be fitted, whereas that to the right one has not. The rear bearing for the centre valve spindle is just visible, this bearing being secured to the front of the motion plate/stretcher by the two bolts above the left-hand centre slidebar. Failure of this rear valve spindle bearing seems to have resulted in major component damage. The arrangement was completely redesigned for the second type of derived motion.

A.E. Glen

point being visible. Additionally, the multiplying lever outputs to the motion rods connected to the 'floating lever' are visible, the top of the left-hand multiplying lever being connected to the bottom of the 'floating lever' via an aperture in the motion plate. The right-hand multiplying lever output is seen connected to the top of the 'floating lever'. The input from the right-hand rocking shaft to the associated multiplying lever is not yet connected, though the boiler is in place, leaving limited access space for the remaining motion installation. To change the motion plate, together with other major valve gear modifications, as was done for both the Stephenson's motion fit and the second form of derived motion, almost certainly would have required a boiler lift.

This first arrangement of the derived motion suffered from a number of drawbacks: first, there are a large number of pin and slide joints, each subject to wear; second, there seemed to be a lack of structural rigidity and stiffness in some members and mountings; third, the multiplying levers and other links all contribute inertial effects arising from their oscillating masses; fourth, component over-stressing seems to have been a significant early problem, resulting in various mechanical failures or plastic deformation.

VALVE EVENTS WITH THE INITIAL DERIVED MOTION

Examination of this initial form of the '956' Class derived motion indicates that when taking account of the multiplying levers, plus sliding and oscillating joints, there can be lost motion 'equivalent' to

fourteen pin/slide joints per side applied to the respective 'floating lever' inputs from the associated right-hand and left-hand motion rods (Figure 31). No data is now available for St Rollox 'limits & fits' tolerances of the period, but equivalent GNR/L&NER data,[23] for Gresley 3-cylinder engines, allowed a build tolerance of 0.004 ins for each pin and slide joint. When applying this build tolerance to the '956' Class motion, two particular running conditions need to be considered. The first relates to low speed operation, in which inertial effects are minimal and only frictional effects are taken into account; the second relates to higher speed operation, where inertial effects become more pronounced.

The Gresley '2:1' derived motion had eleven 'equivalent' pin joints, and when new the lost motion was 0.044 ins, to which an additional 20 per cent could be added for inertial effects at the higher speeds.[23] For the '956' Class initial derived motion, phasing considerations for the 'floating lever' inputs suggest the 'as new' or 'ex shops' lost motion at the centre valve rod could be in the 0.100 to 0.125 in. range, and inertial effects would be greater than for the Gresley motion. To allow some analysis of the '956' Class centre valve motion, a lost motion figure of ⅛ in. has been used, this being assumed as applicable to the locomotive in 'ex shops' condition, but taking no account of any structural deflections or inertial effects.

Interestingly, GNR/L&NER 3-cylinder locomotives entering works for repairs were recorded as having central valve rod lost motion, in worst cases, in excess of ⁵⁄₁₆ in.[23] It is very likely that '956' Class engines may have approached or even exceeded this figure, such a figure of 5/16 in. making the St Rollox 'pin allowance' of 1/8 in., used for valve setting purposes, of questionable value in these circumstances.

The effect of this initial 'ex shops' lost motion varies with cut-off, locomotive speed and valve friction. As wear increases, the effects on valve events will become manifestly greater. If, working at lower speeds, and with cut-off set in the 60 to 65 per cent range (i.e. near full-gear, with port openings around 1¼ ins for the '956' Class, from drawing No. 19947,[12] Figure 27), the effects will be minimal, being around a 5 per cent reduction in set cut-off. For L&NER locomotives in ex shops condition, running with an equivalent long cut-off, the effect of their lost motion was calculated as a reduction of 3 per cent to the set cut-off.[23] However, working the '956' Class at earlier cut-offs, typically 30 per cent (with port openings of 7/16 in.[12]), and assuming, due to carbon build-up, that the valve is stiff in its liner, then the cut-off will be modified due to the minimum 1/8 in. lost motion (from a port opening of 7/16 in. to one of 5/16 in.), the cut-off effectively being almost halved (from 30 per cent to 20 per cent[12] or less). This is because the inside valve moves only a portion of its normal travel and then pauses whilst the remaining movements of the outside valve spindles are absorbed in lost motion.

In these circumstances, the steam entering the cylinder is artificially cut off and the power developed by the centre cylinder might be up to 25 per cent less than the other two. At shorter cut-offs, say 20 per cent and below, where the '956' Class forward gear port openings were less than 5/16 in., and where the centre valve lost motion through wear would exceed 1/8 in., the middle cylinder output could be difficult to determine, as the centre valve travel is again reduced by the amount of the lost motion. Effectively, at cut-offs less than 20 per cent, as lost motion through wear increases and approaches the port opening figure and beyond, the centre cylinder may tend to behave as if it was operating asymptotic to mid-gear. However, since the pin joint wear may be uneven between top and bottom 'floating lever' inputs, the actual events may not be 'centre-based', the events being biased, and changing with wear accumulation.

Exhaust beats in these circumstances, when working at shortened cut-offs could be very strange and irregular. In practice, it may not

have been possible to work the loco at lower than 30 per cent cut-off due to increasing pin joint wear, inertial effects and some lack of structural rigidity.

On the other hand, working at higher speeds and with limited valve-in-liner friction, the centre valve spindle, by virtue of its inertia (including reflected inertias from motion levers), may overshoot its normal travel by an amount equal to the lost motion, so the effective port opening is higher than expected for the set cut-off. At 20 per cent set cut-off (with port openings of 3/8 in. for '956' Class), lost motion effects may give an effective cut-off up to 35 per cent or more, and in these circumstances the power developed by the centre cylinder may be up to 25 per cent above that of the outside cylinders.

The valve events during transition between frictional and inertial effects, coupled with possible resonance in the valve gear operating bandwidth, would be almost unpredictable and would have caused much heart searching for the St Rollox team, since, at that time, few locomotive engineers would have recognised the symptoms. An accurate diagnosis might have proved very difficult, and for Pickersgill to admit to such difficulties external to the company may not have been possible for many reasons.

Not surprisingly, the St Rollox team looked for a different arrangement to solve the problem. In discussing this initial version of Pickersgill's derived motion in 1943, at an ILocoE meeting on locomotive valve gears, E.S. Cox commented[15] that 'Where [the derived motion] involves some 14 pin bearings, as in the Caledonian Railway arrangement ..., it ceases to be a practical proposition at all, and the four engines so fitted were notably unsuccessful'. (However, it should be remembered that the unsuccessful nature of '956' Class performance was by no means wholly related to derived motion problems.)

Initial attempts to rectify various problems were made in October 1921. The St Rollox drawing register[11] notes drawing No. 21352, 'Steady Brackets for Inside Motion Rod, 3 Cyl. Engine' and drawing No 21353,[24] 'Stay for Inside Motion Bracket', being prepared on the 19th of that month. From drawing No. 21353, shown as Figure 37, it seems that unacceptable structural deflections were present at the

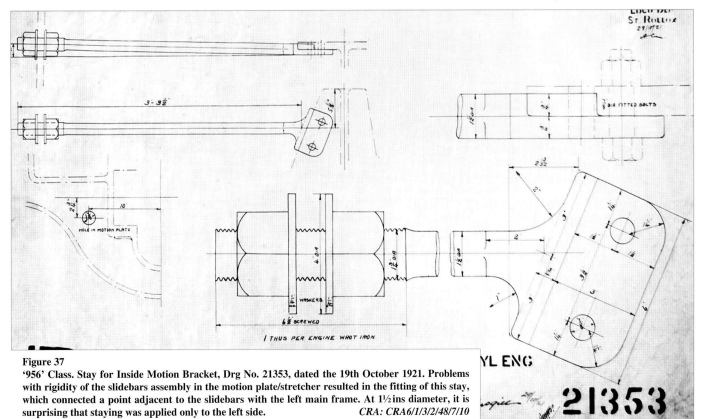

Figure 37
'956' Class. Stay for Inside Motion Bracket, Drg No. 21353, dated the 19th October 1921. Problems with rigidity of the slidebars assembly in the motion plate/stretcher resulted in the fitting of this stay, which connected a point adjacent to the slidebars with the left main frame. At 1½ ins diameter, it is surprising that staying was applied only to the left side.
CRA: CRA6/1/3/2/48/7/10

motion plate (Figure 36), the stay being connected between the left-hand inside frame and the left lower side of the motion plate. It is likely that this additional staying was applied to all locomotives in the class. Moreover, new combination levers were fitted throughout the class, the original drawing No. 19926[25] being altered on the 14th November 1921 to provide a more substantial component, suggesting some service weakness through distortion or failure had taken place.

A further attempt was seemingly made to deal with structural defects in December 1921. Drawing No 21401,[26] 'Details for Altered Motion, Eng. 959', was prepared by Graeme Miller on the 28th of that month, and is stated as being unique to No. 959, but unfortunately the drawing has not been traced. Alan Dunbar[8] noted this work on No. 959 involved modifications to the 'floating lever', and the use of a dashpot, which may have resulted from further discussions

with Professor Mallenby. This specific to No. 959 modification was implemented in early February 1922.[8]

In parallel with this specific to No. 959 initiative, a series of drawings were prepared, starting in December 1921, to allow the fitting of Stephenson's link motion to the centre cylinder, major items being drawing No. 21396, 'Motion Arrangement for 3-Cyl Engine' and drawing No. 21399, 'Expansion Link for 3-Cyl Engine'. Alan Dunbar noted that whilst No. 957 was out-shopped with Stephenson's link motion on the 6th of April and No. 958 on the 27th April 1922, engine No. 956 was not initially so fitted. Around February 1922, the No. 956 derived motion was modified to an arrangement somewhat similar to that which had been fitted to No. 959, which itself was, by April 1922, further modified to mirror the No. 956 fit.[8] Unfortunately, no records or drawings have come to hand detailing this series of modifications to No. 959 and No. 956.

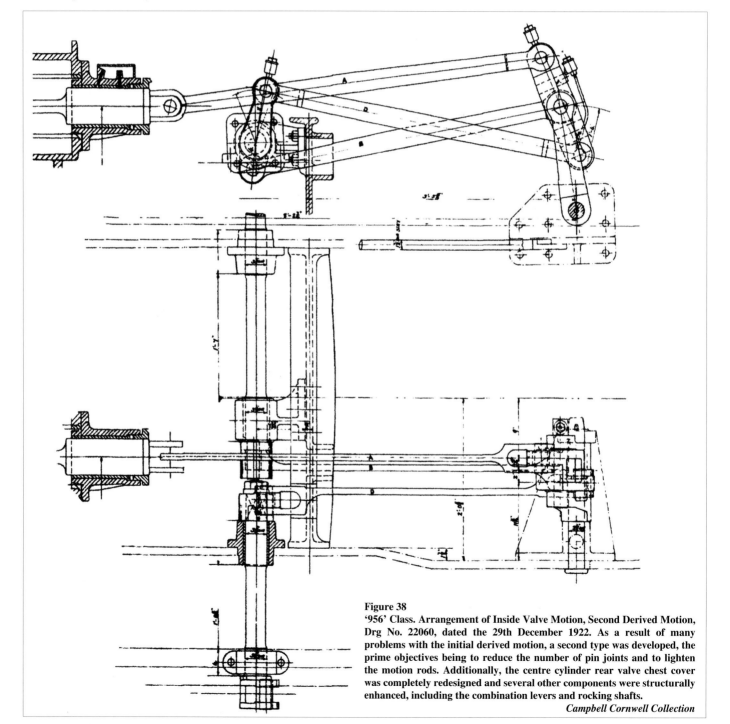

Figure 38
'956' Class. Arrangement of Inside Valve Motion, Second Derived Motion, Drg No. 22060, dated the 29th December 1922. As a result of many problems with the initial derived motion, a second type was developed, the prime objectives being to reduce the number of pin joints and to lighten the motion rods. Additionally, the centre cylinder rear valve chest cover was completely redesigned and several other components were structurally enhanced, including the combination levers and rocking shafts.

Campbell Cornwell Collection

THE SECOND DERIVED MOTION

Putting the fitting of Stephenson's gear to one side for the moment, Pickersgill persevered with the conjugated motion, and drawings were prepared in December 1922 and January 1923 for an 'improved' arrangement.[11] The prime objective was said to have been to shorten, and thus lighten, the motion rods to reduce inertial forces, though the left- and right-hand inputs to this new motion still came from the respective outside valve rod yokes, and various unhelpful dynamic effects would still apply. Additionally, a number of components were re-engineered and structurally enhanced, in the light of operational experience.

This second form of derived motion is shown in Figure 38, St Rollox drawing No. 22060,[27] dated the 29th December 1922, and is effectively a modified form of the Gresley '2:1' arrangement, but set out in the vertical plane. The drawing also shows the rocking shafts arrangement, a perspective layout of this second derived motion being shown as Figure 39, the main components again being identified.

As to the mechanics of the new arrangement, the number of drive rods was reduced from four to three, the 2:1 ratio now being achieved in the length of the inner rocking shaft levers (8 ins on the left side, 4 ins on the right). The 'floating lever' was moved to the back and directly supported from the anchor bracket originally provided for the 1:2 multiplying levers used in the first derived motion. A new rear valve chest cover was provided, using a 5½ ins diameter sleeve bearing and valve guide, which was substituted for the earlier unsatisfactory stuffing box facility. The detail of this new centre valve guide arrangement is illustrated in Figure 40, from drawing No. 22015,[28] the actual valve spindle and sleeve being shown as Figure 41, from drawing No. 22045.[29]

A new motion plate was necessary to accommodate the changed drive rods, the original motion plate depicted on drawing No. 20091,[22] being superseded by a significantly strengthened one to drawing No. 22051,[30] dated the 20th December 1922, shown as Figure 42. The new motion plate had the weight-reducing holes removed, the stay attachment point being retained to the left of the connecting rod aperture, and the upper level of the motion plate structure enhanced. Moreover, larger diameter transverse rocking shafts were substituted, the diameter being increased from 3 to 3½ ins, suggesting that torsional effects in the earlier shafts were a contributor to lost motion and potential valve events phasing mismatch. This change in transverse rocking shaft diameter would almost half the initial

torsional twist associated with the smaller diameter. The original slide-bars were retained, although new upper slide-bar mounted bearing brackets were required due to the rocking shafts' diameter increase.

This 'improved' arrangement seems to have made maximum use of available existing parts, perhaps recognising the Caledonian company's difficult financial position. Engines No. 956 and No. 959 were fitted with the 'improved' conjugated gear in mid-1923, though inertial problems seemingly persisted, since drawing No. 22376,[31] dated the 18th October 1923, and depicted as Figure 43, was prepared to fit a dashpot specifically to No. 956. The Stephenson's gear previously fitted to No. 956 in September 1922 would have been removed in late 1923.

Whilst the numbers of pin and slide joints are much reduced, the 'improved' derived motion still suffers from a number of disadvantages, in that wear is still present and so the valve gear lost motion will continue to increase with time, albeit from a smaller starting point. Moreover, a vertical pivot arrangement is required, which does not apply to the horizontal form of the gear used by Gresley, and lack of structural stiffness, inertial and resonance effects remain, though at reduced levels. Interestingly, on drawing No. 22060,[27] Figure 38, there are the faint remains of some annotated comments, suggesting this modified form of the derived motion was also to be fitted to engine No. 957 (in CR days), providing some corroboration that this motion was so fitted,[9] though no supporting photographic evidence has so far emerged.

Drawing No. 22376,[31] Figure 43, is the first of a series of three consecutive drawings in the St Rollox register for October 1923 which are annotated as relating to fitting of the dashpot arrangement to engine No. 956 only, which was presumably fitted to No. 956 in early 1924. No reference on these drawings is made to engine No. 959, though according to driver George Newlands,[8,9] a dashpot was fitted to it. Also, these three drawings, No's 22376, 22377 and 22378, are the last occasions where '956' Class, order 'Y125' and '3-Cylinder Engine' are mentioned as such in the St Rollox drawing register. Mention of the class just disappears, though examination of individual drawings shows modifications to the inside cylinder (drawing No. 19921) in March 1926 and March 1931, and to piston valve liners (drawing No. 19943) in December 1929. Very strangely, the original motion plate (drawing No. 20091) was 'traced to incorporate changes' by the LM&SR in February 1937.[22]

Graeme Miller[32] recalls having been involved in the production of

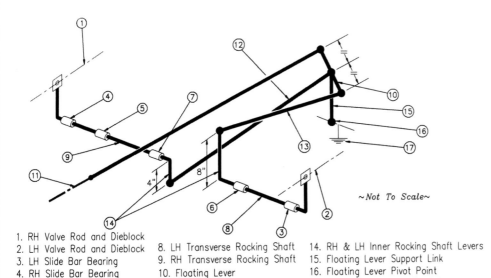

1. RH Valve Rod and Dieblock
2. LH Valve Rod and Dieblock
3. LH Slide Bar Bearing
4. RH Slide Bar Bearing
5. RH Frame Bearing
6. LH Frame Bearing
7. RH Stretcher Bearing
8. LH Transverse Rocking Shaft
9. RH Transverse Rocking Shaft
10. Floating Lever
11. Centre Valve Rod
12. RH Motion Rod
13. LH Motion Rod
14. RH & LH Inner Rocking Shaft Levers
15. Floating Lever Support Link
16. Floating Lever Pivot Point
17. Frame Attachment Bracket

~Not To Scale~

Figure 39
'956' Class. Perspective, Second Derived Motion, based on Drg No. 22060, dated the 29th December 1922. The second derived motion was quite different in layout to the first, a perspective view of the former being illustrated here, with all major components identified. The number of drive shafts was reduced from four to three and the 'floating lever' moved backwards and directly supported by the anchor bracket. Maximum use was made of existing components. Lost motion and inertial effects were reduced, though the basic underlying problems remained. *Author*

a working wooden model of this modified derived gear, and refers to a *'pow-wow'* over the model between Pickersgill and Professor Mallenby, from which Miller suggests the dashpot idea arose. Miller[32] also notes the dashpot emitted a whistle, whose pitch depended upon the size of the holes drilled in it, implying a measure of trial and error in its use. The valve gear model, according to Miller,[32] finally found its way to one of the running sheds and was used in Mutual Improvement Classes.

Facing a continuing problem with centre valve events, St Rollox could have considered tightening up on all the various tolerances associated with this second derived gear. Without exception, all the bushes in the valve motion were specified as *'gun metal'*, an alloy containing around 88 per cent copper and varying proportions of tin, zinc and lead. A harder and better wearing alternative might potentially have been found in one of the phosphor bronzes, which have a tight limit on their zinc content, thus reducing friction and a minimal lead content, thus increasing machinability. These phosphor bronzes are slightly harder than the gun metals, and require their associated shafts and bearing surfaces to be ground to a higher surface finish level, then hardened. This would go some way to

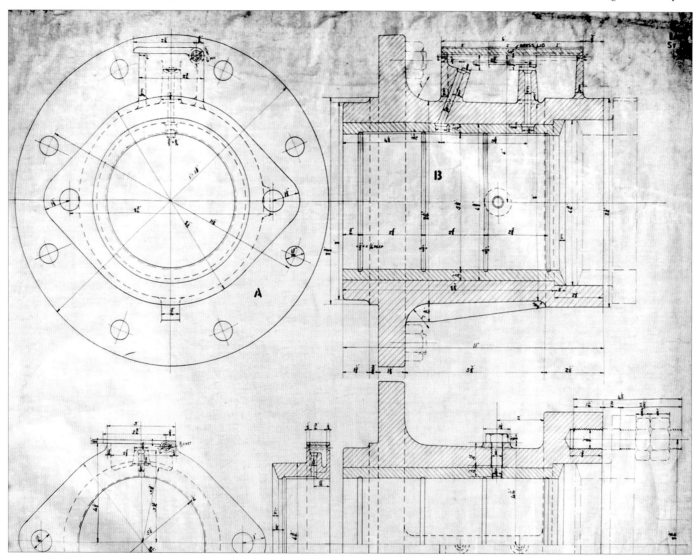

Figure 40
'956' Class. Centre Valve, Steam Chest Cover, Second Derived Motion, Drg No. 22015, dated the 30th November 1922. A major redesign of the middle cylinder rear valve chest cover was needed to overcome problems with the earlier arrangement. With the earlier design a centre valve spindle bearing bracket failure could have caused significant damage to the motion and rendered the locomotive inoperable. It appears this event may have happened more than once. With the new valve chest cover arrangement satisfactory operation seems to have been secured. *CRA: CRA6/1/3/2/48/8/10*

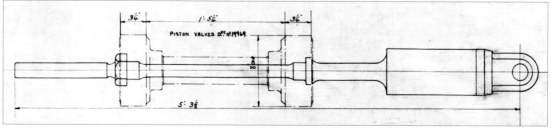

RIGHT: **Figure 41**
'956' Class. Valve Spindle for Centre Cylinder, Second Derived Motion, Drg No. 22045, dated the 18th December 1922. The valve spindle with the revised rear
support arrangements, using a 5½ins diameter sleeve bearing with enhanced lubrication is illustrated. As far as records show, there were no further problems in this area, though the somewhat unusual solution may have been predicated by space constraints. *CRA: CRA6/1/3/2/48/9/5*

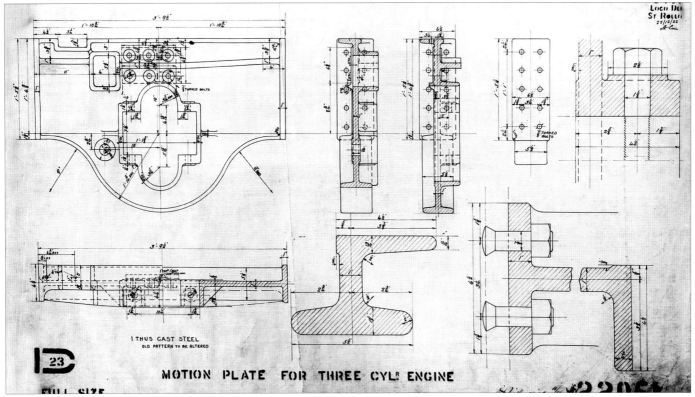

MOTION PLATE FOR THREE CYLR ENGINE

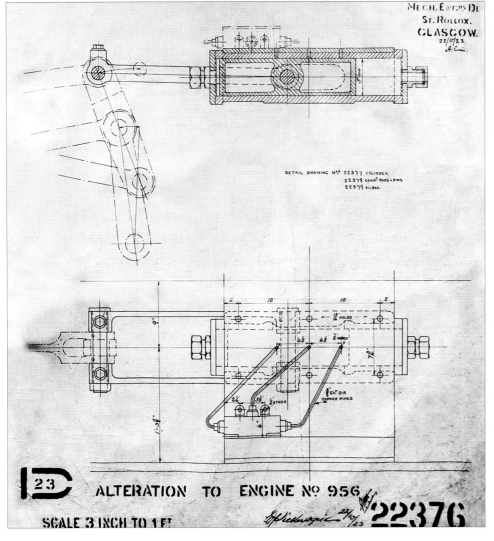

ALTERATION TO ENGINE Nº 956

SCALE 3 INCH TO 1 FT   22376

ABOVE: Figure 42
'956' Class. Motion Plate, Second Derived Motion, Drg No. 22051, dated the 20th December 1922. A new motion plate/ stretcher was necessary to accommodate the changed drive rods, the original being superseded by the significantly strengthened one illustrated. Lightening holes were removed and the upper section of the plate structurally enhanced. Staying to the left-hand main frame was retained.
CRA: CRA6/1/3/2/48/9/7

LEFT: Figure 43
'956' Class. Alteration to Engine No. 956, Dashpot Arrangement, Drg No. 22376, dated the 18th October 1923. Whilst engines No. 956 and No. 959 were fitted with the 'improved' second form of the derived motion in mid-1923, inertial overrun problems persisted and, to counter this, a dashpot was fitted, as illustrated. No details are available as to the success of this oil dashpot arrangement, but George Newlands, the Perth driver who had custody of No. 959, noted its fitting to his engine and that improved performance resulted.   *NRS: GD456, RHP136355/24*

explaining the re-issue of valve rod drawing No. 22063,[18] Figure 32, in January 1923, requiring hardened faces on the cast steel bearing surfaces.

Reducing the machining tolerances to 0.002 or 0.003 in. per slide or pin may have just been possible, though the problem is made worse by the oscillating nature of the bearing surfaces: pressure grease lubrication may have been essential. A successful attempt at such tolerance tightening, when used in conjunction with the modified derived motion and dashpot, would have improved valve events throughout the operational cut-off and speed ranges. The structural design improvements providing increased stiffness in certain components would also have been immensely beneficial, when implemented. In these circumstances, operation at valve events down to 15 to 20 per cent cut-off might have been much more assured, with resonance effects potentially being moved outwith the operating bandwidth.

It may have been possible to consider the use of ball and/or roller bearings to further reduce the lost motion per pin joint, since around this time such bearings were being manufactured for railway use, though due to the oscillating nature of the valve gear components, trials would have been needed to establish the certainty of the application. In mid-1922, attention was drawn to trials[33] being

undertaken by A.J. Hill of the GER into the use of roller bearings, the bearings being supplied by the Chain Roller Bearing Co. of Stockport. Interestingly, George Newlands, who had custody of No 959 at Perth, had the conviction that the fitting of the second form of the derived motion with associated dashpot provided a vast improvement in performance, whereas he considered the fitting of Stephenson's link motion for the centre cylinder was a retrograde step.[9]

Difficulties, however, remain, particularly the indirect oscillating drives from the external valve rod yokes. Fitting Gresley's arrangement in front of the cylinders removes this obstacle, but, as this would have required major surgery and incurred significant cost, it is unlikely that this option was considered at all. Whilst this second form of the derived motion may have given an improved precision to valve events, the oscillating masses may have remained an impediment to higher speed running.

STEPHENSON'S LINK MOTION

Following what seemed to be disappointing test results from the initial form of the derived gear, a decision was made to remove it from engines No. 957 and No. 958 and to fit the centre valve drive with Stephenson's link motion. As previously noted by Graham Miller,

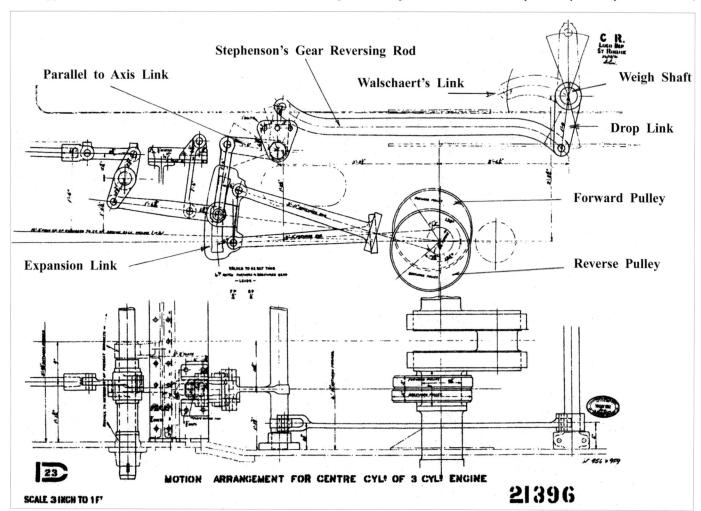

Figure 44
'956' Class. Motion Arrangement (Stephenson's) for Centre Cylinder, Drg No. 21396, dated the 23rd December 1921. Following disappointing test results with the original derived motion, a decision was made to remove it from engines No. 957 and No. 958 and to fit the centre valve drive with independent Stephenson's link motion. This change was seen as *'best port in a storm'*, so there was clearly some pressure on St Rollox, in late 1921, to find an acceptable solution to the centre valve drive difficulties. The two locomotives altered to Stephenson's motion were out-shopped from St Rollox in April 1922. The arrangement of Stephenson's motion chosen was unusual in many respects and commentators of the day noted little improvement, if any, in engine performance. One peculiarity related to the expansion link being raised to engage forward gear with the result that lead was reduced as the gear was notched up.
Campbell Cornwell Collection

'after a period of close observation, Pickersgill had no hesitation in making the bold decision to abandon the gear in its original form and to replace it with Stephenson's independent gear'.[34] In separate correspondence, Miller[35] referred to the installation of Stephenson's gear as equivalent to 'best port in a storm', suggesting, in late 1921, there was some pressure on St Rollox to find an acceptable solution for the middle cylinder valve events difficulties.

Drawing No. 21396,[36] dated the 23rd December 1921 and depicted in Figure 44, details the overall layout arrangement for the Stephenson's motion, the drawing being annotated in the bottom right-hand corner to indicate this motion was to be fitted to engines No. 956 and No. 959, which was perhaps just a simple draughting error. It is not clear if this arrangement was ever fitted to No. 959, and the annotation makes no reference to engines No. 957 and No. 958, which were in fact fitted with the gear in April 1922,[8] No. 956 following in September 1922.[8] Drawing No. 21396, Figure 44, is also annotated to point up specific components in the valve gear.

There are a number of novel and unexplained features in this most unusual arrangement of Stephenson's gear, including the decision to arrange for the expansion link to be raised to engage forward gear. Further, it seems that in putting together these arrangements, an error was made in the drawing office, in that a revised drawing

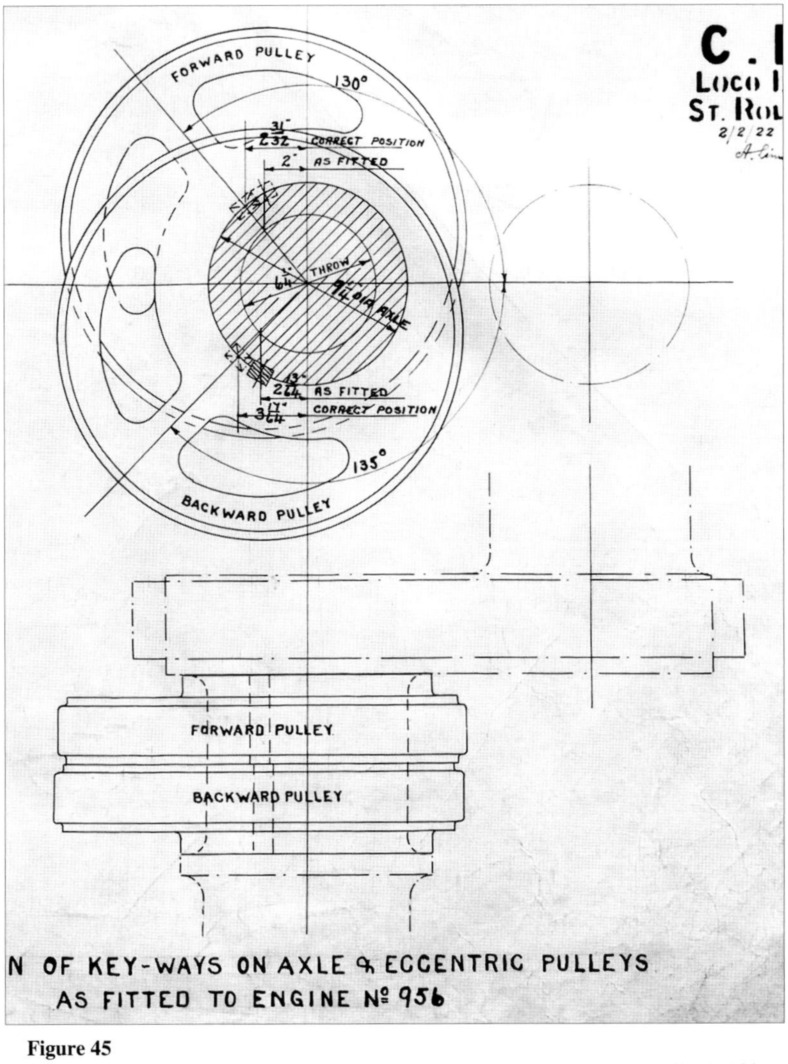

Figure 45
'956' Class. Position of Keyways for Eccentric Pulleys, Engine No 956, Drg No. 21744, dated the 2nd March 1922. An error seems to have been made in the drawing office regarding the eccentric pulley angular settings for the Stephenson's link motion to be fitted to No. 956. This was corrected by issuing the drawing illustrated, which indicates the original and revised angles. It is unclear if any original machining of the crank axle was recoverable. *NRS: GD456, RHP136355/22*

for the eccentric pulleys was issued in March 1922 to confirm the intended positions for the related angular settings on engine No 956. This drawing, No. 21744,[37] is illustrated in Figure 45, it being unclear whether any original crank axle machining was salvageable.

As a matter of passing interest, in a group of December 1921 drawings noted in the register[11] and related to the fitting of Stephenson's link motion, some were prepared by a draughtsman named E.G. Pickersgill. This refers to Edwin Gordon Pickersgill,[38] the Locomotive Superintendent's younger son, who was employed in the St Rollox drawing office at the time. At this time E.G. Pickersgill would have been in his early twenties and went on to become an LM&SR Running Superintendent based at Leeds. When his mother, Mary Ann Pickersgill, Wm Pickersgill's widow, died at Bournemouth in April 1948, Edwin was an executor of his mother's estate and was at that time a British Railways' employee.

Today, it is unclear why this novel arrangement of raising the expansion link for forward gear was chosen. To implement it, the Stephenson's gear reversing reach-rod was attached to the weigh shaft by a drop-link, this link being already extended upwards to connect with the main reach-rod from the cab, the weigh shaft being the pivot. Thus, on moving the cab reversing lever forward, the main reach-rod moved forward and the Walschaert's motion behaved as before, i.e. the die block was lowered in the expansion link for forward running. At the same time, the Stephenson's gear reach-rod moved backwards, thus raising the expansion link for forward gear.

With the existing inside admission piston valve and a space restriction under the boiler necessitating the use of a rocker, together with the eccentric rods appearing 'crossed' to give correct valve events, the raising of the expansion link for forward gear resulted in decreasing lead as the gear was notched up. The steam assisted reversing gear, mounted in the cab, is shown in Figure 46, drawing No. 20233.[39]

A much more satisfactory arrangement of Stephenson's gear would have been to lower the expansion link to engage forward gear, and this could have been arranged by extending the existing reach rod forward to engage the quadrant operating the centre expansion link. One is tempted to enquire if the modified arrangement installed was selected purely for aesthetics, so that the new extended reach rod could be concealed beneath the frame upper level (and thereby conceal the underlying problems!). Certainly, the arrangements chosen by St Rollox provide no obvious clear technical advantage over the more conventional approach in lowering the expansion link for forward gear.

Additionally, one wonders if St Rollox fully appreciated the operational limits of their chosen Stephenson's valve gear arrangement, which was certainly more dimensionally constrained than would normally be the case. Accepting the need to minimise the effects of angularity, specific ratios should be adhered to for the raise/lower quadrant controlling the expansion link. The parallel-to-axis part of the quadrant should be as long as possible,[40] and certainly not less than L/4, where L is the eccentric rod length. The '956' Class arrangements fall just outside this limiting criterion, so it is to be expected that angularity would be greater than accepted limits. Moreover, the eccentric rod/eccentric throw ratio should be as large as practical. It will be recalled that Drummond used 5 ft 6 ins eccentric rods, whereas the '956' Class rods were 3 ft 11 ins, the shortest ever used on any Caledonian company express passenger locomotive – though to assist in the reduction of angularity effects, the expansion link was fitted with 'launch links'.

Drawing No. 21396,[36] Figure 44, shows that the gear was not set out in the same plane as the cylinder and was dimensionally restricted in the vertical, with the rocker arms having 5⅞ ins centres and the suspension link being quite short at 16 ins, which again would contribute to increased angularity. In his 1906 text book on the subject, Professor Dalby analysed[41] an arrangement not unlike the Stephenson's gear fitted to No. 956 and concluded that such an arrangement, would result in a reduction in lead as the gear was notched-up.

To accommodate this Stephenson's gear, a new ¾ in. plate stay between the frames, no less than 1 ft 2 ins wide and riveted to the top flange of the motion plate, was provided solely to carry the top pivot brackets of the suspension link for the intermediate valve rod.

Figure 44 also indicates that at notch 4 cut-off, the lead is to be set at ³⁄₁₆ in. for the forward port and ½ in for the back port, the latter figure being most surprising. From the valve events table shown on

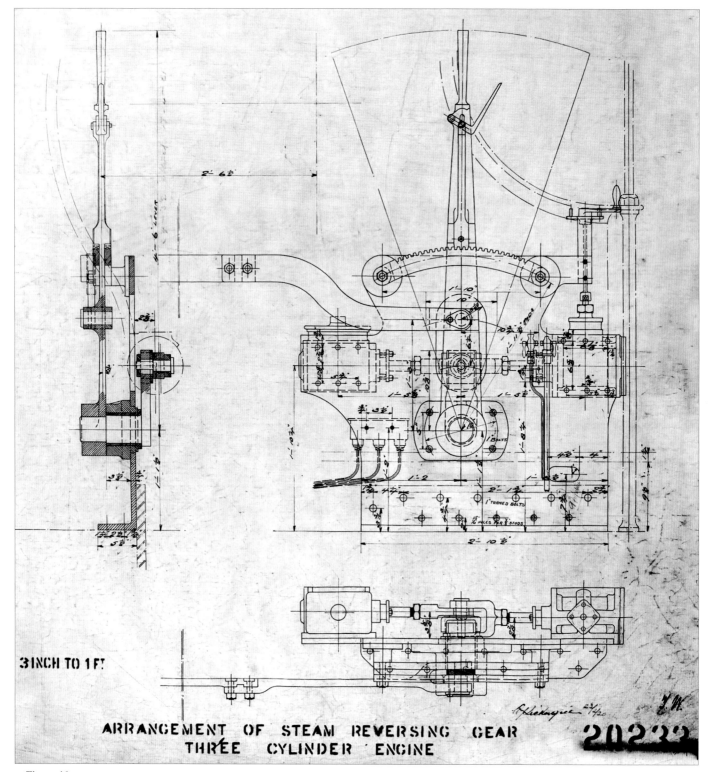

3 INCH TO 1 FT

ARRANGEMENT OF STEAM REVERSING GEAR
THREE CYLINDER ENGINE

20233

Figure 46
'956' Class. Arrangement of Steam Reversing Gear, Drg No. 20233, dated the 22nd October 1919. The steam reversing gear was of standard arrangement, a steam assisting servo being provided. As normal, the main reach rod was connected to the weigh shaft, from which a drop link was provided to a separate reach rod for the Stephenson' gear.
CRA: CRA6/1/3/2/48/5/9

drawing No. 19947,[12] Figure 27, notch 4 provides a 37 per cent cut-off in forward gear and 30 per cent in back gear. For the centre cylinder valve events, with ½ in. lead at the back port, the port is open by a full ½ in. to steam with the crank at back dead centre, inferring that the admission cycle may well have commenced around 30 degrees prior to that point. The back port lead of ½ in. at 37 per cent cut-off can only be explained if one accepts that the lead is reduced as the gear is notched up, the intention being to obtain a lead of say ¼ in. at around 25 per cent cut-off, thus giving compatibility with the fixed outside valves' leads at the latter cut-off. This centre valve setting results in excessive and premature cushioning, which, at longer cut-offs, would contribute to 'sluggishness' in acceleration.

A further point of concern would be the differences in leads at back and front ports, with the potential for inequality of power being developed by each end of the cylinder, a point noted by David Newlands and referred to earlier. No original indicator cards have survived for the front and rear ports on No. 956's centre cylinder in this configuration.

Whilst drawing No. 21396,[36] Figure 44, outlines a scheme where angularity is likely to be greater than normal, the drawing gives no information on how compensation for the effects of angularity is to be achieved. This would usually be provided by offsetting the expansion link pivot point ahead, or in front of, the link arc, but no detail for this is given on the drawing.

One further puzzle arises from the Stephenson's motion fit – shown on drawing No. 21748,[42] dated the 11th March 1921 (wrongly dated, since the drawing was prepared in March 1922), Figure 47 – which details modifications to the centre valve assembly for engines No. 957 and No. 958, and which appears to show different laps on the front and back valve bobbins. Additionally, the valve settings on drawing

No. 21748 do not seem to accord with those set out on drawing No. 21396,[36] Figure 44. No explanation for this is available, and it would seem from the original annotation on drawing No. 21748, these details were initially to be applied to engine No's 956, 957 and 958 (the St Rollox drawing register[11] annotates the drawing as applicable to No's 956, 957 and 958), though this appears to have been altered to exclude No. 956 at this point. No 956 was, of course, subsequently fitted with Stephenson's motion.

As noted previously, the more acceptable technical solution for this application of Stephenson's gear would have been to arrange that forward gear was engaged with the expansion link lowered and to use an 'open' eccentric rod arrangement, in which angularity is minimised. In these circumstances, the lead is increased as the motion is linked up, a position helpful to an express locomotive. Total eccentric throw given on drawing No. 21396,[36] Figure 44, is 6¼ ins, so to align with outside valve events, some minor restriction on the centre valve travel would be needed. Whilst relatively straightforward to achieve, no detail is shown on the drawing.

During trials of engine No. 956, on an ascent of Beattock from the south, in October 1922, and when fitted with Stephenson's gear, indicator diagrams of individual cylinder IHPs were taken. As will be seen from Figure 48,[43] these show the power output of the centre cylinder was disproportionately low when compared to the outside cylinders. The power disparity is in the 15 to 20 per cent range at around 60 per cent cut-off, which was the operating condition pertinent to the trials. The reduced power output from these trials may well have obliged St Rollox to find a more acceptable form of the derived motion.

The trials results shown in Figure 48 were obtained with No. 956 working a 500 ton 'test train' (630 tons including engine and tender),[43]

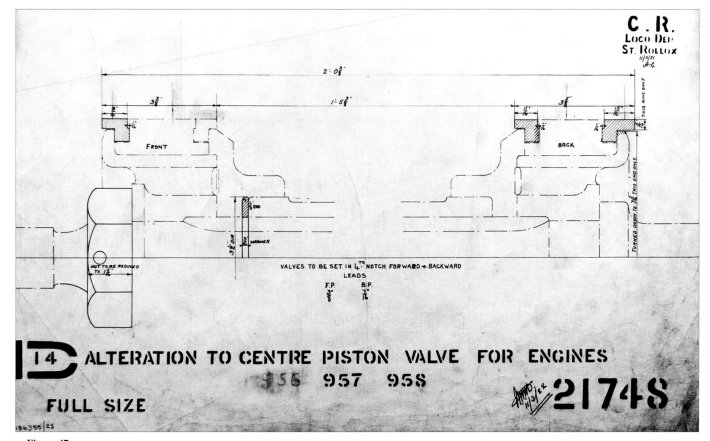

Figure 47
'956' Class. Alteration to Centre Piston Valve for Engines No's 956, 957 and 958, Drg No. 21748, dated the 11th March 1922. As valve events for the centre cylinder must have involved significant compromise, alterations to the centre valve leads seem to have been needed to ensure equal leads to all three valves at around 25 per cent cut-off. The drawing illustrated gives different ring dimensions for front and back valve heads, which suggests unequal lap at front and back ports for the centre cylinder.

NRS: GD456, RHP136355/23

the details of the working being given in Appendix 3. It is noteworthy that No. 956 took 40 minutes for the unaided climb from Beattock station to the summit, normal express passenger service trains being allowed 20 minutes with banking assistance, if needed.

There has been much questioning, over many years, as to whether, when fitting the 'crossed' rods Stephenson's motion arrangement to No. 956, the centre valve lead increased or decreased as the gear was linked up. The question is something of a 'red herring', since the 'crossing' of the rods arose in obtaining correct valve events, having selected a raised expansion link position for forward gear. Theoretically, from Figure 44, the lead reduces as the gear is notched up, a position confirmed by Professor Dalby's 1906 analyses and also by the St Rollox valve setting design, which required a reduction in lead from ½ in. to approximately ¼ in. when linking up from around 35 per cent to about 20 to 25 per cent. Whether the rods are 'crossed' or 'open' is not really a valid question in these circumstances, though theoretically, 'crossed' rods can amplify angularity.

An interesting conversation, on a similar theme, some twenty years later, is reputed to have taken place between Edward Thompson, CME of the L&NER, and Sir William Stanier, his counterpart on the LM&SR. Thompson, concerned in 1941 about the increasing wear in the motion bearings on the 600 plus L&NER locomotives fitted with Gresley '2:1' gear, sought Stanier's advice on this problem. An analysis was produced by E.S. Cox,[23] and was used by Thompson to persuade the L&NER Directors into halting production of locomotives using the Gresley's derived motion. Thompson is reputed to have remarked to Stanier that he was considering replacing the inside derived motion on the Gresley engines with Stephenson's link motion, to which Stanier apparently advised most strongly against such action. Stanier seemingly told Thompson the LM&SR had inherited four

big Caledonian engines 'just like that', and their performance was so poor that they were scrapped prematurely[44] – although this is not quite the whole story.

Exhaust Passages and Valve Chests

From Figure 49,[45] which shows a cross-sectional plan of the valve chests, parallel front and rear exhaust passages run from left to right across the engine, through the centre cylinder exhaust chest, before entering the blast pipe. An interesting and perhaps crucial feature, which has to date been given little attention, concerns the interaction between the cylinder exhausts due to the unusual passage design. This would principally concern the left and inside cylinders' exhausts, which are in tandem along the common exhaust passages to the blast pipe.

As the exhaust port of the inside cylinder begins to close, with pressure a little above atmospheric, the corresponding exhaust port of the left cylinder would begin to open, releasing steam at substantial pressure (perhaps as much as 50 psi, even at shortened cut-offs), to pass through the inside cylinder steam chest (exhaust end), en-route to the blast-pipe. Some of this left cylinder exhaust steam would undoubtedly have entered the inside cylinder, due to pressure differential, before the centre cylinder exhaust port fully closed, trapping the steam there.

The net result of this exhaust steam ingestion, just prior to the inside cylinder compression stage, would be to enhance the compression event and provide a 'quasi' steam admission in advance of that intended. Two potential results arise: first, the mean effective pressure (MEP) is reduced as the indicator diagram is 'thinner', and second, over-compression might result in the steam chest pressure

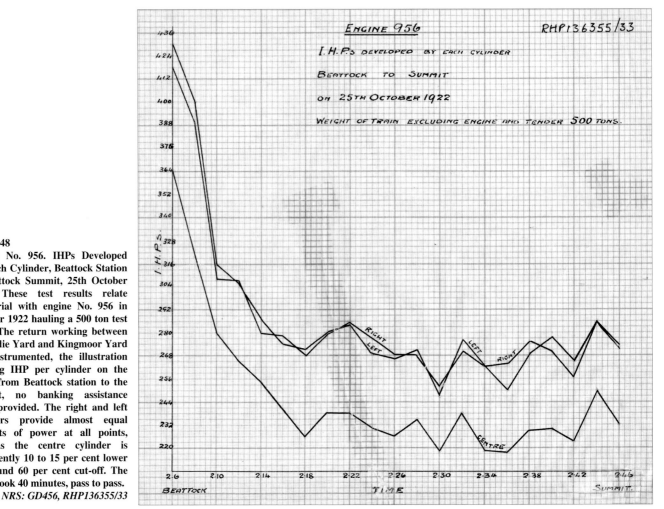

Figure 48
Engine No. 956. IHPs Developed for Each Cylinder, Beattock Station to Beattock Summit, 25th October 1922. These test results relate to a trial with engine No. 956 in October 1922 hauling a 500 ton test train. The return working between Polmadie Yard and Kingmoor Yard was instrumented, the illustration showing IHP per cylinder on the climb from Beattock station to the summit, no banking assistance being provided. The right and left cylinders provide almost equal amounts of power at all points, whereas the centre cylinder is consistently 10 to 15 per cent lower at around 60 per cent cut-off. The climb took 40 minutes, pass to pass.
NRS: GD456, RHP136355/33

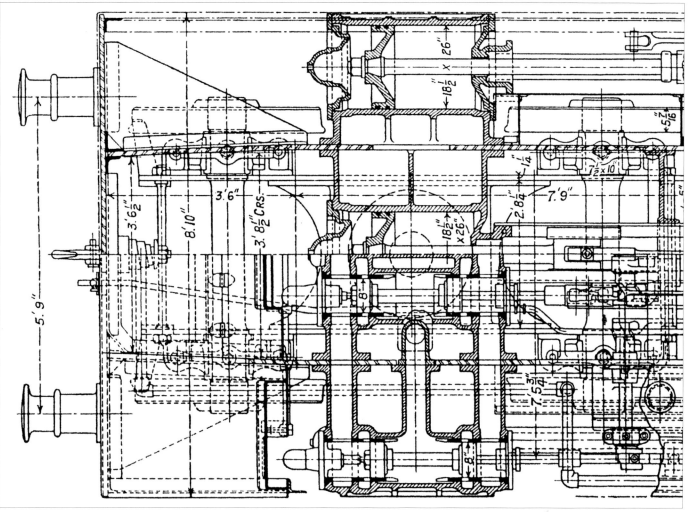

Figure 49
'956' Class. Sectioned Plan in way of Steam Chests. This illustration, taken from the engine GA, shows the parallel exhaust passages connecting the left and centre cylinders to the blast pipe. An interesting and perhaps crucial feature, which has to date been given little attention concerns the interaction of cylinder exhausts, which would have resulted in steam admission to the centre cylinder from the left cylinder exhaust. This would have introduced an earlier admission point in the cycle than was intended. The result would be some over compression, a reduction in centre cylinder mean effective pressure and a measureable reduction in output power for a cylinder already provided with larger than normal lead. It is unlikely that St Rollox knew of this effect.
The Railway Engineer, *October 1921*

being lower than cylinder pressure at the admission point, leading to a marginal retarding of the admission point.

Working at longer cut-offs, near full gear, where at the release point the left cylinder initial exhaust pressure might exceed 90 psi, could effectively provide additional trapped cushioning steam, further reducing the centre cylinder MEP and the output power, hence again contributing to 'sluggish' acceleration, the effects being difficult to identify from trials indicator diagrams. These conclusions would seem applicable to '956' Class performance irrespective of centre valve gear arrangements and might influence the *'accent and tempo'* of the exhaust beats as noted by David Newlands.

Surviving No. 956 traced indicator diagrams, taken during trials workings on the 11th August 1921 between Glasgow Central and Carlisle,[46] suggest there may have been slight over compression, prior to the admission event, but without the original diagrams per cylinder it is difficult to draw definitive conclusions.[47,48] The detail of this August 1921 working is given in Appendix 2. It is of interest to note that some earlier indicator diagrams were seen as having unusual shape.[9] For the Stephenson's motion fit at extended cut-offs, when the centre cylinder lead was already excessive, this additional effect, arising from exhaust passage layout, would have further depressed the MEP.

VALVE GEAR – COMPONENT MECHANICAL DESIGN

Some comment is appropriate on the mechanical design of the derived valve gear assembly, since in certain areas early component failure arose. In particular, the internal and external valve rods, the external upper slide-bars, together with the internal and external valve rod support brackets, were all recorded as the subject of failures.[8,9,10,49,50] Moreover, as already noted, the anchor point for the multiplying levers (Figures 30 and 31) was changed to a more substantial structure and staying added to the lower motion plate (Figure 37), which suggests the original structural support was insufficient. Strengthened combination levers were substituted, the rocking shafts' diameters increased and the main motion plate strengthened, all pointing to some initial components experiencing unexpected and unintended deflection or deformation.

For the first form of derived motion, no substantial support seems to have been initially provided for the fore end of the centre valve spindle, apart from the stuffing box. The rear spindle of the centre valve crosshead assembly was supported by a bearing bracket of similar type to that used externally, as illustrated in Plates 47, 50 and 51. If this rear bearing bracket fractured, which seemed to have been a repeated problem in early days, significant damage to

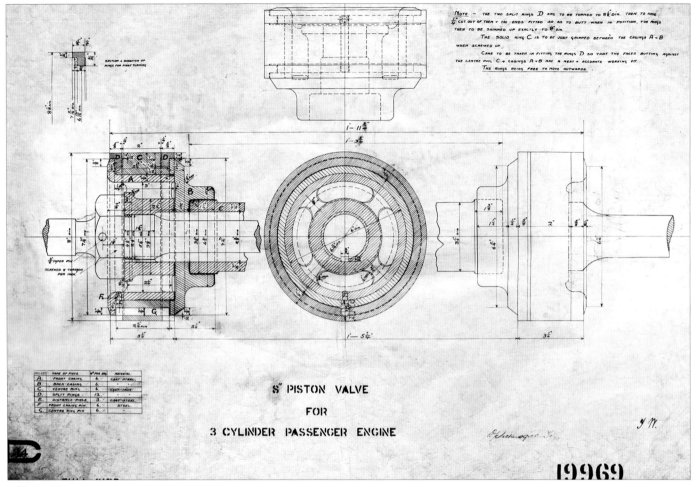

Figure 50
'956' Class. 8 ins Diameter Piston Valve, Drg No. 19969, dated the 22nd May 1919. Whilst Pickersgill had incorporated 11 ins diameter piston valves in his 1918 outside-cylindered 4-4-0 proposals, he reverted to 8 ins diameter valves for the '956' Class. Conventional thinking of the time would have suggested 9 ins or even 10 ins diameter valves. For the sealing of '956' Class piston valves, St Rollox used a design similar to that of the Pennsylvania Railroad Co., details of which had been published in the USA in 1917. The build notes on the St Rollox drawing follow in outline the layout from that PRC publication.
NRS: GD456, RHP136355/9

the 'floating lever', its crosshead and the valve spindle would result. This would come about since, after bracket fracture, the input forces from the motion rods and the weight of the valve spindle itself, plus the 'floating lever' and crosshead weights, would be cantilevered on the stuffing box gland. Such a bearing bracket failure and related consequences might have been quite catastrophic for the centre motion and could probably fail the locomotive completely, possibly requiring the internal derived motion to be partially dismantled prior to the engine being moved. In such circumstances, it is likely a significant number of new motion parts might be needed to repair what could have been extensive damage.

Initially, it would seem that the bearing bracket material was changed from cast iron to cast steel, though a complete redesign of the rear centre valve chest cover was put in hand for the fitting of the second derived motion. The new arrangements, shown on drawing No. 22060,[27] Figure 38, incorporated a 5½ ins diameter sleeve bearing, 12 ins long, having enhanced lubrication. The sleeve bearing housing is shown on drawings No 22015,[28] Figure 40. Post this redesign work, no further problems seem to have arisen.

A similar problem of fracture of external valve rod rear bearing brackets was overcome by again changing the material from cast iron to cast steel. As with the internal bracket failure, damage to motion components may have been extensive. Also, an inherent weakness in the external valve rods themselves, as depicted in Figure 32, can be identified due to the under-cut to 1¾ ins diameter between the

combination lever connection and the rear support bearing. Such an under-cut raises the stressing unnecessarily, with the increased likelihood of fatigue fracture. A much more satisfactory arrangement to support the valve rod would result from the use of extended steam chests (which also give more direct steam ports) incorporating a set of external valve rod slide bars, thus reducing the unsupported length. No undercuts should have been permitted.

Fracture of the upper external slidebars has been variously noted[8,9,10,49,50] and some comment on these components is called for. The accepted way to proceed with slidebar design was to assume the whole of the boiler pressure acted on the piston, with no need to make allowance for increased pressure due to water in the cylinders (which other stressing calculations would acknowledge), or for the inertia of moving parts, since they are negligible at mid stroke. The loadings and deflections were then calculated taking account of connecting rod length and crank radius, recognising the slidebars' support points and the bar section selected.

For the '956' Class slidebars, the positioning of the outboard supporting motion girder was constrained by available frame space and had to support overhung and lengthened slidebars arising from the shortening of the outer connecting rods, which itself arose due to the loco extended front end. In these circumstances, the upper slidebar is subject to both positive and negative loading, pivoted around the outboard support girder and constrained by the cylinder cover attachment.

Between the cylinder cover attachment and the motion girder support, the upper slidebar section is reduced by about 20 per cent arising from the bolts securing the transverse rocking shaft outer bearing bracket, thus producing a stress raiser at a point of significant loading. Moreover, it should be noted that normally only the upper slidebar is cyclically loaded at twice rotational frequency from piston thrust when the engine is running in the forward direction. With an engine maximum speed assumed at 65 mph, upper slidebar cyclic stressing occurs in the 10 Hz bandwidth.

To compound the slide-bar stressing, a further superimposed cyclic force from the rocking shafts is added to the point of potential maximum loading, this force being conditioned by inertial effects from the inside motion oscillating masses, the upper slidebar being the final reaction point for some proportion of these forces, which again occur in the 10Hz bandwidth. In recognition of these imposed stress patterns, a much more pronounced trapezoidal section, often used in such slide-bar applications, would have been more appropriate in countering the imposed stresses. Since piston rod and slide bar lengths were greater than those normally anticipated (to reduce outside connecting rod length for a locomotive with an extended front end), a further reason for using a more pronounced trapezoidal section arises.

Recognising the importance of very tight alignment tolerances for structural elements of this derived motion, it would seem essential that all major components should have been dowelled throughout the scheme: whether this was done, to any extent, is unknown. Since no valve gear stressing calculations for the '956' Class have survived (if they were ever produced), yet major component fractures occurred, it is reasonable to conclude that St Rollox did not really appreciate the related stressing phenomena sufficiently adequately, and that this was a serious weakness in the valve gear design, which initially prejudiced reliability and consequently locomotive availability.

PISTON VALVES

Until the advent of the 956 Class, St Rollox standard practice for piston valves on superheated locomotives used valves in the Schmidt form,[51] with a segmented ring and double ported arrangements. However, on the '956' Class, Pickersgill introduced a different design having sealing rings at each end of the valve bobbin, the details being given on drawing No. 19969,[52] dated the 22nd May 1919, illustrated as Figure 50.

Each valve bobbin essentially consists of two split rings at the extremities and a central solid ring, the arrangement being such that when the clamping is tightened to the correct pressure, the split rings are an accurate circumferential sliding fit between the central solid ring and the related valve body structure. All valve components are manufactured in cast steel, with the exception of the central ring which is of cast iron. The two split rings are specified as being free to move outwards and are turned up to fit the valve chest liner.

This arrangement of piston valve sealing is similar in many respects to that used by the Pennsylvania Railroad Corporation (PRC) and the annotated instructions on St Rollox drawing No. 19969[52] covering the manufacture and fitting of the sealing rings are similar to those outlined in the Yoder and Wharen 1917 publication on the subject.[53] It would seem that the St Rollox team may well have been aware of latest thinking on such matters from the USA.

Unfortunately, little information is available on the performance of these valves in Caledonian company service, although if they were a PRC standard design, Pickersgill would have more than reasonable assurance that many locomotives were so fitted and that performance was entirely satisfactory. Comments made some years later by L.D. Porta[54] suggest steam leakage may have been a problem with this valve arrangement.

SUMMARY OF VALVE GEARS FITTED

As far as can now be ascertained from the restricted amount of photographic evidence available and remarks by various commentators, the following valve gears were fitted to respective locomotives at the times noted:

No. 956
Initially built with first form of derived motion; modifications made to first derived motion in February 1922, followed by further changes in April 1922 to align with fit on No. 959; fitted with Stephenson's gear by CR in mid-1922; fitted with second form of derived motion, almost certainly by the LM&SR, as No. 14800 in late 1923, and thereafter, in 1924, with dashpot to limit inertial effects. (It has been suggested that No 956 may have been fitted with the second form of the derived motion prior to fitting Stephenson's gear.[34] This is unlikely, recognising St Rollox drawing register output dates.)

Plate 26 (page 52) shows No. 956, with original valve motion, at

Plate 52
Engine No. 956, now fitted with Stephenson's link motion for the centre cylinder, is illustrated leaving Balornock shed on the 9th August 1922 to work the 5.00 pm Buchanan Street to Aberdeen Pullman Express. *Ken Nunn, NRM/LCGB3369*

Above: Plate 53
The right side of No. 956 is illustrated at Perth station. The absence of the rocking shaft bearing on the upper slidebar and the yoke on the valve rod indicates that Stephenson's link motion is fitted.
A.B. MacLeod, NRM 341/80

Plate 54
LM&SR official photograph of the former No. 956 as LM&SR No. 14800, now fitted with the second type of derived motion, the rocking shaft bearing on the upper slidebar being evident. It is likely the dashpot was fitted at this time, though only a between-frames view would corroborate that.
NRM/SRX114

Glasgow Buchanan Street in August 1921 with a Perth express, under trials conditions, whilst Plate 52 illustrates this engine, fitted with Stephenson's motion, at Balornock shed on the 9th August 1922 and about to work the 5.00 pm, Buchanan Street to Aberdeen express. Plate 53 highlights the motion changes to No. 956 when running with the Stephenson's motion arrangement and Plate 54 depicts the locomotive as refitted with the second form of the derived motion as LM&SR No. 14800.

No. 957

Initially built with first form of derived motion; fitted with Stephenson's motion by CR in April 1922; as LM&SR No. 14801, refitted with second form of derived motion in the latter part of 1931. (It is not clear if dashpots associated with the second form of derived motion were fitted post 1931.)

No photograph has come to light of No. 957 in CR livery and fitted with the original form of the derived motion. Plates 55 and 56 show

Plate 55
Left-side view of No. 957, fitted with Stephenson's link motion, at Kingmoor shed in 1922. The engine finish seems spotless, yet through continuing problems the Carlisle based engines saw little work.
A.B. MacLeod, NRM/ABM C25

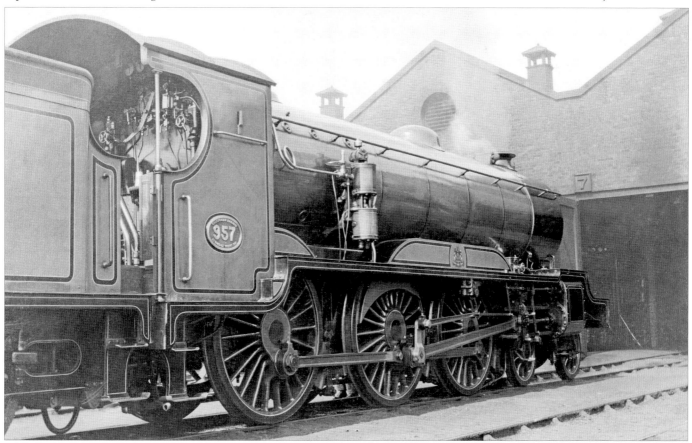

Plate 56
Right-side view of No. 957, fitted with Stephenson's link motion, at Kingmoor shed in 1922. Again the finish is spotless.
A.B. MacLeod, courtesy Jim MacIntosh

RIGHT: Plate 57
The former No. 957, as LM&SR No. 14801, fitted with Stephenson's link motion, at Buchanan Street goods station, Glasgow, in 1930. This engine would be refitted, in the following year, with the derived motion from the withdrawn No. 14800.   *J.F. McEwan*

BELOW: Plate 58
The former No. 957, as LM&SR No. 14801, now fitted with the second type of derived motion, at Kingmoor shed in 1933. The transverse rocking shaft and support bearing on the upper slidebar are prominent. The boiler and frames of No. 14801 were reunited after a general repair at St Rollox works in December 1931 and it seems to have been at this time the second derived motion was fitted.   *CRA460168b*

the left and right sides of No. 957 at Kingmoor in 1922 when fitted with Stephenson's link motion. No. 14801 retained its Stephenson's motion for some time, as depicted in Plate 57 at Buchanan Street goods station in 1930, and in Plate 29 on a local passenger train at Carlisle station. Plate 58 illustrates No. 14801 at Kingmoor in 1933 when fitted with the second form of derived motion; the rocking shaft bearing on the upper slidebar is clearly visible.

It seems that the second form of derived motion fitted to No. 14801 almost certainly would have come from the withdrawn No. 14800.

No. 958

Initially built with first form of derived motion; fitted with Stephenson's gear by CR in April 1922; no evidence of further changes to motion thereafter.

Plate 44 shows No. 958, with original derived motion at Edinburgh in 1921, whilst Plate 59 depicts the engine fitted with Stephenson's motion at Perth on the 29th October 1922. Plates 60 and 61 illustrate right and left sides of the locomotive as LM&SR No. 14802. In Plate 60, No. 14802 stands at the ash pits at Balornock in the 1930s, whilst Plate 61 shows the engine at Annan goods yard in 1926, when carrying early LMS livery.

No. 959

Initially fitted with first form of derived motion; fitted with changes to original derived motion in late 1921; fitted with second form of derived motion by CR, possibly mid 1923; dashpot fitted in late 1923 to early 1924; no known changes to motion fit thereafter. No photographic evidence of Stephenson's motion being fitted has come to light, though annotations to St Rollox drawings suggest otherwise. (Fitting of dashpot to No. 959 confirmed by driver George Newlands and by David Newlands.)

Plate 62 shows the locomotive at Perth in 1923, whilst Plates 63 and 64 depict the respective right and left sides of the engine as LM&SR No. 14803, the former location being Kingmoor, the latter being Balornock.

It would seem that No. 958 was never fitted with the second form of the derived motion, and that No. 959 never had Stephenson's gear applied, but Graham Miller's remarks[34] (that engine No. 957 and No. 958 were fitted with second derived motion) and further comments in the section on anecdotal evidence need to be taken account of.

Moreover, it seems that engines No. 956 (LM&SR No. 14800) and

ABOVE: Plate 59
No. 958, fitted with Stephenson's link motion, at Perth shed, on the 29th October 1922, again appearing quite majestic.
A.W. Croughton, CRA460231a

Plate 60
The former No. 958, as LM&SR No. 14802, fitted with Stephenson's link motion, at Balornock shed ash pits in the 1930s.
J.F. McEwan, CRA460173

Plate 61
The former No. 958, as LM&SR No. 14802, fitted with Stephenson's link motion and carrying the earlier LM&SR livery, on shunting duties, probably for a pick-up freight working at Annan goods yard in 1926.
J.J. Cunningham, courtesy A.F. Swann

ABOVE: Plate 62
No. 959 at Perth shed in 1923 and fitted with derived motion. It is not possible to tell from this image if No. 959 had been fitted with the second form of the derived motion at this time. Only a glance between the frames could give the answer. The centre driving wheels are chocked so it appears the engine was receiving attention. *Courtesy Jim MacIntosh*

Plate 63
Right-side view of the former No. 959, as LM&SR No. 14803, at Kingmoor shed and carrying the earlier LM&SR livery. It is assumed to be fitted with the second form of derived motion by this time.

CRA460174

Plate 64
Left-side view of the former No. 959, as LM&SR No. 14803, with second LM&SR livery style, at Balornock shed in the 1930s.   *NRM/LPC43963*

No. 957 (LM&SR No. 14801) were potentially the subject of the greatest number of valve gear variations. No. 956 was initially built with derived motion, which was twice modified prior to the fitting of Stephenson's motion, which in turn was subsequently removed, *prima facie*, in late 1923 by the LM&SR and replaced with the second derived motion, which itself was then fitted with a dashpot. No. 957, again originally fitted with the first derived gear, was subsequently fitted with Stephenson's motion, the LM&SR removing the Stephenson's gear and refitting derived motion in the latter part of 1931.

The first two locos to be withdrawn, No. 14800 and No. 14803, were carrying derived motion at the time, as too was No. 14801, whereas No. 14802 was withdrawn carrying Stephenson's link motion. Could this infer that, as George Newlands suggested,[9] the second form of the derived gear gave better performance than the Stephenson's link motion? Why, otherwise, would the LM&SR have substituted derived motion on No. 14801 in 1931, when withdrawal was not far off? This substitution would have been implemented in the pre-Stanier era, perhaps, as noted earlier, under the instructions of John Barr.

It is not now known if new parts were manufactured for the 1931 valve gear changes to LM&SR No. 14801, or whether existing items were re-used. Most likely, new bearing inserts for the motion rods would be manufactured to minimise initial lost motion 'ex shopping', although the frames would have required work to incorporate items from the second derived motion which were different to those fitted for the first type and Stephenson's motion fits, for example through frame bearings for the rocking shafts, slidebar mounted bearings, centre motion rear valve cover and the main between-

frames motion plate. The St Rollox drawing register is silent on these matters, though it is most probable that a boiler lift would have been necessary to gain access for the modifications, and indeed was the case (note earlier comments on boiler record cards).

It has been suggested that the identities of engines No. 14800 and No. 14801 may have been transposed in the 1930 to 1931 period. By this, the boiler and smokebox from No. 14801 may have been fitted to the frames and engine of No. 14800, whose boiler had been condemned, the resulting amalgam taking the No. 14801, which in its latter years was photographed several times fitted with derived motion. No evidence to support this proposition has been discovered and the boiler record cards[55] clearly demonstrate no interchange of boilers between locomotives, so *prima facie*, this suggestion can be discounted.

OBSERVATIONS

One suspects that in overall terms, the '956' Class 3-cylinder derived valve gear design was a 'bridge too far' for St Rollox. Whilst the number of cylinders and their dimensions cannot be faulted, and the use of long lap, long travel valve gear can be applauded, much of the derived valve gear system cannot escape criticism. The initial selection of the derived motion type, whilst theoretically correct, was completely lacking in practicability, and it is possible that through increasing wear, structural and inertial effects, the gear could not be operated successfully below 30 per cent cut-off. Additionally, the oscillating masses, and the *'disturbing effects throughout the whole gear'*[34,35] (which probably refers to resonance effects), may well have constrained engine speed to just above 60 mph. Again, the choice of Stephenson's motion for the inside cylinder was not practical because of the scheme selected and the space constraints, resulting in an abnormal arrangement with unconventional and inefficient valve settings. Accurate valve setting may have been problematic, a point noted by P. Ransome Wallis in September 1924.

One enigma remains unresolved, that being why St Rollox persisted with the design of a rocking shaft driven derived gear scheme in 1919, when Gresley's experience with a broadly similar scheme, fitted to GNR engine No. 461 in May 1918,[56] had attracted considerable adverse technical criticism due to the number of pin joints? Indeed, there was much technical debate on such matters in the ILocoE and technical press of the day, which could not have escaped St Rollox notice.

Whilst the second derived motion design was moving in the right direction, with manufacturing tolerance tightening and the potential use of roller bearings, the generic lost motion and oscillating masses problems could not be entirely removed without further major alterations. Additionally, it should have been obvious to St Rollox, when comparing the first No. 956 trials results with those from No. 60 in 1917, the most compelling problem related to a poorly steaming boiler aggravated by low superheat.

The fitting of independent Walschaerts' gear for the centre cylinder would have assisted the power output only marginally (by around 8 per cent increase over derived valve gear in 'ex shops' condition), but should have eliminated the *'disturbing effects throughout the whole gear'*[32,34] by removing any related resonance effects and any valve motion conditioned speed constraints. The reality of the August 1921 '956' Class trials[57] was that throughout the operating speed range, No. 956 seemed to struggle to produce the equivalent power of a '60' Class engine.

In a broad mechanical engineering sense, St Rollox should have recognised that with machinery operating at an average of 200 rpm for four hours each day and, say, 100 days per year, and capable of operating for at least three years between major repairs, it would have to be made robustly. Clearly, since some of the 'unique-to 956-Class' components could not get beyond the first few months without repeated fractures, there were significant stressing shortfalls, and a lack of appreciation at St Rollox of the finer points of detailed design.

REFERENCES

1. A.J. Powell papers, NRM, 956 Class material, uncatalogued
2. J.F. McEwan paper, William Patrick Library, Kirkintilloch, ref T25/1, etc
3. *Locomotive Engineers' Pocket Book 1935* (The Locomotive Publishing Co.), pp. 78ff
4. A.E. Glen Collection, private collection, courtesy Dr Ann Glen
5. *An Illustrated History of LNWR Engines*, Edward Talbot (OPC, 1984), Fig. 125, p. 274, and Fig. 134, p. 297
6. *The LNER 2-6-0 Classes*, John F. Clay and J. Cliffe (Ian Allan, 1978), pp. 26ff
7. *Locomotive Engineers' Pocket Book 1935* (The Locomotive Publishing Co), p. 52 and Steam Tables, p. 307
8. 'Y125 – And All That?', Alan Dunbar, in *SLS Journal*, August 1948, pp. 192, 193ff
9. *Fifty Years with Scottish Steam*, Alan G. Dunbar and I.A. Glen (Bradford Barton), pp. 40, 41ff
10. *Scottish Locomotive History 1831-1923*, Campbell Highet (George Allen & Unwin, 1970), p. 225
11. St Rollox Drawing Register, NRS, BR/CAL/5/56
12. St Rollox Drg No. 19947, dated 8th May 1919, Montague Smith Collection, NRS, GD 456, RHP136355/7
13. Private correspondence, Graeme Miller to C.P. Atkins, May 1978
14. St Rollox Drg No. 19968, dated 22th May 1919, NRS, RHP132397
15. 'The Evolution of Valve Gears', T.H. Shields, ILocoE Paper No. 443, 1943 (Vol. 33)
16. The Gresley Pacifics, O.S. Nock (David & Charles, 1973), p. 14
17. 'Scottish Topics – Past and Present', O.S. Nock, in *The Railway Magazine*, January 1965, pp. 20ff
18. St Rollox Drg No. 22063, dated 2nd January 1923, CRA6/1/3/2, Archive Group 48
19. St Rollox Drg No. 20032, dated 26th June 1919, CRA6/1/3/2, Archive Group 48
20. St Rollox Drg No 20030, dated 25th June 1919, CRA6/1/3/2, Archive Group 48
21. St Rollox Drg No. 20037, dated 28th June 1919, CRA6/1/3/2, Archive Group 48
22. St Rollox Drg No 20091, dated 12th August 1919, CRA6/1/3/2, Archive Group 48
23. 'Report on "2 to 1" Valve Gear, L.N.E.R. 3-Cylinder Locomotives', dated 8th June 1942, from the Chief Mechanical Engineer's office at Watford, written by E.S. Cox for Sir William Stanier, who passed it to Edward Thompson, NRM, Cox 2/20
24. St Rollox Drg No. 21353, dated 19th October 1921, CRA6/1/3/2, Archive Group 48
25. St Rollox Drg No. 19926, dated 2nd May 1919, altered 14th October 1921, Montague Smith Collection, NRS, GD456, RHP136355/6
26. St Rollox Drg No. 21401, St Rollox Drawing Register, NRS, BR/CAL/5/56
27. St Rollox Drg No. 22060, dated 29th December 1922, Campbell Cornwell Collection
28. St Rollox Drg No. 22015, dated 30th November 1922, CRA6/1/3/2, Archive Group 48
29. St Rollox Drg No. 22045, dated 18th December 1922, CRA6/1/3/2, Archive Group 48
30. St Rollox Drg No. 22051, dated 20th December 1922, CRA6/1/3/2, Archive Group 48
31. St Rollox Drg No. 22376, dated 18th October 1923, Montague Smith Collection, NRS, GD456, RHP 136355/24
32. Private correspondence, Graeme Miller to C.P. Atkins, May 1978
33. 'Bearing Trials on GER', in *The Railway Magazine*, July/December 1922, pp. 315ff
34. Private correspondence, Graeme Miller to D. Newlands, 1st September 1966
35. Private orrespindence, Graeme Miller to C.P. Atkins, May 1978
36. St Rollox Drg No. 21396, Campbell Cornwell Collection
37. St Rollox Drg No. 21774, dated 2nd March 1922, Montague Smith Collection, GD456, NRS, RHP136355/22
38. 'Pickersgill, A Relative View', Ralph Needham, in *The Caledonian Journal*, No. 5, 1988, pp. 11ff
39. St Rollox Drg No. 20233, CRA6/1/3/2, Archive Group 48
40. *Steam Locomotive Design, Data and Formulae*, E.A. Phillipson (The Locomotive Publishing Co.), pp. 330ff
41. *Valves and Valve Gears*, W.E. Dalby FRS (Arnold, London, 1906), pp 145-62
42. St Rollox Drg No. 21748, dated 11th March 1921 (should be 1922), Montague Smith Collection, NRS, GD456, RHP136355/23
43. Engine No. 956, Cylinder IHPs (Beattock to Summit), 25th October 1922, Montague Smith Collection, NRS, GD456, RHP136355/33
44. The Pickersgill 4-6-0s of the Caledonian Railway, Morrison Bryce, in *The True Line*, No 82, October 2003, p. 22
45. 'New 3-Cylinder 4-6-0 Locomotives', Caledonian Railway, in *The Railway Engineer*, October 1921
46. Indicator Diagrams, Engine No. 956, 11th August 1921, Glasgow to Carlisle Working, NRM, ID685 ALS3/7/4/G
47. 'Steam Engine Indicators and Valve Gears', Llewellyn V. Ludy, American Technical Society 1913, pp. 74-5
48. *Locomotive Performance*, Prof. W.F.M. Goss (John Wiley, New York, 1911), pp. 267ff
49. 'Scottish Topics – Past and Present', O.S. Nock, in *The Railway Magazine*, January 1965, p. 20
50. 'The Heavenly Blue Enigmas, CR 956 Class 4-6-0s', C.P. Atkins, in *BackTrack*, February 2009, p. 108
51. *The Application of Highly Superheated Steam to Locomotives* (Schmidt Superheater Co., 1910)
52. St Rollox Drg No. 19969, dated 22nd May 1919, Montague Smith Collection, NRS, GD456, RHP136355/9
53. *Locomotive Valves and Valve Gears*, J.H. Yoder and G.B. Warren (Pennsylvania Railroad Co., 1917), pp. 20-34 and fig. 30
54. *Advanced Steam Locomotive Development*, L.D. Porta, various papers, published 1969-2000, p. 54
55. 956 Class Boiler Record Cards, NRS, GD344/4/32/1-3
56. *Master Builders of Steam*, H.A.V. Bulleid (Ian Allan, 1970), p. 50
57. Appendices 1 and 2 of this publication

1928 BRIDGE STRESS COMMITTEE – LOCOMOTIVE HAMMER BLOW ANALYSES

CLASS	ENGINE NUMBER	TYPE	NUMBER OF CYLINDERS	DIAMETER OF DRIVERS	SPEED AT 6RPS (MPH)	MAX. AXLE LOAD (TONS)	HAMMER BLOW (IN TONS AT 6RPS)			MAX. AXLE LOAD (IN TONS AT 6RPS)	
							WHOLE ENGINE	AXLE	WHEEL	AXLE	WHEEL
CR '60'	14650	4-6-0	2	6 ft 1 ins	78	19.30	23.5	10.6	9.3	31.0	18.9
CR '944'	15350	4-6-2T	2	5 ft 9 ins	74	18.50	29.7	11.6	8.4	30.1	17.6
CR '191'	14619	4-6-0	2	5 ft 6 ins	71	15.70	26.9	11.0	7.8	26.7	15.6
CR '938'	14756	4-6-0	2	6 ft 0 ins	77	17.75	1.7	4.2	3.7	21.4	12.3
HR 'Clan'	14762	4-6-0	2	6 ft 0 ins	77	15.33	15.3	7.1	5.4	22.4	13.1
HR 'Goods'	17950	4-6-0	2	5 ft 3 ins	67	13.92	16.6	6.3	5.6	20.2	12.6
HR 'Castle'	14691	4-6-0	2	6 ft 0 ins	77	15.45	16.3	8.0	6.6	23.2	14.2
CR '908'	14609	4-6-0	2	5 ft 9 ins	74	18.00	10.5	6.9	5.1	24.0	14.1
CR '179'	17905	4-6-0	2	5 ft 9 ins	74	18.25	6.4	8.0	5.7	26.2	14.8
LM&SR	13000	2-6-0	2	5 ft 6 ins	71	19.60	11.7	6.8	5.2	26.4	15.0
L&NER	'A1'	4-6-2	3	6 ft 8 ins	86	22.05	2.3	2.6	4.3	24.7	15.3
L&NER	'K3'	2-6-0	3	5 ft 8 ins	73	20.00	1.9	3.5	5.0	23.5	15.0

Figure 51
Bridge Stress Committee Report, 1928. Locomotive Hammer Blows Analyses. This figure, illustrating hammer blow values, is taken from the 'Bridge Stress Committee' publication of 1928. The committee's published results show the CR '60', '944' and '191' classes had significantly greater hammer blow profiles than might have been expected and these locomotives would have punished the track much more severely than the ex-HR 'River', 'Superheated Goods' and 'Clan' classes. It would seem that Pickersgill balanced a higher proportion of reciprocating mass than other CMEs or builders. By comparison the excellent balancing of the Gresley 'K3' and 'A1' class engines should be noted. *HMSO, 1928*

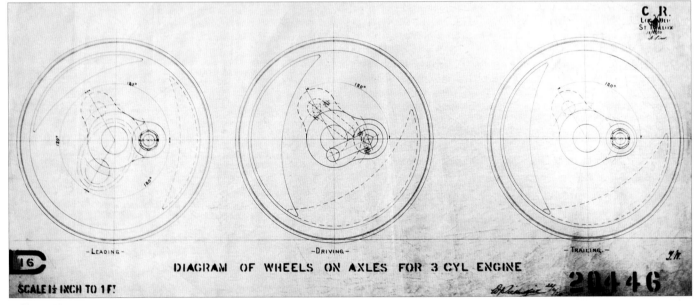

Figure 52
'956' Class. Diagram of Wheels on Axles, Drg No. 20446, dated the 18th February 1920. Unfortunately, no calculations are now available to show how St Rollox handled the balancing of the '956' Class, though this drawing of wheels on axles indicates what was intended. No weights data is given, though it is very likely that balancing to the criteria used on the '60' and '944' Classes would have been used. *CRA: CRA6/1/3/2/48/7/6*

CHAPTER 16

BALANCING AND MECHANICAL DESIGN

BALANCING

The objective in balancing a locomotive is twofold; first, to make the engine run as steadily as possible, and second, to ensure that the pull on the drawbar is more nearly uniform than otherwise would be the case. The standard text on the subject in the pre-1914 period came from the pen of the ever present Professor Dalby.[1] The normal approach to balancing was to ensure that all revolving parts were balanced on the wheels to which respective parts were attached. For the balancing of reciprocating parts, for example, pistons and piston rods, crosshead, connecting rod, etc, the related proportionate weight per side to be balanced was established and divided over all the coupled wheels, but not necessarily in equal quantities.

The proportion of total reciprocating weight to be balanced was, in early years, arbitrarily selected in the range 30-66 per cent of the related reciprocating masses. On account of the resultant variation of pressure of driving wheels on the rails, caused by the balance weights, a preference developed to balance 40-50 per cent, of the reciprocating parts. The greater the proportion of reciprocating weight balanced, the less the tendency to horizontal drawbar fluctuations, but the greater the cyclical pressure, termed 'hammer blow', between driving wheels and rail, which in exceptional circumstances could cause the individual driving wheels to lift off the rails.

Due to the need to understand more fully the fluctuating forces between locomotive driving wheels and rails at various speeds, and particularly their impact on bridge stresses, in 1923 the Bridge Stress Committee[2] was set up and investigated the subject most thoroughly. To assist their analyses, the committee, which included Professor Dalby, undertook detailed analyses of the hammer blow characteristics of many UK locomotive classes.

The St Rollox drawing register[3] records that hammer blow analyses were undertaken, in February 1927, on a number of Northern Division engines, no doubt in support of Professor Dalby's work. The actual drawings covering these calculations are randomly grouped in the No's 23856 to 23906 series, which also includes former G&SWR and HR classes. From a detailed examination of the drawing register data, no '956' Class hammer blow analysis seems to have been provided by St Rollox to support the bridge stress committee work (and no data on '956' Class[4] hammer blow analysis is extant in the committee's papers at the National Archives, Kew), but the committee's published results do cover a large number of LM&SR Northern Division locomotives (including the CR '60', '179', '191', '908', '938' and '944' Classes)[2] and other LM&SR and L&NER[5] types, which allow some insight of CR balancing policy and how St Rollox was likely to have treated the '956' Class.

Whilst Figure 51 illustrates details of wheel and axle dynamic loadings for various engine classes then in service, taken from the committee's 1929 publication,[6] the St Rollox drawings giving the detailed calculations for each of these classes have not been located. It is likely they have not survived.

One immediate conclusion seems clear from Figure 51, in that the Caledonian company has to be judged, in Pickersgill's tenure, as an organisation which balanced a higher than seemed appropriate proportion of reciprocating masses, leading to larger than normal balance weights and, consequently, larger proportionate hammer blow forces. Thus, for the '60', '944' and '191' classes the hammer blow per axle exceeds 10 tons, leading to axle loadings in excess of 30 tons for the '60' and '944' classes, and in excess of 26 tons for the

'191' Class, these figures being calculated at 6 revs per second (rps), this being the standard reference speed used by the committee in their analyses.[2]

Since the hammer blow characteristic, for a given balanced system, is a function of the square of rotational speed, one might argue that at 6 rps, a higher than normal reference speed was being used. However, even at 4 rps (approximately 48 mph) on the '191' Class, the hammer blow was almost 5 tons per axle, giving a total axle loading in excess of 20 tons, which, for the Callander & Oban route, exceeded the strictly enforced Civil Engineer's 15½ tons per axle limit.[7] Additionally, whilst one might doubt '60' Class locomotives consistently reached 78 mph (6 rps), at 5 rps (65 mph) the hammer blow per axle was almost 7 tons, giving a total axle loading of approximately 26 tons, again well above the civil engineering limit of 20 tons. By contrast, the CR '938' Class at 78 mph was balanced to minimise hammer blow at 4.2 tons per axle, giving an all up axle loading of 21.4 tons.

Comparison of hammer blow forces on contractor-supplied ex-HR 4-6-0 classes, also given in Figure 51,[6] suggests that St Rollox, during Pickersgill's tenure, was not at the forefront of contemporary thinking on balancing and related locomotive-to-track interactions. This seems especially so when one considers the specific positions engineered on the GNR/L&NER 'A1' and 'K3' classes and the '938' Class. In the McIntosh era, the balancing of the '908' and '179' classes suggests St Rollox followed Professor Dalby's advice,[1] with around 50 per cent of reciprocating weights balanced, though maximum axle loads still exceeded the Civil Engineer's limits, albeit to a lesser extent than in the Pickersgill period.

Drawing No. 20446,[8] dated the 18th February 1920 and shown as Figure 52, outlining the layout of wheels on axles for the '956' Class has survived, and indicates the position of balance weights per wheel and their respective physical sizes, so some analysis seems to have been put in hand. There is, unfortunately, no annotation on this drawing to suggest what weights, in numeric terms, might have been specified.

Interestingly, the highest recorded speed for a '956' Class locomotive under normal service conditions was 65½ mph[9] (5 rps), by No. 956, on the 8th September 1922, when working a 415 tons (gross) train from Glasgow Central to Carlisle, the engine being fitted with Stephenson's motion. This was the working noted earlier with Lord Monkswell on the footplate, the 65½ mph being recoded as an average between MP 19 and MP 17. A speed of 64½ mph[10] was recorded by C.J. Allen in September 1921, by the nearly new No. 957, when working a 260 tons (gross) train from Carlisle to Symington, the engine being fitted with the first form of derived motion.

A synthesised speed for No. 956 of 68½ mph,[11] fitted with Stephenson's motion in 1923, and working a 420 tons (gross) train from Carlisle to Beattock was prepared by A.J. Powell,[11] but this was recognised as unrepresentative of normal '956' Class performance. Powell made a comparison of the '956' Class performance against a BR Standard Class '5', an engine he considered as of broadly similar size and power output.

The highest recorded speed of a '956' Class engine under trials conditions was for No. 956 itself when operating the Up leg of the Glasgow Central to Carlisle return working on the 11th August 1921. This trials trip is covered in detail in Appendix 2, speeds of 66 mph being recorded on two occasions.

Photographic evidence suggests the '956' Class balance weights per wheel are proportionately similar to the '60', '944' and '191' classes, with a marginally smaller centre axle weight and a different arrangement for the leading coupled axle. From the available information, it can be inferred that, for the '956' Class, a figure of perhaps around 66 per cent of the reciprocating mass was again used for balancing purposes. Whilst the natural balance of the 3-cylinder engine could have been of assistance to St Rollox, there may have been a lack of appreciation as to how to tackle the more complex divided drive arrangement. For the '956' Class it is unlikely the proportionate hammer blow per axle would have been less than those figures for the '60' Class.

St Rollox was not the only design office using large percentages of reciprocating masses in their balancing policy; the Great Central company in their 'C4' Class 4-4-2s,[12] balanced 79 per cent of the reciprocating weights, which lifted the driving wheels off the track at 85 mph, and the L&NWR 4-6-0, 19 in. goods engines,[12] lifted its wheels at 51 mph, both designs being seen as somewhat unrepresentative of 1920 good practice. Interestingly, Professor Dalby and his team found the hammer blow detailed calculations provided by the various railway companies for their respective locomotives were often considerably lower than those computed by the committee.

The largest variations[12] between railway company and committee hammer blow calculations related to the ex-NER 'T2' Class, where the difference was a factor of 2½, the Urie ex-L&SWR 4-6-0s being not far behind.

MECHANICAL DESIGN

Little can be offered today by way of analytical commentary on the overall '956' Class mechanical design, since limited definitive information survives, though a few drawings are available in the CRA and NRS Archives. It is upon these that the following observations are offered.

The plate frames were certainly of heavy construction at 1¼ ins. A good guide to contemporary framing policy is to be found in the LM&SR Horwich 2-6-0,[13] schemed out in 1924, where the frames were 1 1/16 ins, with significant horizontal staying and diagonal bracing, the whole frame assembly being the most rigid on the LM&SR. Later LM&SR frame investigations acknowledged the Horwich design having as good a record of freedom from cracks as any LM&S standard type, and certainly much better than the Class '5' 4-6-0s.[13] On the other hand, the MR 4-4-0 Class '4P' compound, with one of the most flexible frames on the LM&SR, was equally good.

The Caledonian 4-6-0s were regarded as the best classes with regard to frame cracks on the whole LM&SR,[13] so from the aspect of frame durability the Pickersgill approach has much merit, though as noted earlier, '60' Class frame fractures had been reported in 1919.[14]

Regarding connecting and coupling rods, some comment on design and stressing is appropriate. For connecting rods, two major factors need to be taken account of: first, the strength to resist buckling in the horizontal plane, and second, dealing with inertial stressing

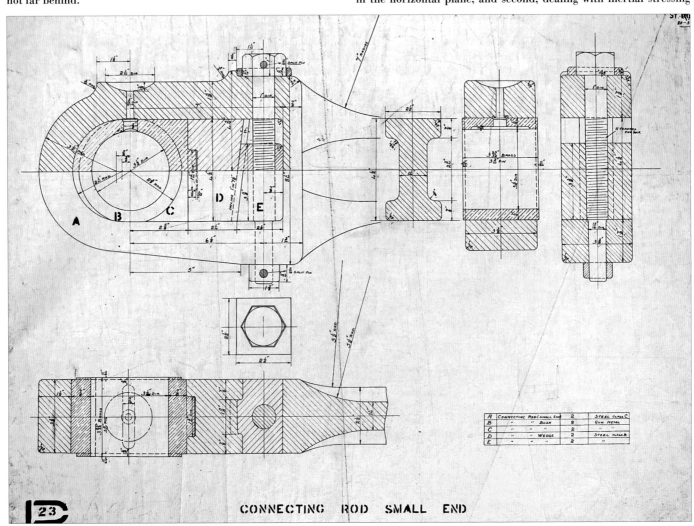

CONNECTING ROD SMALL END

Figure 53
'956' Class. Connecting Rod Small End, Drg No. 19878, dated the 20th March 1919. The illustration shows the substantial nature of the connecting rod and its small end, designed to accommodate rotational plus tensile/compressive stresses and buckling effects. Whilst there is no evidence of failures, it was not unknown for rods to be bent in service and having to be straightened.
NRS: GD456, RHP136355/2

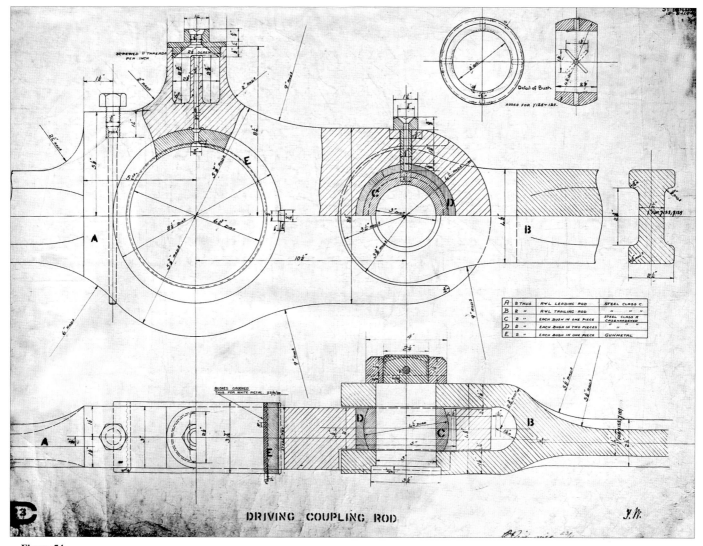

DRIVING COUPLING ROD

Figure 54
'956' Class. Driving Coupling Rod, Drg No. 19887, dated the 26th March 1919. Whilst this drawing relates directly to the '956' Class coupling rods, it is annotated to show that rods of similar type, with modified dimensions, were to be used on St Rollox orders Y128 and Y129. These latter orders refer to the '191' Class 4-6-0s intended for the Callander & Oban route, it being the initial intention to construct the two orders at St Rollox.

NRS: GD456, RHP136355/3

due to rotation,[15] both of which would have been appreciated by St Rollox. Since there is no evidence of any failures, it can be assumed that alternating compressive and tensile stressing plus any bending moments and buckling tendency were satisfactorily accommodated with appropriate factors of safety. It was not, however, unknown for rods to be bent in service, the rods on Southern Railway N15 engines *'continually being sent to the works for straightening after being bent in service; some are bent to an alarming extent and it would appear that they are running on a very close safety line'*.[16] Drawing No. 19878,[17] Figure 53, shows the '956' Class connecting rod small end bearing arrangement.

Coupling rod stressing was progressed in broadly the same way, by calculating the force necessary to slip wheels and then calculating the alternating compressive and tensile stresses for the section chosen and again taking account of inertial and potential buckling loads. Once more there seem to have been no recorded faults, so one has to assume the necessary calculations would demonstrate adequate margins. Drawing No. 19887,[18] Figure 54, shows the coupling rod bearing arrangements on the centre coupled axle and indicates that both leading and trailing rods are of the same grade forged steel section. The trailing rods are provided with knuckle articulation, allowing some rear coupled axle lateral movement.

One point of interest on the coupling rods drawing No. 19887, Figure 54, relates to annotated changes proposed for orders Y128 and Y129, for which the web cross section was to be reduced from 1¼ ins to 1 in. Orders Y128 and Y129 refer to the '191' Class locomotives, which were initially proposed for construction at St Rollox, but ultimately were supplied by the North British Locomotive Co. It is presumed that when '191' Class build at St Rollox was intended, coupling rods of similar form to the '956' Class, with reduced centres and cross section were to be used.

For the '956' Class coupling rods the cross section is approximately 7½ sq. ins, giving an equivalent rod tensile and compressive stressing of around 2.1 tons per sq. in. for the 16 tons slip wheel value associated with the '956' Class. Grade B forgings, used for coupling rods, would have a minimum UTS of around 26 tons per sq. in.,[19] giving a static factor of safety (FoS) of around twelve. Whilst an FoS of twelve might be considered very much on the high side, it is realistic for the available knowledge of the day, recognising the tensile, compressive, buckling and inertial stresses involved. The LM&SR CME 1939[20] edition of the standards to be applied to the design of connecting and coupling rods requires an FoS of nine to be applied for the above conditions at 7 rps, assuming a modulus of elasticity of 30×10^6 lbs per sq. in.

Surprisingly, springing on the two leading coupled axles was provided by coiled springs, with semi-elliptical leaf springs on the rear coupled wheelset, the arrangement on the driving axle being shown on drawing No. 19866,[21] Figure 55. Whilst from 50 to 60 per cent lighter in weight, and requiring less space, coiled springs were generally not employed in more modern contemporary locomotive design practice since they are rather too sensitive and, further, a fracture may have a more immediate effect on the availability of the engine. For these reasons, and the fact that semi-elliptic leaf springs offered an improved resiliency over coiled springs, the former were almost universally employed. Apart from weight constraints, no obvious reason for the use of coiled springs in the '956' Class has been uncovered. GWR practice, on their 4-6-0s, from inception of the type, was to use semi-elliptic leaf springing throughout, and in his '956' Class rebuild considerations, A.J. Powell advocated their use.[11]

The initial '956' Class crank axle design is shown on drawing No. 19848,[8] Figure 56. The main journals, at 9½ ins x 11 ins, are more than adequate for the weight per axle, resulting in a pressure of 215 psi, excluding hammer blow effects, this providing around a 10 per cent positive margin over the accepted static bearing pressure limits of 240 to 250 psi.[22] It would have been helpful if mechanical lubrication had been provided for the rear coupled axle. By comparison, the bearings on the '938' Class, at 8½ ins x 10 ins, carrying a static axle load of 17¾ tons, result in a bearing pressure of 235 psi; for the '903' Class, the equivalent loading is 215 psi.

Various changes are annotated on drawing No. 19848, including a reduction in journal diameters to 9.0 ins from 9½ ins for main bearings and to 9.0 ins from 9¼ ins for the big end, similar changes being annotated on the corresponding axle-boxes (St Rollox drawing

No. 20130) and connecting rod big ends. In reducing the journal diameters, St Rollox must have been confident of their initial design margins. Additional changes were made to drawing No. 19848 by the LM&SR in May 1924 and again in September 1930, suggesting this type of crank axle was still be in service.

In 1924, the LM&SR produced an updated drawing, 19848A,[8] shown as Figure 57, proposing a different crank axle arrangement and, by inference, manufacturing process. The main changes were the removal of what appear to be shrunk on hoops (usually fitted to keep the webs in compression) and the provision of a fitted through-bolt to protect the big end journal from catastrophic failure in fatigue mode. As with drawing No. 19848, the journal diameters were again reduced.

It is unclear why a change in the crank axle manufacturing route was necessary. There are no extant records relating to crank axle problems, though the effects of inertial overrun on the centre valve may have caused a rethink by the LM&SR authorities on crank axle provision for those locomotives retaining the second version of derived motion. The reduction in journal diameters result in around 5 per cent increase in journal bearing pressures, which is acceptable. Lower speed operation on freight workings may have figured in the LM&SR thinking, Plate 65 showing No. 14801 heading south from Solway Junction with a pick-up freight working in 1929.

'956' CLASS BOGIE

A new bogie was designed to accommodate the front end weight increase and a sectioned plan of the leading axle and central mounting for this is shown as Figure 58, drawing No. 20267,[23] dated

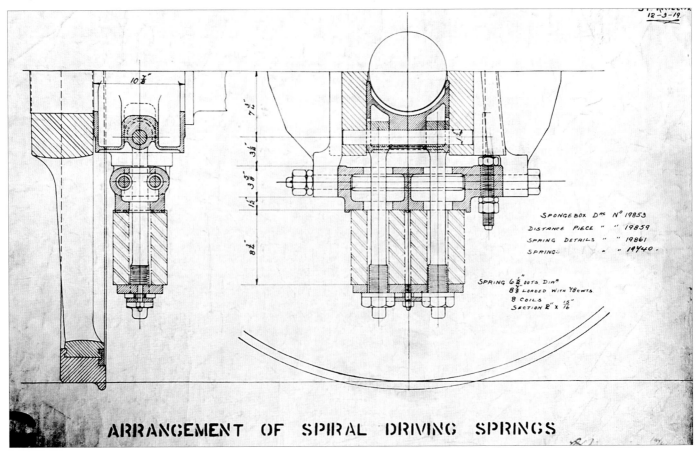

Figure 55
'956' Class. Arrangement of Spiral Driving Springs, Drg No. 19866, dated the 12th March 1919. Surprisingly, springing for the two leading coupled axles was provided by coil springs, with semi-elliptical springs being fitted to the rear coupled axle. Whilst lighter in weight, coiled springs were generally not used for driving wheels in contemporary locomotive practice, as they were rather too lively. Apart from weight constraints, no obvious reason for the use of coiled springs on the '956' Class has been established.
NRS: GD456, RHP136355/1

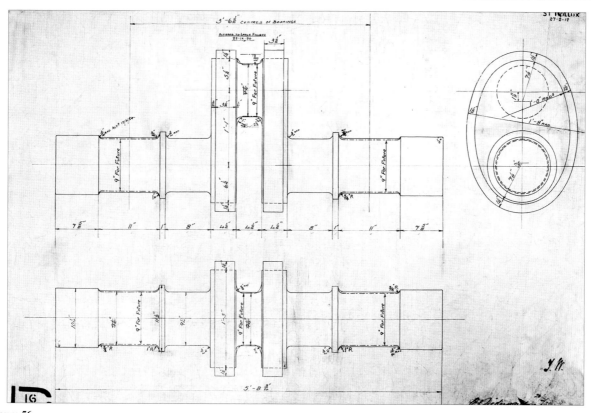

Figure 56
'956' Class. Crank Axle, Drg No. 19848, dated the 27th February 1919. The initial form of the '956' Class crank axle is illustrated, though various changes are annotated on the drawing, including a reduction in journal diameters from 9½ ins to 9 ins for the two outer bearings and from 9¼ ins to 9 ins for the connecting rod big end. Further modifications were made by the LM&SR in 1924 and 1930, suggesting this type of crank axle was still in service then.
CRA: CRA6/1/3/2/48/1/5

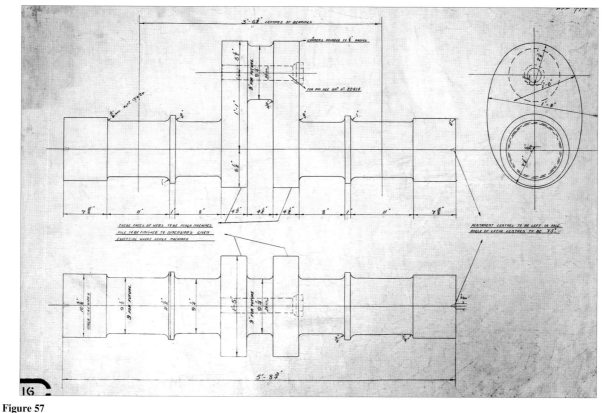

Figure 57
'956' Class. Crank Axle (Modified), Drg No. 19848A, dated the 1st February 1924. In 1924, the LM&SR produced an updated crank axle drawing, proposing a different arrangement and, by implication, manufacturing process. The main changes were the removal of what appear to be shrunk on hoops (usually fitted to keep the webs in compression) and the provision of a fitted through-bolt to protect the big end journal from failure. As with the previous type of crank axle, the journal diameters were similarly reduced. *CRA: CRA6/1/3/2/48/1/6*

Plate 65
The former No. 957, as LM&SR No. 14801, heads south from Solway Junction with a pick-up freight working in 1929. The engine is fitted with Stephenson's link motion, and would be refitted with the second form of derived motion in the latter part of 1931.

J.J. Cunningham, courtesy A.F. Swann

the 5th November 1919, the original drawing not being of the best quality, seemingly having seen much use.

The centre pin for the 7 ft wheel based bogie was placed 1 in. forward of the centre of the wheel base, weight being transferred to the bogie by a centre slide casting and then to the axle-boxes independently by pairs of volute coil springs. The bogie side play was restrained by short helical springs each side of the central pin casting. From drawing No 20267,[23] these side control springs have a compressed length of 6⅜ ins, and an external diameter of 5 ins, being wound with six effective turns of what scales to be ⁹⁄₁₆ in. diameter material. The available remaining uncompressed length is marginally over 2 ins, after which the spring will 'bottom'.

Thus the bogie may move by ±2 ins from the central position laterally under the control of the associated side spring, at which point any further movement would be immediately impeded, with some lateral shock impact to the locomotive. It is not clear from the GA drawings for the '956' Class, if 'bump stops' were also fitted.

Ernest Glen photographed one of the '956' Class bogies during construction,[24] this being depicted in Plate 66. The main vertical springing is in place on the bogie stretcher, though the volute springs for individual axleboxes have yet to be fitted.

One has to bear in mind that the '956' Class, with no less than 10 ft 3 ins between the leading coupled axle and the bogie pin centre, compared to 8 ft 10 ins for the '938' Class[25] and 8 ft 6 ins for the HR 'Clan' Class,[25] would have needed fairly heavy side control springing if 'nozing' at speed was to be avoided. Moreover, with this lengthened front end, together with the increased forward weight of three cylinders, and an intended running speed of up to 70 to 75 mph, St Rollox should have recognised the need for special attention in this area.

Whilst oscillation of a locomotive around its vertical centre of gravity, especially at the higher speeds, was not well understood at this time, the basics of bogie design and the use of appropriate side control springing was reasonably well established by around 1900, C.E. Wolff's text[26] on the subject laying out the detail. Wolff quotes design data from contemporary GCR and NER locomotives, with side plays of just below ±2 ins, using a cross slide arrangement similar to that in the '956' Class, these being seen as satisfactory in service. According to Wolff's criteria, the side control spring initial compression is set so that, at maximum deflection to one side, a small compression is still retained on the opposite spring. Spring rates of around 1 ton per inch are quoted, with an initial compression determined by the slide play needed. In the cases quoted by Wolff,[26] 1¾ ins movement per side required 1¾ tons initial compression and *pro-rata* for other displacements.

For the '956' Class, selecting an initial compression per side of 2 tons at the requisite spring rate noted, would provide a re-centring force of around 4 tons at maximum bogie deflection, with friction in the slide being sufficient to dampen any oscillations and just retaining the opposite spring in compression. Whilst no spring rate data is given on drawing No. 20267,[23] Figure 58, an estimate of this can be made from the available geometric data on the drawing. Assuming a Shear Modulous (G)[27] for the spring material of 11.4×10^6 lbs per sq. in., gives a spring rate of around 350 lbs per in. This suggests an initial compression of 700 lbs and a maximum re-centring force of approximately 1,400 lbs, at 2 ins deflection, which would be considered inadequate for a locomotive of this front end weight, intended speed and extended front end dimensions.

In commenting on the '956' Class bogie centring spring arrangements, A.J. Powell noted: *'the springs look wholly inadequate for*

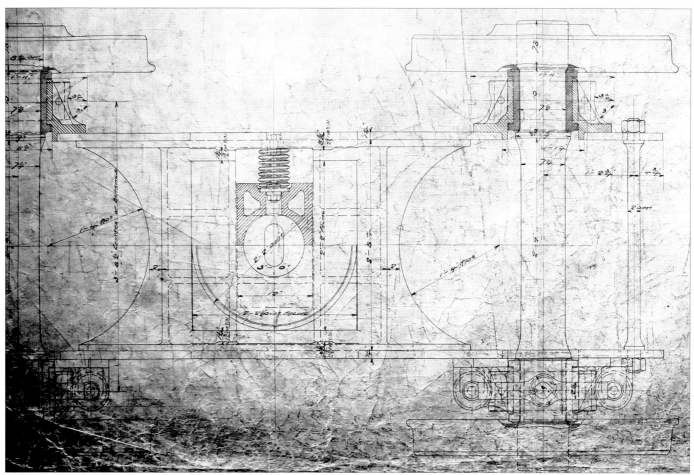

ABOVE: Figure 58
'956' Class. Front Bogie Assembly, Sectioned Plan, Drg No. 20267, dated the 5th November 1919. A new bogie was designed to accommodate the increased forward weight of the '956' Class, though the side control springing was inadequate to control 'nozing' of the front end, which is likely to have resulted in rough and uncomfortable conditions for the footplate crew at higher speeds.
NRS: GD456, RHP136355/27

Plate 66
A partially completed '956' Class bogie sits in the St Rollox works erecting shop. The main vertical springing is in place on the bogie stretcher, the volute springs for individual axleboxes having yet to be fitted.   *A.E. Glen*

the forces likely to be developed by a locomotive of this size'.[11] He goes on to suggest:

> 'that this inadequate side control could be expected to permit nozing of the engine up to the limits of the bump stops, when such movement would be violently arrested. This would likely be translated into vicious lateral oscillations at the cab end.'

In conclusion, Powell notes: '*The impression is given that drivers were almost afraid to allow them to run to anything over 65 mph*'. Campbell Cornwell[28] also notes '*that on the faster stretches, riding tended to be rather wild, the extensive use of coil springs perhaps being responsible for this*'.

For '956' Class operation in these circumstances, the use of coil springs in the main suspension would do little to dampen any rolling or lateral motion, and at speed, engine movement may well have been a mixture of rolling and yawing, up to suddenly arrested limits; a corkscrewing motion which could be very uncomfortable for the enginemen.

It is noticeable from '956' Class trials results and timed workings, that speeds above 60 mph are very rare. Even on downhill stretches, where smart running at speeds in the 70 to 75 mph range would have been necessary and expected, these higher speeds were never achieved. As already noted, the maximum recorded speed for a '956' Class engine in normal service was 65½ mph.[9] The bogie was never tested at the upper end of its 70 to 75 mph operating range. By comparison, Caledonian company No. 49, the first McIntosh 4-6-0 express locomotive, with 6 ft 6 ins wheels was timed at over 80 mph.[29]

On the HR 'Clan' Class 4-6-0 engines supplied by Hawthorn, Leslie & Co., a much more acceptable bogie side control spring regime was provided, the GA for the class noting that bogie lateral control was obtained using 'Spencers Patent Concentric Springs'.[30] In the bogie central position, the respective side control springs are noted at 8½ ins in length and having ±2¼ ins maximum lateral deflection. An initial compression of 2¼ tons per side was provided, the centring force at maximum deflection being around 4 tons, which mirrors Wolff's criteria noted earlier.[26] The 'Clan' Class bogie carried 16¾ tons in full load condition.

Recognising the front end dynamics of 4-6-0 locomotives operating in the 60 to 90 mph speed range were not well understood, leading bogie initial lateral spring compressions were set, even in the 1920s, around ¾ ton per side or less,[31] somewhat short of the criteria previously set out by Wolff,[26] who was dealing with lower speeds. In 1930, the high speed partial derailment of LM&SR 'Royal Scot' Class engine No. 6131 *Planet*[31] at Weaver Junction, and a similar partial derailment nine days later of 'Lord Nelson' Class engine No. E853 *Sir Richard Grenville*[31] on Southern metals, caused some detailed analyses to be focused on the side control springing issue. As a result, for the 'Royal Scot' Class, the initial side control spring compression of 1,344 lbs, with a maximum compressive load of 2.34 tons at maximum bogie deflection, was increased to an initial compression of around 2 tons,[31] with a corresponding increase in maximum compressive load to around 4 tons, and even at that, LM&SR engineers considered it still too light, recognising that speeds up to 85 mph were called for. For some unknown reason, Wolff's 1907 citing of criteria used by the GCR and NER for side control spring initial compression and centring forces appears to have been lost during the intervening years.

OBSERVATIONS

The basic design of the frame and related components seems structurally sound, the whole arrangement being built ruggedly to withstand the forces associated with the operation of a 1,500 IHP, 65 to 75 mph express passenger locomotive. There is, however, the suggestion of over-engineering of the framing, this point being valid in the context of the weight balance equation of the whole locomotive. For example, could a higher boiler pressure, perhaps needing a marginal increase in plate thickness, have been traded against a frame weight reduction? Further, the provision of what has been termed 'massive construction' does not, of itself, necessarily provide immunity from mechanical failure, evidenced by the additional staying required to support the internal motion plate, by the structural enhancements to increase rigidity in the derived valve gear and the failure of motion components in early service.

The '956' Class balancing can only be considered as crude and resulting in excessive hammer blow, when measured against the best practice of the time, as exemplified and refined by Gresley's team in his 'A1' and 'K3' class locomotives.[6] In comparison with balancing on contractor-supplied locomotives, such as the '938' Class[6] and

the ex-HR 'Clan' Class,[6] the St Rollox approach must be seen as somewhat removed from contemporary best practice. Additionally, the main axle springing should have used semi-elliptic leaf springs, which would have assisted damping, were the engines to exhibit any tendency to roll.

There is more than a suggestion that bogie side control springing may have been inadequate, though even the mighty LM&SR seemed unaware of the fundamentals affecting such matters, which were only brought into focus as a result of the high speed derailment at Weaver Junction in 1930. Rough riding could well have been a major problem above 60 mph for the '956' Class, leading to limitations on operational speeds. No explanation for reducing the journal bearing diameters throughout the class in the early LM&S period has been established.

REFERENCES

1. *The Balancing of Engines*, Professor W.E. Dalby, FRS, 2nd edition, (Edward Arnold, London, 1906)
2. *Report of the Bridge Stress Committee* (HMSO, 1928)
3. St Rollox Drawing Register, NRS, BR/CAL/5/56
4. The National Archives (TNA): DSIR 3/34-36: Main Committee Meetings of Bridge Stress Committee
5. The National Archives (TNA): DSIR3/39: Details of Hammer Blow Calculations from LMS/LNER/SR Locomotives
6. *Report of the Bridge Stress Committee* (HMSO, 1928), Locomotive Hammer Blow Analyses
7. E.S. Cox memo to R.A. Riddles, of 12th July 1933, giving axle loads for C&O and Highland lines, NRM, ESC2/2/13/2
8. Campbell Cornwell Collection of CR '956' Class drawings, CRA6/1/3/2, Archive Group 48
9. Lord Monkswell's Note Books, Running of CR No 956, 8th September 1922, courtesy Ted Talbot
10. 'British Locomotive Practice & Performance', C.J. Allen, in *The Railway Magazine*, January 1922, pp. 102ff
11. A.J. Powell papers, NRM, 956 Class material, uncatalogued
12. The National Archives Kew (TNA): DSIR3/36, Paper No. 68, Conrad Gribble paper, Locomotive Hammer Blow
13. 'Locomotive Frames', E.S. Cox and F.C. Johansen, ILocoE paper No. 473, November 1947, pp. 93ff
14. *The Locomotive News and Railway Notes*, 24th May 1919
15. *Modern Locomotive Practice*, C.E. Wolff (The Scientific Publishing Co., Manchester, 1907), Chapter IX, pp. 162ff
16. Southern Railway, Eastleigh Works Manager to CME, 3rd Jan 1947, NRM, ID685, AJ53/7/4/G
17. St Rollox Drg No. 19878, dated 20th March 1919, Montague Smith Collection, NRS, GD456, RHP 136355/2
18. St Rollox Drg No. 19887, issue dated 26th March 1919, Montague Smith Collection, NRS, GD456, RHP136355/3
19. *The Locomotive Engineers' Pocket Book* (The Locomotive Publishing Co., 1936), Strength of Materials, p. 310
20. LM&SR CME&E's Dept, Rules for Design of Connecting Rods and Coupling Rods, May 1939, NRM, ALS3/7/4G
21. St Rollox Drg No. 19866, dated 12th March 1919, Montague Smith Collection, NRS, GD456, RHP136355/1
22. *Locomotive Engineers' Pocket Book 1935* (The Locomotive Publishing Co.), p. 127
23. St Rollox Drg No. 20267, dated 5th November 1919, Montague Smith Collection, NRS, GD456, RHP136355/27
24. A.E. Glen Collection, private collection, courtesy Dr Ann Glen
25. *Highland Railway Locomotives, Book 2*, J.R.H. Cormack and J.L. Stevenson (RCTS, 1990), pp. 101, 131
26. *Modern Locomotive Practice*, C.E. Wolff (The Scientific Publishing Co., Manchester, 1907), pp. 43-9ff
27. *The Model Engineer's Handbook*, Tubal Cain (Argus Books, 1981), Chapter 13 pp. 13.1ff
28. *Forty Years of Caledonian Locomotives 1882-1922*, Campbell Cornwell (David & Charles, 1974), p. 184
29. *Trains Illustrated*, October 1953, Montague Smith, Letter to the Editor
30. Hawthorn, Leslie & Co., HR 'Clan' Class General Arrangement Drg, NRS, RHP15048
31. For details of Weaver Junction derailment, see, *Chronicles of Steam*, E.S. Cox (Ian Allan, London, 1967), pp. 35ff

CHAPTER 17

SOME OVERALL CONCLUSIONS

A prophet is without honour in his own land

Mark Ch. 6, v. 4

It is appropriate to summarise conclusions on the major elements in the overall '956' Class design, noting where straightforward and timeous improvement might have been put in hand. Of course, the financial climate at St Rollox may have impeded even the most compellingly simple modifications post the August 1921 trials, a position not assisted by the impending statutory railway company amalgamations.

STEAM RAISING PLANT AND STEAM CIRCUIT

For the boiler and related steam circuit, one has to say this was far from being an unqualified success. Apart from the boiler proportions, which were not ideal, major shortfalls were associated with drafting, grate and ashpan layout and the steam circuit. The provision of unnecessarily low SHS, a lower than acceptable flue gas flow regime and superheater elements being insufficient in cross section, worsened the position. From trials results,[1] specific alterations, had they been possible post August 1921, could potentially have removed what appeared to be relatively straightforward difficulties with the ashpan and draughting layouts.

Of course, there may have been major dilemmas at St Rollox in determining the main source of the difficulties and prioritising remedial actions. Valve gear mechanical problems may have masked the draughting and low SHS plus flue-gas ratio shortfalls, and confused the technical way forward. Which area to concentrate on may not have been particularly clear and St Rollox may, unfortunately, not have appreciated the implications of reduced steam temperatures and higher superheater pressure loss from No. 956 trials compared to those on No. 60 in 1917,[2] nor recognised the former's cylinder exhaust passage peculiarity and its potential to reduce power output.

In these straightened financial circumstances, as a consequence of which St Rollox employee lay-offs were being implemented,[3] further modification work on the '956' Class tubeplates, ashpan and draughting, no doubt involving boiler lifts for each locomotive, might have been quite impossible to progress. But for the Chairman's edict[3] on expenditure, this boiler remedial work might, in normal circumstances, have been implemented, had St Rollox been alive to the technical problems. Of more concern, however, is that in putting forward the 2-6-0 goods engine design in 1923,[4] Pickersgill persisted with a low superheat policy, which suggests St Rollox may not have appreciated the true nature of the overall '956' Class boiler problems, a point made by E.S. Cox.

The new owner's attitude to these four engines can perhaps be best gauged by there being no overt mention of any '956' Class related work in the St Rollox drawing register between the provision of dashpots for No. 956 in November 1923 and withdrawal of the last of the class in 1935. It would seem that any expenditure to improve their performance was unequivocally denied and the whole class, with the exception of No. 14800, were thereafter consigned to goods traffic workings.

Most unfortunately, for the '956' Class, a series of avoidable design shortfalls and errors in the steam raising plant, each having a measurable impact, coupled to lack of foresight in the provision of adequate superheat conditions, conspired, as an amalgam, to produce a somewhat feeble and most unsatisfactory result. In essence, steam supply was such that the required power output could not be met.

VALVE GEAR

The selection of outside Walschaert's motion, using valves with 1½ ins lap and almost 6 ins travel at maximum cut-off, should be seen as progressive and applauded. The real failure was the use of a theoretically correct derived motion, which, due to inertial effects, unforeseen structural deflections and the number of pin joints needed to implement it, proved to be virtually unworkable mechanically. Even with the tightest of machining tolerances, performance at lower cut-offs was never likely to be assured. As such, the '956' Class valve gear arrangements must, unfortunately, be seen as a major failure, not only from the centre valve events position, but also from a series of avoidable mechanical component failures.

The extent of Professor Mallenby's involvement in the first form of the derived motion is also not clear, with Graham Miller[5] suggesting the professor's input came later and was focused on dashpot matters. The major disappointment, however, is that the best brains at St Rollox, perhaps supported by professorial input, failed to appreciate the effects of lost motion plus inertial and structural deficiencies on the derived motion design and centre valve events. Gresley's initial experiences seem to have been completely overlooked.

Whilst the derived motion mechanical problems could potentially have been overcome more simply and expeditiously by the fitting of an independent inside Walschaert's motion, this opportunity was missed with the fitting of an inappropriately engineered Stephenson's motion, and again when Pickersgill persisted with a modified derived motion in the Gresley style. Unfortunately, however, changing or altering the valve gear was not the solution, since until the steam circuit and boiler problems had been overcome, it mattered not-at-all which type of valve gear was fitted. Independent Walschaert's gear for the centre cylinder would, of course, have potentially eliminated resonance effects and should have removed any valve motion constraints on upper speed limit, but would not have resolved matters relating to the exhaust passage layout.

One could be forgiven for suggesting that Pickersgill's focus in this period was perhaps more concerned with potential loss of face from the poor operational performance of his derived valve gear and the salvaging of his reputation. The continued focusing of nugatory effort on the valve gear, whilst the steam raising plant seemingly got little or no attention, will never be understood other than in terms of questionable technical judgement.

MECHANICAL DESIGN

On the general subject of weight, stressing and balancing, certain components, such as the frame plates, were perhaps marginally over-engineered, any criticism really being brought into focus in the overall locomotive weight equation. The natural balancing of the 120 degree cranks on the '956' Class could potentially have been used much more effectively, but may not have been understood at St Rollox. The bogie design, particularly the use of inadequate side control springing, may well have led to rough riding and inhibited higher speed working.

One should recall that the '956' Class weight ranked them as the largest tender engines built for a Scottish railway company and they were also amongst the heaviest pre-grouping 4-6-0s, sharing that accolade with the 81 ton L&SWR Urie H15 locomotives.[6]

Summary

Unfortunately, one has to record that, in a design and performance sense, the '956' Class must be considered as falling well short of expectations as a main line express locomotive – performance at times verged on what can only be described as wretched. The fortunate acquisition of the well-engineered '938' Class in 1915 should have been a clear signal to Pickersgill of what the future potentially held but, regrettably, he and his staff seemed to disregard all these technical indicators. As noted, the attitude of John Barr,[7,8] the Assistant Locomotive Superintendent for running matters, may well have been lukewarm or ambivalent to the '956' Class.

If the '938' Class draughting, ashpan, boiler and superheater regimes had been transferred into the '956' Class design, matters would have proceeded very differently. Indeed, an enhanced boiler based on the '938' Class steam raising plant, plus the provision of separate steam and exhaust lines for each cylinder, and independent Walschaerts' gear for all cylinders, may have provided the CR with a locomotive which could have become an LM&SR standard class and allowed St Rollox to bask in reflected glory.

In comparative terms, one of the most successful Scottish express passenger engines was the G&SWR '128' Class 4-6-0, of which, unfortunately, only two were built, ensuring they could never become an LM&S standard class. In the late 1920s,[9] these two locos, in a four-engine link with two LM&SR compounds, worked the 1.50 pm Glasgow to Liverpool expresses from Central station to Carlisle, returning to Glasgow via former G&SWR metals. When the Edinburgh portion was added at Strawfrank Junction, trains of over 400 tons were at times worked forward to Carlisle,[9] this being a turn from which the '956' Class had long been banished.

Plates 67 and 68 show respectively the former No. 129, as LM&SR No. 14674 at Ayr shed in 1930, and the erstwhile No. 128, as LM&SR No. 14673, in the same period. On withdrawal in November 1934, No. 14674 had accrued over 615,000 miles.

Some commentators[5,10] have the view that the '956' Class design was an heroic effort by St Rollox to move into the modern, big locomotive scene, and, with certain alterations, much might have been heard of those magnificent machines, had the grouping not come about. The author finds this hard to accept, recognising the many technical shortfalls inherent in the class, the knowledge of locomotive design generally available at the time, and the previous achievements of the Caledonian company, together with the achievements of CMEs, such as Gresley and Maunsell in the same time frame. What can be said is that St Rollox had the aspiration to break new ground, but unfortunately the technical staff resources to achieve the desired end were not made available and the engineering imperatives of the day ignored.

One can only conclude that this next step in St Rollox locomotive progression, the design and production of the '956' Class, intended to handle unaided any express passenger working on the Caledonian main line, was unaccountably badly fumbled by St Rollox, notwithstanding the wartime and financial pressures of the day.

Interestingly, in addition to the recruitment of Dugald Drummond, St Rollox seemingly did, over the years, attract one or two unusually talented and technically able people to the drawing office. One such individual was Chief Draughtsman, Robert W. Urie, who apparently schemed out an outside cylindered 4-6-0 before the appearance of the HR 'Jones Goods' Class, only to have his proposal curtly condemned by McIntosh, resulting in his seeking pastures new.

Urie's successor as Chief Draughtsman, Thomas Weir, who must be given significant credit for the McIntosh era progress, may have found himself in the same position as Urie, in that his significant experience and sharp technical judgement were over-ruled in the context of the '956' Class, precipitating his departure, without pension. If these two circumstances are reflective of McIntosh and Pickersgill's respective management styles, then not for the first or last time would undoubted technical talent be sacrificed on the 'alter of expediency' by those of lesser ability.

A Prophet is Without Honour in His Own Land

Not for the first or last time would

'A prophet be without honour in his own land.'

E.S. Cox[11] perhaps put his finger on the real problem in locomotive drawing offices in general, when he wrote:

'what is to be blamed is the insular and self-satisfied outlook which reigned in nearly all technical offices at the time. We have forgotten, in these more aware and open days, what total resistance there could be to any suggestion that one should look at, let alone try, anything which seemed to be bringing the other fellow some advantage. Not least among the resisters were the hardy Scots and it is graven on my memory for ever what blood, tears and sweat had to be expended upon Messers Anderson, Henderson and Campbell of the old Midland company and early LM&SR, to get them to consider long travel valve gear, to mention only one example.'

References

1. Appendices in this publication
2. Trials Data, Engine No. 60, 18th May 1917, Montague Smith Collection, NRS, GD456, RHP136352/49
3. Caledonian Railway, Directors' Reports and Minutes of Board Meetings, NRS, BR/CAL/1/67, held as CRA2/3/1/10
4. St Rollox Drg No. 21020, 16th October 1923, NRS, RHP132337
5. Private Correspondence, Graeme Miller to C.P. Atkins, May 1978
6. *Trains Illustrated*, September 1953, Letter to the Editor from J. Burt, p. 339
7. *The Caledonian Railway*, O.S. Nock (Ian Allan, 1963), p. 143
8. *The Caledonian Dunalastairs*, O.S. Nock (Ian Allan, 1968), p. 101
9. *Locomotives of the G&SWR*, David L. Smith (David & Charles, 1976), pp. 113ff
10. *Trains Illustrated*, October 1953, Letter to the Editor from Montague Smith
11. Private Correspondence, E.S. Cox to A.G. Dunbar, 6th May 1968, NRS, GD344/6/12

Plates 67 and 68
Plate 67 (*above*) illustrates ex G&SWR '128' Class 4-6-0 No. 129 as LM&SR No. 14674 at the north end of Ayr shed, in 1930, whilst Plate 68 (*below*) shows the former No, 128 as LM&SR No 14673 in the same period. This most successful small class of two locomotives was built by the North British Locomotive Co. in 1911 to James Manson's requirements, each being fitted with a Schmidt superheater. In the late 1920s, these two engines shared a Glasgow Central to Carlisle express passenger link with two LM&SR '4P' 4-4-0 compounds, duties from which the '956' Class had long been banished. In this link, trains exceeding 400 tons were worked forward, unaided, over Beattock from the north. No. 14674 accrued over 600,000 miles prior to withdrawal in November 1934.
Author

No. 956, fitted with an indicator shelter, heads a train out of
Glasgow Buchanan Street.   *J.G. Barr, SRPS24371*

No. 959 at Perth station waiting departure.

R.D. Stephen, NRM/RDS C12

APPENDICES

CALEDONIAN RAILWAY '956' CLASS TRIALS: TRIALS DATA FROM 1921 AND 1922

Fortunately, three sets of data related to the operation of engine No. 956 under trials conditions have survived, being held by the Montague Smith Collection[1] in the National Archives of Scotland, the corresponding indicator diagrams for two of these trials workings being held at the NRM,[2] York. The respective trials are covered in Appendices 1 to 3.

Two sets of this data relate to workings in August 1921, just six weeks after No. 956 emerged from St Rollox works, the locomotive being fitted with the first form of derived motion. The August 1921 data covers return workings between Glasgow Buchanan Street and Perth on the 9th August, and between Glasgow Central and Carlisle on the 11th August. Indicator diagrams are available for each working. The third set of data gives the results of a trial in October 1922, when No. 956 was fitted with Stephenson's link motion to operate the centre cylinder. At the time of this publication, no indicator diagrams have come to hand for this 1922 working. Moreover, no trials data has emerged relating to the operation of any '956' Class member when fitted with the second type of derived motion.

Each set of trials data takes the form of 'Tables of Diagrams', the information being presented graphically by which various locomotive operating parameters are plotted against the related route mileage. Each diagram is overlaid with the associated gradient map plus both booked and achieved running times.

Specific comment on the individual trials scenarios, measurements taken and the performance of the locomotive is given in each of the Appendices, the structure being such that each Appendix can be treated as a stand-alone document.

The following information was recorded on trials charts and diagrams:
- Weight of train in tons, including passengers and luggage, but excluding locomotive and tender.
- Water used on outward and return working in gallons.
- Weight of coal used on outward and return working in pounds (lbs).
- Boiler pressure in pounds per square inch (psi).
- Steam chest pressure in pounds per square inch (psi) (from Indicator Diagrams, held at NRM, York).
- Cylinder MEP in pounds per square inch (psi) (from Indicator Diagrams held at NRM, York).
- Regulator openings in square inches, full regulator being 16 sq. ins.
- Speed in miles per hour (mph).
- Engine cut-off, measured as a percentage, with a maximum of 65 per cent (full gear).
- Actual and booked times, with notes for signal and P.W. checks.
- Indicated horse power (IHP), from indicator diagrams, taken at various specific points (mileposts given).
- Gradients for the route, taken from CR Gradient Profile Charts.
- Route mileage, taken from CR Milepost data.
- Average temperature of superheated steam during trials in degrees Fahrenheit (°F).
- Maximum temperature of superheated steam during trials in degrees Fahrenheit (°F).
- Smokebox vacuum, maximum value recorded in inches of water gauge (ins WG).
- Temperature of tender water in degrees Fahrenheit (°F).
- All timetabled stops on outward and return working.

APPENDIX 1: GLASGOW TO PERTH RETURN WORKING, 9TH AUGUST 1921
This appendix covers the operation of engine No. 956, under trials conditions, heading a return express passenger working from Glasgow (Buchanan Street) to Perth on the 9th August 1921.

APPENDIX 2: GLASGOW TO CARLISLE RETURN WORKING, 11TH AUGUST 1921
This appendix covers the operation of engine No. 956, under trials conditions, heading a return express passenger working from Glasgow (Central) to Carlisle on the 11th August 1921.

APPENDIX 3: POLMADIE TO KINGMOOR RETURN WORKING, 25TH OCTOBER 1922
This appendix covers the operation of engine No. 956, under trials conditions, heading a return special 500 ton 'test train' working from Polmadie Yard (Glasgow) to Kingmoor Yard (Carlisle) on the 25th October 1922.

REFERENCES
1. Trials Data, 956 Class Engine No 956, August 1921 and October 1922, Montague Smith Collection, NRS, GD456, RHP136355
2. Indicator Diagrams, Engine No 956, August 1921, NRM, ID685, ALS3/7/4/G

APPENDIX 1:
GLASGOW TO PERTH RETURN WORKING, 9TH AUGUST 1921

ENGINE: No. 956
WORKING: 1.30 PM PASSENGER TRAIN, GLASGOW BUCHANAN STREET TO PERTH AND RETURN

COMMENTS ON INFORMATION RECORDED

Whilst on this trial total IHP figures are recorded from indicator diagrams, the output of individual cylinders is not available. It is not therefore possible to pass any comment, from these results, on the performance of No. 956's derived motion. Further, from the NRM traced indicator diagrams, only one diagram is given for each recorded point, there being no annotation referring to the cylinder from which it was obtained.

The calorific value of the coal used is not given, though it is assumed that the best grade available on the CR for express passenger duties would be used. This is estimated to have a calorific value of around 13,500 BTU/lb.

No information is provided on the post-trial weight of deposits accumulated in the smokebox, from which an estimate could have been made of unburned coal carry-over. Allowing for expected ash (as a percentage of the coal weight fired), some measure of boiler combustion efficiency could have been estimated, but owing to lack of data this cannot be done.

Details on the expected operation of the locomotive and train is not provided, though it is assumed that the locomotive working would be such as to maintain the timetable, make up for any lost time and avoid blowing off. Whilst the weight of the train is known, its composition is not, though it is assumed to be of bogie corridor stock, normally used on a service of this type. No data is given for the loaded weight of the locomotive and tender, and this is assumed to be approximately 130 tons at commencement of each trial.

At several points on the workings the regulator was fully closed, but no detail is given on the related operating cut-offs. Additionally, there is no indication given for boiler water levels, or injector use, or blowing off

No data is recorded as to the engine crew, any senior officers present, or the names of those in the trials team.

WORKING: 1.30 PM PASSENGER TRAIN, GLASGOW TO PERTH

Specific trials information has been taken from the CR trials chart, held in the Montague Smith Collection, the National Records of Scotland, ref. RHP136355/26.

Weight of train, including passengers and luggage	351 tons
Water used on outward working	2,460 gallons
Coal used on outward working	3,024 lbs
Water evaporated per mile	39.04 gallons
Pounds of water evaporated per pound of coal	8.1 lbs
Coal used per gallon of water evaporated	1.2 lbs
Greatest vacuum created in smokebox	4 ins WG
Maximum temperature of superheated steam	555 °F
Average temperature of superheated steam	529 °F
Temperature of water in tank	62 °F

TIMINGS FROM 1.30 PM AT BUCHANAN STREET				
	ARRIVE		DEPART	
	BOOKED	ACTUAL	BOOKED	ACTUAL
Buchanan Street (MP 0)	–	–	1.30	1.30
Larbert (MP 22.1)	2.04	2.04	2.07	2.07
Stirling (MP 30.2)	2.21	2.19	2.24	2.24
Gleneagles (MP 47.4)	2.52	2.54	2.54	2.56
Perth (MP 63.2)	3.07	3.07	–	–

COMMENTARY ON TRIALS CHARTS

Figure A1.1 (ref. RHP136355/26) shows the overall trials chart for this working from Glasgow, Buchanan Street to Perth.

BUCHANAN STREET TO LARBERT (MP 0 TO MP 22.1)

The start was made on time from Buchanan Street at 1.30 pm with 65 per cent cut-off (full gear) and 9/16th regulator plus boiler pressure at 180 psi. It is assumed that no banking assistance was provided through to Robroyston, since there is no related annotation on the trials chart. Passing through St Rollox station, cut-off was shortened to 40 per cent and indicator diagrams taken, showing the locomotive developing 673 IHP on the 1:80 gradient (speed 13 mph, cut-off 40 per cent, regulator 9/16th, pressure 175 psi, gradient 1:80 up). At MP 2, the regulator was opened to 15/16th and remained there until the summit at Robroyston was cleared. Indicator diagrams taken at Robroyston (MP 3.2) show 910 IHP being developed (speed 26 mph, cut-off 35 per cent, regulator 15/16th, pressure 170 psi, gradient level). Speed picked up to 47 mph through Stepps Road station, though at this point the train was two minutes behind booked time, the three mile climb from Buchanan Street to Robroyston being somewhat laboured.

At MP 6.5, on the relatively level section between Stepps and Glenboig, further indicator diagrams were taken, showing No. 956 to be developing 958 IHP (speed 54 mph, cut-off 35 per cent, regulator 2/16th, pressure 174 psi, gradient level). However, on the slight rise to Glenboig speed fell away and a further one minute is recorded as having been lost. After Glenboig, the regulator was closed to 1.5/16th and speed picked up to 57 mph on the approach to the 1 in 99 climb to Cumbernauld. Indicator diagrams were taken on the 1 in 99 gradient at MP 12.2, showing that 789 IHP was being developed (speed 54 mph, cut-off 35 per cent, regulator 2/16th, pressure 175 psi, gradient 1 in 99 up).

After passing Cumbernauld, at MP 13.2, the regulator was closed and speed gradually fell to 47 mph, before the regulator was opened progressively to 1.5/16th for the climb to Greenhill, then closed again for the run down to Larbert where arrival was on time. Boiler pressure from Cumbernauld to Larbert remained at 175 psi.

It is unclear why the two minutes time lost climbing to Robroyston was not made up more speedily, though it would seem that the boiler was taxed by the climb, with pressure falling to 170 psi and remaining at that mark for several miles of broadly level track. Interestingly, closing the regulator to 1.5/16th after Glenboig, on a short rising gradient caused the boiler pressure to rise and speed to pick up to the maximum on this section, 57 mph.

LARBERT TO STIRLING (MP 22.1 TO MP 30.2)
Departure from Larbert was on time at 2.07 pm, with 65 per cent cut-off, 2/16th regulator and pressure at 175 psi. On the downhill 1 in 164, approximately one mile out of Larbert, cut-off was reduced to 35 per cent, regulator increased to 4/16th, and indicator diagrams taken. These showed No. 965 to be developing 950 IHP (speed 32 mph, cut-off 35 per cent, regulator 4/16th, pressure 170 psi, gradient 1 in 164 down). For the 1 in 126 climb to Plean station, the regulator was opened to 9.5/16th and speed rose to 52 mph, before falling back to 46 mph at Plean Summit. Most surprisingly, the boiler pressure fell to 155 psi at the summit, where the speed had fallen to 46 mph, suggesting again the boiler was not steaming well. Just before Plean Summit, indicator diagrams were taken showing that 996 IHP was being developed (speed 44 mph, cut-off 35 per cent, regulator 9.5/16th, pressure 155 psi, gradient 1 in 126 up). Boiler pressure did not pick up to 160 psi until half way down the 1 in 118 to the north of Plean, when the regulator was closed for the run into Stirling.

With the benefit of a clear downhill run from Plean to Stirling and speed rising to 55 mph just to the north of Bannockburn, the arrival at Stirling was two minutes ahead of booked time. There seemed to be the suggestion of boiler steaming problems on the ascent to Plean Summit, recovery to 160 psi being only achieved with a closed regulator. Plean Bank is only two miles at 1 in 126, hardly a significant incline; perhaps there is the suggestion of a deliberate attempt to evaluate No. 956's performance by starting the climb at a lower pressure and seeing how things developed.

STIRLING TO GLENEAGLES (MP 30.2 TO MP 47.4)
Full use was made of the five-minute stop at Stirling to re-establish boiler pressure at 180 psi, this no doubt being considered essential for the six mile climb from Cornton Crossing to Kinbuck. The first three miles from Cornton through Bridge-of-Allan to Dunblane has a ruling gradient of approximately 1 in 100, followed by a more taxing three miles at 1 in 88 to MP 38, just north of Kinbuck. The climb to Kinbuck from Cornton Crossing was considered one of the most arduous CR sections handling express passenger traffic, comparable to tackling Beattock from the south.

No. 956 departed on time from Stirling using 65 per cent cut-off and 4.5/16th regulator, the cut-off being eased first to 40 per cent when crossing the River Forth, and then to 35% per cent. Concurrent with easing the cut-off to 40 per cent, the regulator was opened out to 7/16th, pressure remaining steady at 175 psi. Indicator diagrams were taken just before Cornton Crossing, showing that 1,067 IHP was being developed (speed 37 mph, cut-off 35 per cent, regulator 7/16th, pressure 175 psi, gradient level).

At MP 33, just north of Bridge-of-Allan, speed peaked at 44 mph, at which point the regulator was fully opened (16/16th), speed falling over the next two miles to 40 mph at Dunblane where, in recognition of falling boiler pressure, the regulator was eased to 8/16th. Cut-off was lengthened to 40 per cent for the remainder of the climb, speed falling further to 26 mph and boiler pressure to 165 psi as the summit was breasted. Just before the summit, indicator diagrams were taken, showing 999 IHP being developed (speed 26 mph, cut-off 40 per cent, regulator 8/16th, pressure 167 psi, effective gradient 1 in 88 up).

On the brief 1½ miles of 1 in 750 downhill after Kinbuck Summit, the regulator was progressively eased to 4.5/16th, cut-off shortened to 35 per cent with boiler pressure recovering to 170 psi. Indicator diagrams were taken at MP 39.5, showing 860 IHP being developed (speed 32 mph, cut-off 35 per cent, regulator 3/16th, pressure 170 psi, gradient 1 in 750 down). The regulator was momentarily closed at MP 40, with no obvious increase in boiler pressure, the trials chart showing that No. 956 kept to booked time passing Kinbuck Summit.

From Greenloaning to Gleneagles a further series of uphill gradients

TRIALS TRIP SUMMARY OF RECORDED VALUES, 9TH AUGUST 1921

MP	LOCATION	GRADIENT	SPEED MPH	REGULATOR N/16TH	CUT-OFF PER CENT	POWER IHP	BOILER PRESSURE PSI	STEAM CHEST PRESSURE PSI	MEP PSI
0	Buchanan Street	–	–	–	–	–	180	–	–
1.1	St Rollox	1:80 up	13	9	40	673	175	160	106
3.2	Robroyston	level	26	15	35	910	170	160	72
6.5	–	level	54	2	35	958	174	120	43
9.0	Glenboig	level	48	2	35	–	180	–	–
12.2	–	1:99 up	54	2	35	789	175	100	29
18.5	Greenhill	level	46	1.5	35	–	175	–	–
22.1	Larbert	–	–	–	–	–	175	–	–
23.0	–	1:164 down	32	4	35	950	170	140	62
26.0	Plean	1:126 up	44	9.5	35	996	155	120	54
30.2	Stirling	–	–	–	–	–	180	–	–
32.3	Cornton Crossing	level	37	7	35	1,067	175	150	60
34.5	Dunblane (South)	1:100 up	43	16	35	–	175	–	–
37.5	Kinbuck	1:147 up	26	8	40	999	167	150	80
39.5	–	1:750 down	32	3	35	860	170	125	52
42.5	–	level	44	2	35	884	167	100	41
45.1	Blackford	1:310 up	48	2	35	–	165	–	–
47.4	Gleneagles	–	–	–	–	–	166	–	–
49.4	Auchterarder	1:100 down	58	1	35	–	166	–	–
53.6	Dunning	1:137 down	58	1	35	–	177	–	–
56.5	Forteviot	1:368 down	58	1.5	35	–	180	–	–
62.0	–	level	50	1	35	–	175	–	–
63.2	Perth	–	–	–	–	–	175	–	–

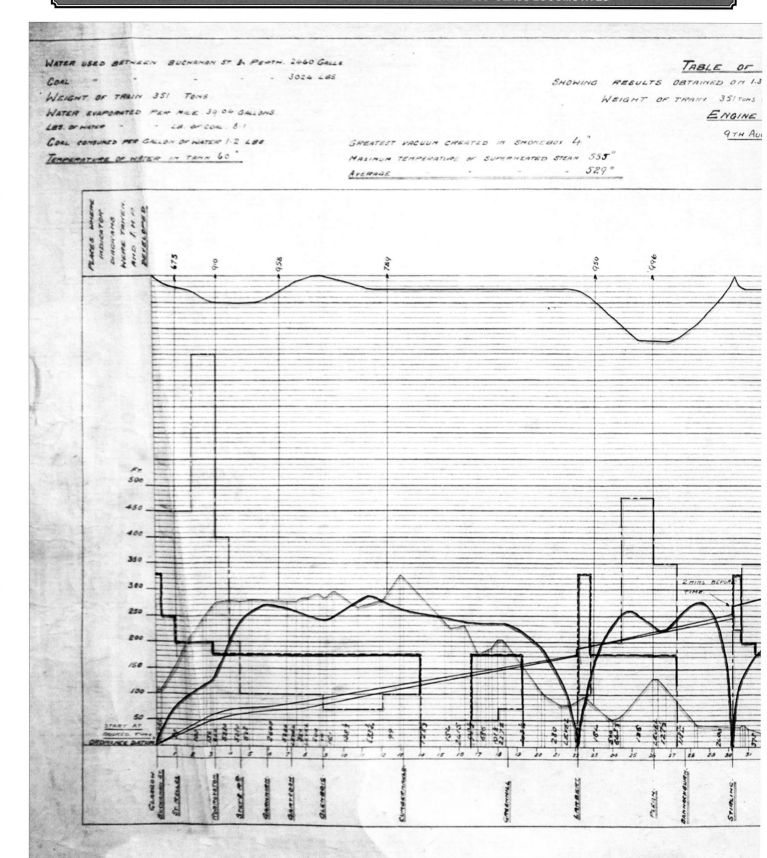

Figure A1.1
Caledonian Railway Co. 'Trials Chart' for the 1.30 pm Passenger Train, from Glasgow (Buchanan Street) to Perth on the 9th August 1921. Engine No. 956.
NRS: GD456, RHP136355/26

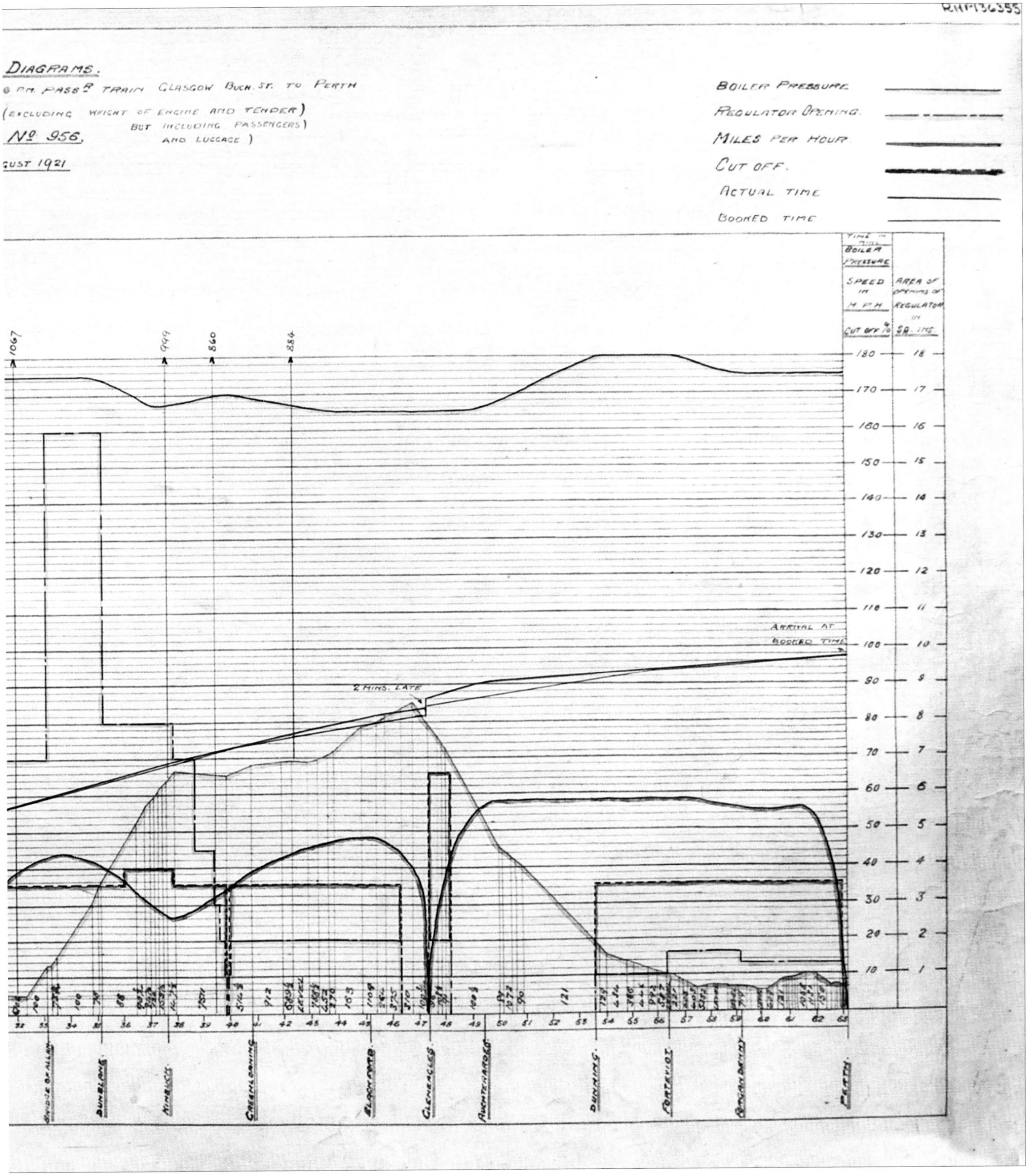

RHM136355
DIAGRAMS.
6 P.M. PASSR. TRAIN GLASGOW BUCH. ST. TO PERTH
(EXCLUDING WEIGHT OF ENGINE AND TENDER)
BUT INCLUDING PASSENGERS)
AND LUGGAGE)
No. 956.
GUST 1921
BOILER PRESSURE
REGULATOR OPENING.
MILES PER HOUR
CUT OFF.
ACTUAL TIME
BOOKED TIME
TIME IN MINS.
BOILER PRESSURE
SPEED IN M.P.H.
CUT OFF %
AREA OF OPENING OF REGULATOR IN SQ. INS.
ARRIVAL AT BOOKED TIME
2 MINS. LATE
BRIDGE OF ALLAN
DUNBLANE
KINBUCK
GREENLOANING
BLACKFORD
GLENEAGLES
AUCHTERARDER
DUNNING
FORTEVIOT
FORGANDENNY
PERTH

is encountered, the most severe being 1 mile at 1 in 163 and several hundred yards at 1 in 100 just short of Gleneagles station. There are several level sections, one being at MP 42.5, where indicator diagrams were taken showing 884 IHP being developed (speed 44 mph, cut-off 35 per cent, regulator 2/16th, pressure 167 psi, gradient level).

No further indicator diagrams were taken on the climb through Blackford to Gleneagles station, which is unfortunate as, with regulator set at 2/16th and cut-off sustained at 35 per cent, boiler pressure declined to 165 psi and speed, whilst maximising at 48 mph, then fell away to 43 mph at MP 46.4, at which point the regulator was closed. Speed dropped quickly on the run into Gleneagles station, where arrival was two minutes behind booked time.

Time was progressively lost after breasting Kinbuck summit, with boiler pressure at 166 psi. Whilst pressure recovered marginally to 170 psi on the more level sections around Greenloaning, when the train was ascending the 1 in 163 towards Gleneagles, pressure fell again, this time to 165 psi, this latter value being maintained to the stop at Gleneagles. It would seem the boiler may have again been 'winded' by the climb to Kinbuck, and subsequently did not recover to anywhere near normal working pressure post the climb.

A question might be asked here on locomotive working, especially if an 'easier' working stance was being taken on such matters during the trials. Total coal consumed on the trip is given as 3,024 lbs and the time to Perth from Buchanan Street (excluding stops) is 87 minutes net. With No. 956 having a grate area of 28 sq. ft, the equivalent average firing rate for the full trip is 75 lbs per sq. ft of grate per hour. The pro-rata figure to Gleneagles would be nearer 90 lbs per sq. ft per hour, recognising that the following section to Perth is almost all downhill. Design criteria suggest that a well-designed locomotive boiler should produce full steam output at a firing rate of around 100 lbs per sq. ft per hour. So, with an average in the 80 to 85 lbs per sq. ft per hour range for the trip as far as Gleneagles, and higher figures during hill climbing, it can be concluded that No. 956 was not being worked in an 'easier' style during this trial.

Gleneagles to Perth (MP 47.4 to MP 63.2)

Departure from Gleneagles was two minutes behind booked time, with 65 per cent cut-off, 2/16th regulator and pressure at 165 psi, no effort having seemingly been made to recover pressure during the Gleneagles stop, or, if efforts were made, they were unsuccessful. One mile out of Gleneagles station, the regulator was closed fully with speed building up rapidly to 58 mph at Auchterarder on the downhill 1 in 100 section. This speed of 58 mph was sustained through to Dunning, by which point, with the regulator still closed, the boiler pressure had recovered to 180 psi. At Dunning the regulator was opened to 1/16th, with cut-off set to 35 per cent, this cut-off being maintained to the stop at Perth.

Speed between Dunning and MP 61 (two miles south of Perth) was maintained in the 58 to 56 mph range, the arrival in Perth being at booked time. Interestingly, the trials charts show that the downhill running out of Gleneagles was slower that the timetable allowed, the time through Auchterarder being a full four minutes behind booked time. Whilst this deficit was recovered by Perth, in the two miles of downhill between Gleneagles and Auchterarder, No. 956 conspired to lose two minutes, suggesting that speeds in the high 60s or low 70s were essential to maintain booked time, speeds which No. 956 was unable to achieve.

Surprisingly, no indicator diagrams were taken on the Gleneagles to Perth section.

General Comments on No. 956 Performance

Attention has already been focused on the apparent poor steaming capability of No. 956's boiler and it possibly being 'winded' and unable to quickly recover post the climbs to Robroyston, Plean and Kinbuck. It is also clear that the engine was being handled in the normal manner for an express passenger working with normal rates of coal firing.

Recorded steam temperatures, with an average of 529°F and a peak at 550°F, confirm that superheat was too low, it being the norm to design for maximum values of 650 to 675°F. A lower than expected superheated steam temperature would result from the selected '956' Class tube-to-flue free-gas area ratio, the flue free-gas area being proportionately too low, a position not assisted using short return loop elements. Further, with a reduction of 100°F in steam temperatures, around 10 per cent more steam would be required to produce the same work.

Smokebox vacuum conditions, stated as a maximum of 4 ins WG, also seem too low, though it is uncertain where the measurements were made. A normal level of 8 to 9 ins WG, perhaps marginally higher, at the centre of the tube-plate and 1 ft behind the blast nozzle, was to be expected using an efficient drafting arrangement under near maximum working conditions. Examination of the '956' Class smokebox layout and ashpan design has already suggested the drafting arrangements were not ideal, and this would certainly adversely affect steaming capability, especially if the rear grate section contained a poorly burning fire.

One strange point seen throughout this trip was the working of the locomotive at relatively long cut-offs accompanied by corresponding lower regulator settings. With the exception of starting from station stops, in which cut-offs were invariably 65 per cent (full gear), the locomotive was worked at cut-offs in the range 35 to 40 per cent, irrespective of route topology.

Concerns around operation of the centre valve mechanism, leading potentially to cut-off and train speed restrictions, might explain why overall top speed seemed constrained and also why downhill running lacked any sparkle, resulting in the inability to recover lost time. The top downhill speeds on this working were 57 mph running from Glenboig, 52 mph from Larbert, 55 mph from Plean and 58 mph from Gleneagles. At no point on the working did speed reach 60 mph, yet speeds of at least 70 mph would be essential to meet normal timetable requirements, and an even greater speed needed if accelerated schedules were to be introduced.

Coal burned was stated as 47.8 lbs per mile and the evaporation rate is given as 8.1 lbs of water per lb of coal fired. These figures might be questioned, since coal usage for the outward and return workings was identical. Perhaps an approximate usage was established by dividing total coal usage by two.

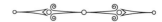

Working: 5.25 pm Passenger Train, Perth to Glasgow

Specific Trials Information has been taken from the CR trials charts held in the Montague Smith Collection the National Records of Scotland, ref. RHP136355/27.

Weight of train, including passengers and luggage	
a) Perth to Larbert	414 tons
b) Larbert to Glasgow	289 tons
Water used on return working	2,437 gallons
Coal used on return working	3,024 lbs
Water evaporated per mile	38.6 gallons
Pounds of water evaporated per pound of coal	8.0 lbs
Coal consumed per gallon of water evaporated	1.2 lbs
Greatest vacuum created in smokebox	4 ins WG
Maximum temperature of superheated steam	555°F
Average temperature of superheated steam	530°F
Temperature of water in tank	62°F

TIMINGS FROM 5.25 PM AT PERTH	ARRIVE		DEPART	
	BOOKED	ACTUAL	BOOKED	ACTUAL
Perth (MP 63.2)	–	–	5.25	5.31
Gleneagles (MP 47.4)	5.50	5.59	5.52	6.01
Stirling (MP 30.2)	6.14	6.27	6.18	6.29
Larbert (MP 22.1)	6.29	6.43	6.31	6.45
Buchanan Street (MP 0)	7.07	7.17	–	–

COMMENTARY ON TRIALS CHARTS

Figure A1.2 (ref. RHP136355/27) shows the overall trials chart for this working from Perth to Glasgow, Buchan Street.

PERTH TO GLENEAGLES (MP 63.2 TO MP 47.4)

The departure was made six minutes late (no reason are noted on the chart, but may have been related to a connection from the north), with boiler pressure at 170 psi and cut-off at 50 per cent, which was shortened to 35 per cent within half a mile of the station and which remained at that setting until Auchterarder (MP 49.5). The regulator was set at 2/16th on departure and remained there until passing Dunning (MP 53.5).

With these settings, and boiler pressure stabilised at 175 psi, speed rose to 53 mph passing Forgandenny (MP 59.5), where indicator diagrams were taken, showing 995 IHP being developed (speed 53 mph, cut-off 35 per cent, regulator 2/16th, pressure 175 psi, gradient 1 in 719 up). Whilst boiler pressure remained steady at 175 psi, speed fell on the climb to Forteviot, further indicator diagrams being taken at MP 57, half a mile north of Forteviot, which showed 1,033 IHP being developed (speed 50 mph, cut-off 35 per cent, regulator 2/16th, pressure 175 psi, average gradient 1 in 403 up).

After falling slightly, speed again recovered to 50 mph passing Dunning, which marks the start of the 1 in 121 followed by 1 in 100 up gradients through Auchterarder to Gleneagles. At Dunning, the regulator was opened to 4.5/16th and indicator diagrams taken on the 1 in 121 up, at MP 52, showing 1,101 IHP being developed (speed 32 mph, cut-off 35 per cent, regulator 4.5/16th, pressure 173 psi, gradient 1 in 121 up). With speed falling to 26 mph just prior to Auchterarder, the regulator was opened from 9.5/16th to fully open, 16/16th, the cut-off lengthened to 50 per cent and indicator diagrams taken on the 1 in 100 up gradient at MP 49.5 (speed 34 mph, cut-off 50 per cent, regulator 16/16th, pressure 165 psi, gradient 1 in 100 up); these diagrams showed 1,067 IHP being developed.

Just before Gleneagles station the regulator was closed with boiler pressure at 160 psi for an arrival nine minutes late on booked time, i.e. an additional three minutes had been lost on the booked schedule from Perth to Gleneagles.

GLENEAGLES TO STIRLING (MP 47.4 TO MP 30.2)

The timetabled two-minute stop time at Gleneagles was maintained, departure being nine minutes late at 6.01 pm, with 40 per cent cut-off and 9.5/16th regulator setting, boiler pressure being just above 160 psi. Indicator diagrams were taken just before the Gleneagles summit at MP 46.8, which showed 767 IHP being produced (speed 14 mph, cut-off 40 per cent, regulator 9.5/16th, pressure 170 psi, gradient 1 in 100 up). After breasting the summit, the regulator was progressively closed to 2/16th by Blackford and 1.5/16th by Greenloaning, cut-off remaining constant at 35 per cent. Speed progressively rose to 50 mph at the foot of the 1 in 163 gradient at MP 43.5, where indicator diagrams were again taken, showing 955 IHP being developed (speed 50 mph, cut-off 35 per cent, regulator 2/16th, pressure 175 psi, gradient 1 in 452 down).

A P.W. restriction at MP 39 resulted in the regulator being closed

and speed falling from 59 mph to 38 mph just before Kinbuck summit – this restriction caused two minutes delay to booked time and, most surprisingly, the boiler pressure is recorded as declining to 167 psi. It is not know why pressure fell, or what blower or injector action had been taken. The regulator was opened passing Kinbuck Summit (MP 38) to 1.5/16th, with 35 per cent cut-off, for just over a mile (to MP 37) and then fully closed, the train coasting down the 1 in 88 and 1 in 100 gradients through Dunblane and Bridge-of-Allan for 5½ miles. Speed rose initially from 38 mph to 54 mph whilst the regulator was opened for the mile in question, though boiler pressure fell to 155 psi and recovered only to 170 psi during the latter part of the downhill coasting period. From closing the regulator, speed only increased by a further 6 mph to 60 mph on this downhill section. There is no comment on the chart pointing to the use of brakes to limit downhill speed.

After a short period of steaming on the level, arrival at Stirling was timed at 6.27 pm, 13 minutes behind booked time. In other words, another four minutes delay from Gleneagles, of which two minutes was the result of a P.W. check and a further one minute put down to signals.

STIRLING TO LARBERT (MP 30.2 TO MP 22.1)

The stop at Stirling was shortened to two minutes, compared to the booked four, departure proceeding with 40 per cent cut-off and 1.5/16th regulator, boiler pressure being 172 psi. Cut-off was shortened to 35 per cent a mile south of Stirling station, where it remained for the whole journey to Larbert. The regulator was opened out to 4.5/16th, then 7/16th on the 1 in 118 rise for two miles to Plean. On the 1 in 127 incline indicator diagrams were taken, showing that 1,118 IHP was being developed (speed 35 mph, cut-off 35 per cent, regulator 7/16th, pressure 175 psi, gradient 1 in 127 up).

On breasting Plean summit, with a two mile run downhill to Alloa Junction, the regulator was eased to 4.5/16th, then to 1.5/16th, though during this period, inexplicably, boiler pressure had fallen to 165 psi. A maximum speed on this section of 55 mph was recorded at MP 24, nearing the bottom of the downhill run from Plean.

Boiler pressure had recovered to 175 psi on arrival in Larbert station at 6.43 pm Owing to boiler pressure reduction in climbing Plean Bank and a slower than necessary downhill running to the south of Plean, further time was lost on the Stirling to Larbert section. Booked time for the 8.1 miles was 11 minutes, requiring an average speed of 44 mph. No. 956 and its train took 14 minutes, losing three minutes in 8.1 miles, and achieving an average speed of 35 mph. Something was clearly wrong with both steam production and downhill running.

LARBERT TO BUCHANAN STREET (MP 22 TO MP 0)

Departure from Larbert, after the booked two-minute stop, was made with 4/16th regulator, 35 per cent cut-off (which was not altered on the whole mileage to Buchanan Street) and boiler pressure at 175 psi. On the two-mile climb to Greenhill at 1 in 103 gradient, indicator diagrams were taken at MP 19, showing 1,029 IHP being developed (speed 42 mph, regulator 4/16th, cut-off 35 per cent, pressure 175 psi, gradient 1 in 103 up). Speed rose to 58 mph just after Greenhill (MP 19), though in climbing the 1 in 98 and the following 1 in 128 to Cumbernauld, boiler pressure again started to fall. Indicator diagrams were taken at MP 14 on the 1 in 128 climb to Cumbernauld, showing 1,006 IHP being developed (speed 38 mph, cut-off 35 per cent, regulator 2.5/16th, pressure 167 psi, gradient 1 in 128 up).

On breasting the Cumbernauld summit, the regulator was eased to 1.5/16th, in the face of boiler pressure registering 164 psi and falling. On the relatively level stretch between Glenboig and Robroyston, with cut-off maintained at 35 per cent and a 1.5/16th regulator setting, boiler pressure fell to 160 psi, recovered to 165 psi, then fell

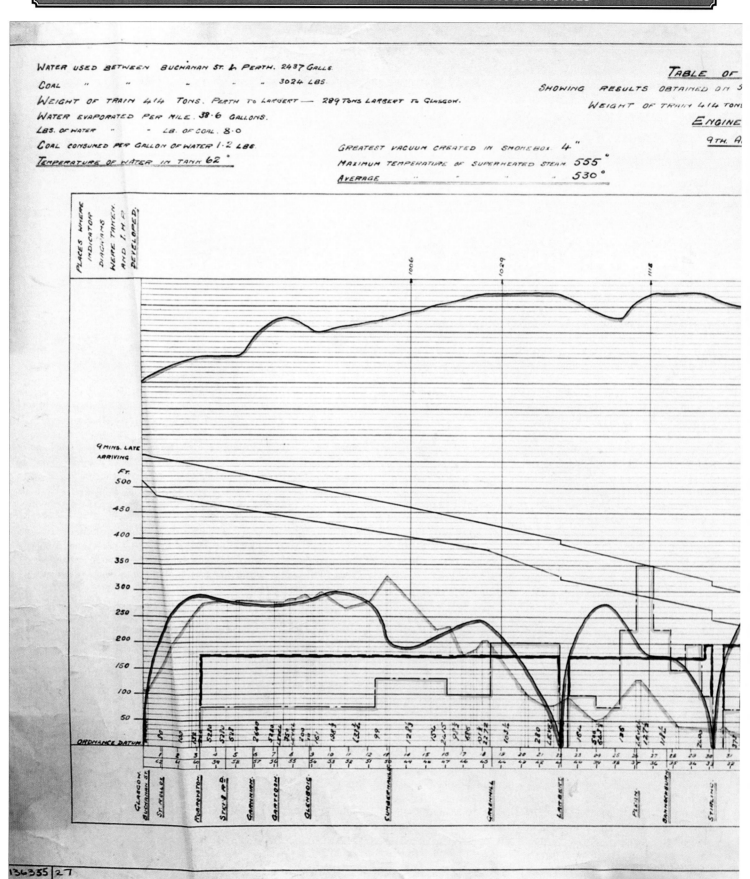

Figure A1.2
Caledonian Railway Co. 'Trials Chart' for the 5.25 pm Passenger Train, from Perth to Glasgow (Buchanan Street) on the 9th August 1921. Engine No. 956.
NRS: GD456, RHP136355/27

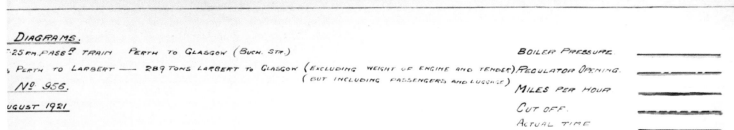

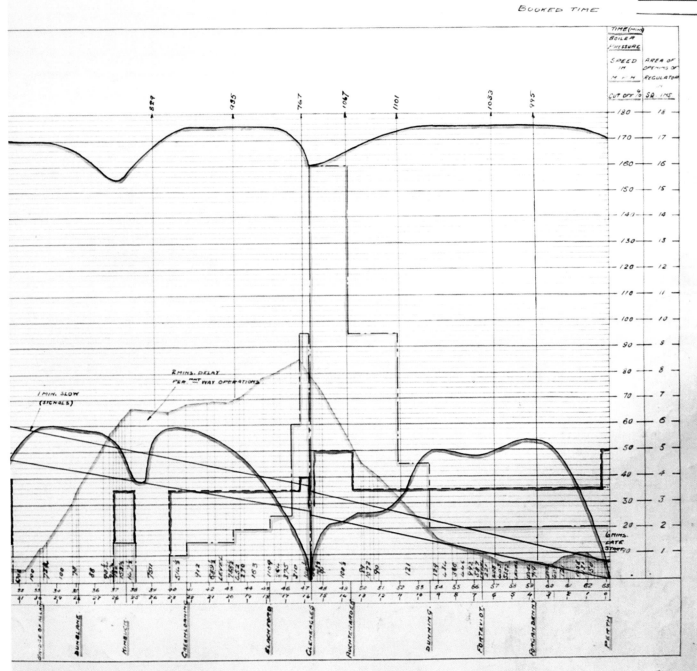

to 150 psi. The regulator was fully closed passing Robroyston with pressure at 150 psi.

Arrival at Buchanan Street was timed at 7.17 pm, No. 956 having arrived with the boiler registering 140 psi, and no time made up between Larbert and Buchanan Street. The results on this section are particularly disappointing, since the train weight was reduced to 289 tons at Larbert, where the Edinburgh portion was detached.

GENERAL COMMENTS ON No. 956 PERFORMANCE

Whilst there was no need to arrive at Buchanan Street with a full head of steam, the overall effect of locomotive performance on this working must have been dispiriting to the crew, who may well have lost heart on the final part of this latter section. It is possible that No. 956 'limped' into Buchanan Street and may not have been able to carry on had Buchanan Street not been the train termination point.

All seemed to be reasonably well on the relatively level section from Perth to Forteviot, but when No. 956 tackled the major gradients to the south of Dunning, speed initially fell quickly. Opening the regulator progressively to fully open and lengthening the cut-off did not improve the speed, whereas boiler pressure was prejudiced further. Half a mile before Gleneagles station, with a fully open regulator and 50 per cent cut-off, speed had fallen to 15 mph and boiler pressure to 160 psi. These circumstances suggest the boiler was again severely tested and found wanting on the initial climb through Dunning, and was not producing sufficient steam to master the more severe gradients which followed. Latterly, on this section, No. 956 was being worked near 'all out' conditions, where speed stability on the incline seemed entirely at the mercy of the boiler's thermal inertia.

The performance on the Gleneagles to Stirling section really defies explanation. On one of the best downhill stretches on the CR main line, over six miles in all, with no signal or P.W. checks and a train of normal weight, the most powerful locomotive owned by the CR was unable to exceed 60 mph and to make up the time lost from Perth to Gleneagles. Indeed, No. 956 conspired to lose more time.

Whilst it would seem the boiler was steaming very poorly, the locomotive seemed incapable of being worked at more than 60 mph, irrespective of any boiler pressure constraints. The speed constraints were perhaps valve gear related, due to the 'disturbing influences' noted by Graham Miller and already mentioned, probably arising from centre valve mechanism resonances and inertial effects from oscillating masses. Rough riding due to 'nozing' at higher speeds may also have been a contributory factor. Overall, the performance of No. 956 on this section would have left the St Rollox design team much to ponder.

One might question what servicing was undertaken at Perth, during the two-hour turn-round period, in the way of ashpan clearance and clinker removal from the fire. The trials data is silent in this regard.

Superheater performance was broadly similar to the morning Down working, so the same remarks apply. By comparing the No. 956 performance with equivalent No. 139 and No. 60 data, St Rollox may have established the higher than normal superheater pressure loss, caused by the elements' cross-section being too small. The Up train was worked in similar regulator and cut-off style to the earlier Down train, with smokebox vacuum conditions being identical. The indicator diagram summations demonstrate, that for an engine supposedly capable of producing at least 1,500 IHP, the values obtained were disappointingly well below those anticipated, with approximately 1,100 IHP being the maximum developed, the boiler perhaps being mortgaged in the process.

In short the overall performance of No. 956 on this section was uninspiring at best.

TRIAL TRIP SUMMARY OF RECORDED VALUES, 9TH AUGUST 1921

MP	LOCATION	GRADIENT	SPEED MPH	REGULATOR N/16TH	CUT-OFF PER CENT	POWER IHP	BOILER PRESSURE PSI	STEAM CHEST PRESSURE PSI	MEP PSI
63.3	Perth	–	–	–	–	–	170	–	–
59.5	Forgandenny	1:719 up	53	2	35	995	175	120	47
57.0	–	1:403 up	50	2	35	1,033	175	115	41
53.6	Dunning	1:121 up	49	5	35	–	175	–	–
52.0	–	1:121 up	32	4.5	35	1,101	173	150	60
49.5	Auchterarder	1:100 up	34	16	50	1,067	165	155	72
47.4	Gleneagles	–	–	–	–	–	160	–	–
46.8	–	1:100 up	14	9.5	40	767	167	160	104
43.5	–	1:750 down	50	2	35	955	175	125	39
38.0	Kinbuck	1:167 down	40	1.5	35	–	155	–	–
33.3	Bridge-of-Allan	1:100 down	60	–	–	–	170	–	–
30.2	Stirling	–	–	–	–	–	175	–	–
26.6	Plean Bank (n)	1:127 up	35	7	35	1,118	175	150	61
25.0	Plean Bank (s)	1:136 down	50	4.5	35	–	165	–	–
22.1	Larbert	–	–	–	–	–	175	–	–
19.0	Greenhill (s)	1:103 up	42	4	35	1,029	175	150	61
14.0	–	1:128 up	38	2.5	35	1,006	167	100	52
3.2	Robroyston	level	58	1.5	35	–	150	–	–
0	Buchanan Street	–	–	–	–	–	140	–	–

APPENDIX 2:
GLASGOW TO CARLISLE RETURN WORKING, 11TH AUGUST 1921

ENGINE: No. 956
WORKING: 10.00 AM PASSENGER TRAIN, GLASGOW TO CARLISLE AND 3.35 PM RETURN

COMMENTS ON INFORMATION RECORDED

Whilst on this trial, total IHP figures are recorded from indicator diagrams, with one exception, individual IHP figures per cylinder are not available. The exception relates to the return Down working to Glasgow, where individual cylinder IHPs are given for the climb from Beattock station to Beattock Summit. It is therefore possible to pass some comment on the performance of the initial derived motion used on '956' Class, as measured on this trial.

It is not clear from the trials charts at which specific points on the working the IHPs were actually measured, the total IHP values being plotted as a continuous variable. However, it has been possible to correlate the chart graphical representation with the individual indicator diagrams.

WORKING: 10.00 AM PASSENGER TRAIN, GLASGOW CENTRAL TO CARLISLE

Specific trials Information has been taken from the CR trials chart held in Montague Smith collection, the National Records of Scotland, ref. RHP136355/28.

Weight of train, including passengers and luggage:	
a) Glasgow to Symington	261 tons
b) Symington to Carlisle	346 tons
Water used on outward working	3,598 gallons
Coal used on outward working	3,920 lbs
Water evaporated per mile	35.7 gallons
Pounds of water evaporated per pound of coal	9.1 lbs
Coal consumed per gallon of water evaporated	1.0 lbs
Greatest vacuum created in smokebox	4 ins WG
Maximum temperature of superheated steam	590°F
Average temperature of superheated steam	539°F
Temperature of water in tank	60°F

TIMINGS FROM 10.00 AM AT GLASGOW CENTRAL

	ARRIVE		DEPART	
	BOOKED	ACTUAL	BOOKED	ACTUAL
Glasgow (MP 102.3)	–	–	10.00	10.00
Motherwell (MP 88.9)	10.20	10.20	10.24	10.24
Symington (MP 66.8)	10.56	10.56	11.01	11.01
Beattock Summit (MP 49.6)	11.27	11.24	11.27	11.24
Carlisle (MP 0)	12.20	12.20	–	–

COMMENTARY ON TRIALS CHARTS

Figure A2.1 (ref. RHP136355/28) shows the complete trials chart for this working from Glasgow Central to Carlisle.

GLASGOW TO MOTHERWELL (MP 102.3 TO MP 88.9)
Departure was on time, with 35 per cent cut-off, 4.5/16th regulator and a boiler pressure of 175 psi. Rutherglen (MP 98.5) was passed at 52 mph, indicator diagrams showing No. 956 was developing 890 IHP (speed 52 mph, regulator 2/16th, cut-off 35 per cent, pressure 175 psi, gradient level). Speed fell marginally to 45 mph on the climb at 1 in 165 through Cambuslang to Hamilton Junction (MP 95.6), where further indicator diagrams showed 1,040 IHP was developed (speed 45 mph, regulator 2/16th, cut-off 35 per cent, pressure 180 psi, gradient level).

Passing Uddingston Junction (MP 93.3), the regulator was eased to 1/16th, notwithstanding the climb at 1 in 134 followed by 1 in 118 to Motherwell (MP 88.9). Indicator diagrams showed power developed at Uddingston Junction (MP 93.3) was 540 IHP (speed 48 mph, regulator 1/16th, cut-off 35 per cent, pressure 175 psi, gradient 1 in 134 up). Continuing the climb to Motherwell, the regulator was progressively opened to 4.5/16th, cut-off remaining at 35 per cent. On the level section at MP 90, just before Lesmahagow Junction, 1,080 IHP was developed by No. 956, though boiler pressure had reduced to 170 psi (speed 26 mph, regulator 4.5/16th, cut-off 35 per cent, pressure 170 psi, gradient level).

Arrival at Motherwell was at booked time of 10.20 am.

MOTHERWELL TO SYMINGTON (MP 88.9 TO MP 66.8)
Departure from Motherwell was on time after the booked four-minute stop, boiler pressure being 175 psi. With cut-off again set at 35 per cent, the regulator was progressively opened to full open (16/16th), in tackling the gradient of approximately 1 in 130 to the summit at MP 78.3. Indicator diagrams were taken on the approach to Wishaw at MP 86.5 with 1,160 IHP being developed (speed 30 mph, regulator 16/16th, cut-off 35 per cent, pressure 170 psi, gradient 1 in 102 up). With boiler pressure reducing, the regulator was eased to 9.5/16th at MP 86.6 and then to 7/16th at Carriongill Junction (MP 84.5), the boiler pressure stabilising at 170 psi.

Indicator diagrams taken passing Carluke (MP 82), on the 1 in 100 upgrade, showed 1,170 IHP being developed (speed 39 mph, regulator 7/16th, cut-off 35 per cent, pressure 170 psi, gradient 1 in 100 up), and further diagrams taken at MP 79.5, showed 1,060 IHP was produced (speed 36 mph, regulator 7/16th, cut-off 35 per cent, pressure 170 psi, gradient 1 in 132 up).

Having breasted the summit at MP 78.5 at 38 mph, the regulator was eased to 2/16th, and then closed fully just before Cleghorn (MP 76), boiler pressure having dropped to 165 psi and speed rising to 50 mph. Recognising the additional climb from Strawfrank Junction, it is surprising that the boiler pressure was allowed to drop to 160 psi. The regulator was then opened to 1/16th at MP 74.5, then 2/16th passing through Carstairs (MP 73.5), and indicator diagrams taken at MP 69.8, showed 1,060 IHP being produced (speed 48 mph,

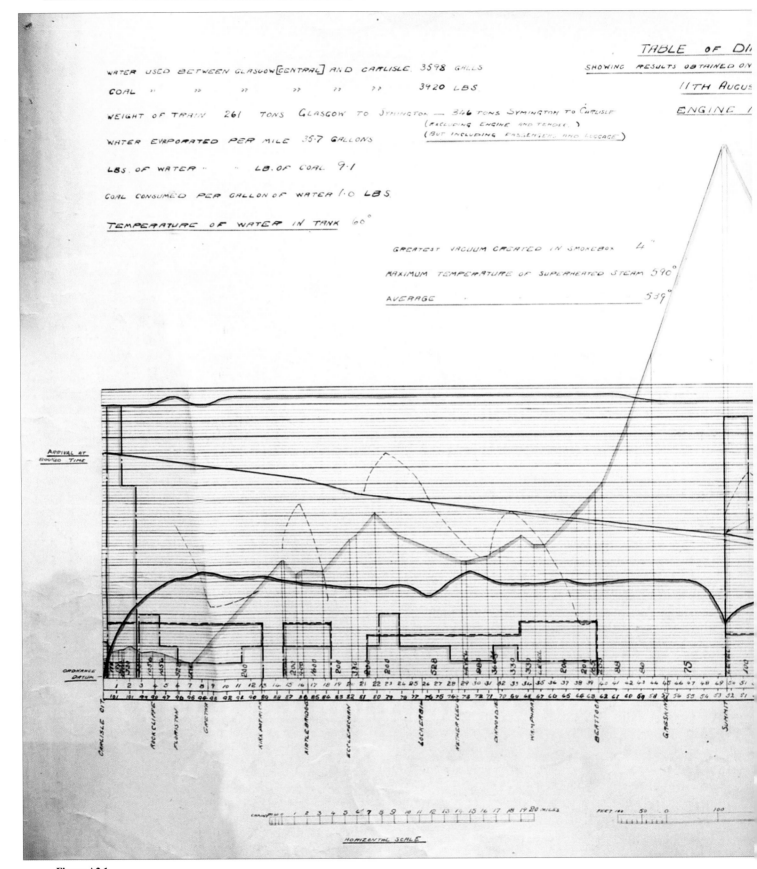

Figure A2.1
Caledonian Railway Co. 'Trials Chart' for the 10.00 am Passenger Train, from Glasgow (Central) to Carlisle on the 11th August 1921. Engine No. 956.
NRS: GD456, RHP136355/28

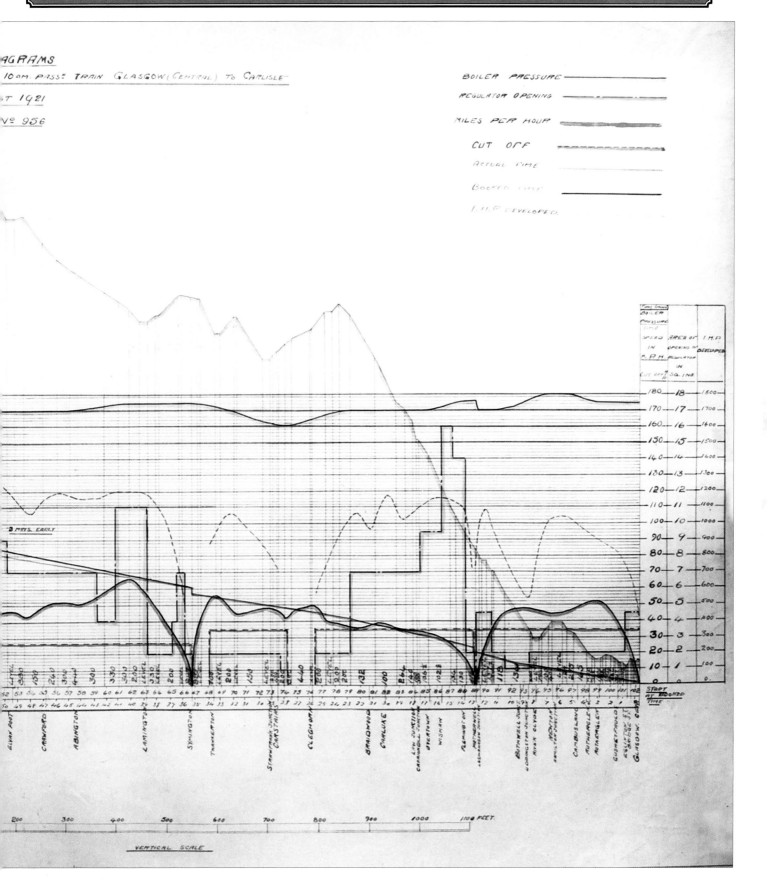

AGRAMS

10 a.m. PASS™ TRAIN GLASGOW (CENTRAL) TO CARLISLE

ST 1921

N° 956

BOILER PRESSURE
REGULATOR OPENING
MILES PER HOUR
CUT OFF
ACTUAL TIME
BOOKED TIME
I.H.P DEVELOPED.

regulator 2/16th, cut-off 35 per cent, pressure 170 psi, gradient 1 in 200 down).

At Thankerton (MP 68), the regulator was closed, the Symington arrival being on time at 10.56 am

SYMINGTON TO BEATTOCK SUMMIT (MP 66.8 TO MP 49.6)

It is convenient to treat the next section as running from Symington to Beattock Summit, even though no stop was made at the summit. Departure from Symington, on schedule, was made at 11.01 am, the Edinburgh portion having been added to the train, whose weight (gross) was now 346 tons. Cut-off was set at 27 per cent, regulator at 2/16th, increased to 7/16th at MP 66, with boiler pressure at 175 psi, speed building up for the climb to Beattock Summit at gradients varying from 1 in 300 up to 1 in 100 up.

Indicator diagrams taken at MP 62, showed 1,200 IHP being developed (speed 65 mph, regulator 11/16th, cut-off 27 per cent, pressure 175 psi, gradient 1 in 200 up), with boiler pressure fading a trace. The gradient at MP 61.8 reduces to 1 in 300 and at this point the regulator was eased to 4/16th, before being opened again at MP 59.2 to 7/16th, cut-off remaining at 27 per cent. At MP 56 (between Abington and Crawford), measurements were again taken showing 1,190 IHP being developed (speed 52 mph, regulator 7/16th, cut-off 27 per cent, pressure 175 psi, gradient 1 in 300 up)

Speed through Elvanfoot (MP 52.2) steadied at 46 mph, as the gradient levelled, at which point the regulator was fully opened (16/16th) for the final two miles at 1 in 100 up to the summit. Beattock Summit was passed three minutes ahead of booked time at 11.24 am, against the timetabled 11.27 am Just prior to the summit (at MP 51.5), indicator diagrams were taken, showing 1,250 IHP being developed (speed 46 mph, regulator 16/16th, cut-off 27 per cent, pressure 170 psi, gradient 1 in 100 up).

This run by No. 956 on the Symington to Beattock Summit section, using 27 per cent cut-off and producing 1,250 IHP, with only a small reduction in boiler pressure to 170 psi at full regulator, and on which a three-minute gain was made on booked time, suggests the locomotive was being handled well and responding appropriately. With a train weight of 346 tons (gross), the boiler seemed to recover well, even allowing for a reduction in pressure to 160 psi prior to Symington. If boiler pressure could have been maintained at 180 psi throughout, IHPs in the range 1,325 to 1,350 could have been achieved and if superheater pressure losses had been lower, perhaps 1,400 IHP might have been exceeded.

BEATTOCK SUMMIT TO CARLISLE (MP 49.6 TO MP 0)

The summit was breasted at 34 mph, with boiler pressure steady at 170 psi, at which point the regulator was fully closed for No. 956 to coast down the 10 miles of 1 in 75, then 1 in 80, followed by 1 in 88 to Beattock station. Speed rose to 60 mph some three miles to the south of the summit, and was maintained at this level, dropping to 58 mph passing through the station, where the regulator was opened to 1/16th and the cut-off set to 35 per cent.

Whilst it is surprising that speed was held at 60 mph during the decent, it may well have been decided to limit No. 956 to 60 mph to ensure that the full power developing potential of the locomotive could be explored on the forthcoming climb at 1 in 200 to the summit at MP 22 between Lockerbie and Ecclefechan. However, there is always the concern that speed was limited due to valve gear effects and rough riding influences. The extent of any braking effort applied to constrain train speed during the descent is not recorded.

At MP 32.8 on the 1 in 300 down, measurements showed 1,020 IHP being developed (speed 58 mph, regulator 2/16th, cut-off per cent,

TRIALS TRIP SUMMARY OF RECORDED VALUES, 11TH AUGUST 1921

MP	LOCATION	GRADIENT	SPEED MPH	REGULATOR N/16TH	CUT-OFF PER CENT	POWER IHP	BOILER PRESSURE PSI
102.3	Glasgow	–	–	–	–	–	175
98.5	Rutherglen	level	52	2	35	890	175
95.6	Hamilton Junction	level	45	2	35	1,040	180
93.3	Uddingston Junction	1:134 up	48	1	35	540	175
90.0	Lesmahagow Junction	level	26	4.5	35	1,080	170
88.9	Motherwell	–	–	–	–	–	175
86.5	Wishaw	1:102 up	30	16	35	1,160	170
82.0	Carluke	1:100 up	39	7	35	1,170	170
79.5	–	1:132 up	36	7	35	1,060	170
69.8	–	1:200 down	48	2	35	1,060	170
66.8	Symington	–	–	–	–	–	175
62.0	–	1:200 up	65	11	27	1,200	175
56.0	–	1:300 up	52	7	27	1,190	175
51.5	Beattock Summit	1:100 up	46	16	27	1,250	170
32.8	–	1:300 down	58	2	27	1,020	175
29.5	–	1:980 down	66	1	27	–	175
23.0	–	1:200 up	56	4	27	1,390	175
16.5	Kirtlebridge	1:1600 up	58	2	35	1,070	175
8.5	Gretna	1:200 down	66	1	35	–	170
0	Carlisle	–	–	–	–	–	170

NOTE:
The IHP, speed, cut-off and other measurements taken against mileage in the above table have been extracted from the overall trials chart. At times the data given on the indicator diagrams shows marginal variation from the data given on the chart. The indicator diagram data has been used for any numerate analysis.

pressure 175 psi, gradient 1 in 330 down). With cut-off maintained at 27 per cent, and the regulator eased to 1/16th at Dinwoodie, a maximum speed of 66 mph was recorded at MP 29.5, pressure remaining at 175 psi. The regulator was opened progressively to 4/16th for the climb to MP 22 and diagrams taken at MP 23 showed No. 956 developing 1,390 IHP (speed 56 mph, regulator 4/16th, cut-off 27 per cent, pressure 175 psi, gradient 1 in 200 up).

Further indicator diagrams were taken at MP 16.5, passing Kirtlebridge, though for some unknown reason the cut-off had been lengthened to 35 per cent. Power developed at this point was 1,070 IHP (speed 58 mph, regulator 2/16th, cut-off 35 per cent, pressure 175 psi, gradient 1 in 1600 up). On the 1 in 200 run down for seven miles passing Gretna, speed again touched 66 mph, with regulator set at 1/16th and 35 per cent cut-off.

Arrival at Carlisle station was to booked time at 12.20 pm, with boiler pressure of 170 psi. The three minutes gained to the north of Beattock Summit was lost between the summit and Lockerbie, though this can probably be attributed to an operational decision to limit the downhill speed to 60 mph. Perhaps, also, there was no pressure to arrive at Carlisle ahead of booked time.

GENERAL COMMENT ON No. 956 PERFORMANCE

Overall, the highpoint of this trial run was the gaining of three minutes between Symington and Beattock Summit with a 346 ton (gross) train. Over a distance of eight miles between MP 63 and MP 55, No. 956 sustained continuous outputs in the 1,150 to 1,200 IHP range, followed by 1,250 IHP on the 1 in 100 grade just prior to the summit. Cut-off setting between Symington and Beattock Summit was initially 27 per cent and remained at that setting, with more extensive use of the regulator. This contrasts with earlier running at 35 per cent cut-off.

Clearly the locomotive responded well when handled at shorter cut-offs, there being no *prima facie* evidence of valve gear concerns which might have suggested the longer cut-offs being needed and speed restrictions being applied. During this part of the run, boiler pressure remained in the 170/175 region and throughout the working was rarely less than 170 psi.

A maximum speed of 66 mph was recorded twice during the working, though note must be taken of the 60 mph maximum on the descent from Beattock Summit. Cut-offs at 27 per cent were in regular use in the initial part of the working, with no apparent recorded adverse effects on centre valve mechanism operation being noted.

Coal consumption was a very reasonable 38.13 lbs per mile and the water evaporated per lb of coal fired at 9.1 is a very respectable figure. A figure of 1.0 gallons of water per lb of coal fired is considered a good figure to aim for and indicates both fuel combustion and heat transfer was achieved efficiently.

Smokebox vacuum conditions, with a recorded maximum of 4 ins WG, would suggest combustion conditions were less than ideal, though the boiler seemed to perform reasonably well. Normally, on the tube-plate centre line and 1 ft behind the blast orifice, a figure of at least 9 ins WG was considered as satisfactory.

Whilst average superheat temperatures at 539°F could have been higher, a maximum steam temperature of 590°F was measured.

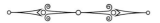

WORKING: 3.35 PM PASSENGER TRAIN, CARLISLE TO GLASGOW CENTRAL

Specific trials information has been taken from the CR trials charts, held in the Montague Smith Collection, the National Records of Scotland, ref. RHP136355/29 and RHP136355/30.

Weight of train, including passengers and luggage	343 tons.
Water used on return working	3,720 gallons
Coal used on return working	5,936 lbs
Water evaporated per mile	36.4 gallons
Pounds of water evaporated per pound of coal	6.2 lbs
Coal consumed per gallon of water evaporated	1.5 lbs
Greatest vacuum created in smokebox	4 ins WG
Maximum temperature of superheated steam	580°F
Average temperature of superheated steam	538°F
Temperature of water in tank	60°F

TIMINGS FROM 3.35 PM AT CARLISLE	ARRIVE		DEPART	
	BOOKED	ACTUAL	BOOKED	ACTUAL
Carlisle (MP 0)	–	–	3.35	3.39
Lockerbie (MP 25.8)	4.07	4.13	4.10	4.17
Beattock Stn (MP 39.6)	4.27	4.34	4.31	4.38
Beattock Summit (passing) (MP 49.6)	4.53	5.05	4.53	5.05
Carstairs (MP 73.6)	5.20	5.35	5.25	5.42
Glasgow (MP 102.3)	6.10	6.21	–	–

COMMENTARY ON TRIALS CHARTS

Figure A2.2 (ref. RHP136355/29) shows the complete trials chart for this working, whilst Figure A2.3 (ref. RHP136355/30) gives details of the individual cylinder IHPs from Beattock station to Beattock Summit.

CARLISLE TO LOCKERBIE (MP 0 TO MP 25.8)

Departure from Carlisle was four minutes late, probably due to a late running connection from the south, with boiler pressure at 175 psi, cut-off at 35 per cent (shortened to 30 per cent after 2.5 miles) and a regulator setting of 2/16th, speed increasing to 56 mph by MP 7.

Indicator diagrams taken passing Rockcliffe (MP 4), show 950 IHP being developed (speed 43 mph, regulator 2/16th, cut-off 30 per cent, pressure 175 psi, gradient near level). On passing Gretna at MP 8.5 the regulator was increased to 14/16th for the 1 in 200 climb up through Kirkpatrick and indicator diagrams taken at MP 8.5 show 1,140 IHP being developed (speed 45 mph, regulator 14/16th, cut-off 30 per cent, pressure 174 psi and easing, gradient 1 in 200 up). Further diagrams taken at MP 12 show No. 956 developing 1,120 IHP (speed 45 mph, regulator 14/16th, cut-off 30 per cent, pressure 170 psi, gradient 1 in 200 up).

On breasting the summit of the 1 in 200 at MP 14.6, with boiler pressure at 170 psi, the regulator was eased to 4/16th, then to 2/16th at MP 16.5, cut-off remaining constant at 30 per cent. At MP 19.3, indicator diagrams taken on the 1 in 200 climb through Ecclefechan, showed 990 IHP being developed (speed 51 mph, regulator 2/16th, cut-off 30 per cent, pressure 170 psi, gradient 1 in 200 up). A further indicator diagram was taken at MP 22.5, showing 1,020 IHP being developed (speed 46 mph, regulator 2/16th, cut-off 35%, pressure 175 psi, gradient 1 in 200 down).

The regulator was fully closed at MP 25.2, arrival at Lockerbie being at 4.13 pm, against a booked 4.07 pm, i.e. a further two

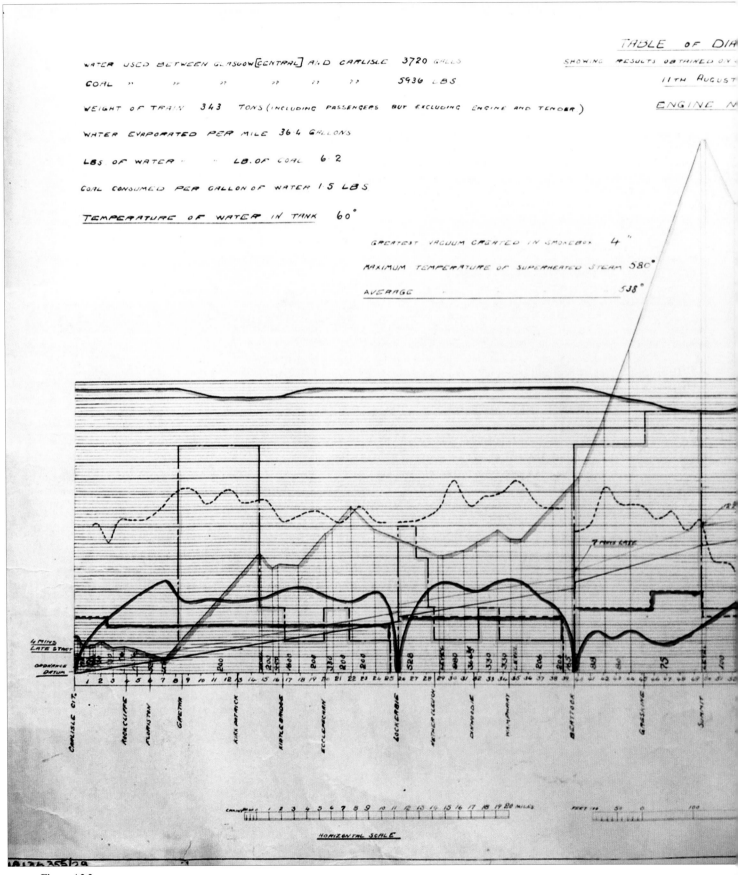

Figure A2.2
Caledonian Railway Co. 'Trials Chart' for the 3.35 pm Passenger Train, from Carlisle to Glasgow (Central) on the 11th August 1921. Engine No. 956.
NRS: GD456, RHP136355/29

GRAMS
3 *EXPRESS* TRAIN CARLISLE TO GLASGOW (CENTRAL)

1921

956

BOILER PRESSURE
POWER OF OPENING
MILES PER HOUR
CUT OFF
ACTUAL TIME
BOOKED TIME
TOTAL I.H.P.

VERTICAL SCALE

minutes had been lost on the booked schedule to Lockerbie, which is surprising. One would have thought that some of the initially lost four minutes, related to the late start, might have been recovered. One assumes it was not the intention to lose time in relatively favourable running conditions, which suggests that perhaps the footplate crew were having some difficulties. Noticeably, the locomotive was worked on this section with no cut-off less than 30 per cent.

LOCKERBIE TO BEATTOCK STATION (MP 25.8 TO MP 39.6)

An additional one minute was added to the Lockerbie stop (no details are given on the trial's chart), the train departing at 4.17 pm with 175 psi available, cut-off set at 35 per cent, and regulator at 9/16th. On the downhill 1 in 528, speed rose to 56 mph at MP 29.5, indicator diagrams taken at MP 30.2 showing 1,180 IHP being developed (speed 54 mph, regulator 2/16th, cut-off 35 per cent, pressure 175 psi, gradient 1 in 980 up) and further diagrams at MP 35 again showed 1,180 IHP being developed (speed 57 mph, regulator 2/16th, cut-off 35 per cent, pressure 175 psi, gradient level).

Arrival at Beattock station was timed at 4.34 pm, against a booked time of 4.27 pm, i.e. seven minutes late, so there was no recovery of lost time. Strangely, No. 956 was worked at 35 per cent cut-off for the whole of the 14 miles from Lockerbie, no attempt having been made to notch up further, which is a rather different style to the working of No. 956 earlier in the day. There may have been reasons for this, including a concern on boiler steaming becoming progressively more difficult.

BEATTOCK STATION TO BEATTOCK SUMMIT (MP 39.6 TO MP 49.6)

Whilst no stop was made at the summit, it is appropriate to split this section of the working there, and to review No. 956's performance in more detail, since indicator data per cylinder has survived. The trials chart does not mention banking assistance being provided and it is assumed none was taken.

Departure from the station was made seven minutes late, with pressure at 175 psi, using 14/16th regulator and 40 per cent cut-off. At MP 42, where the gradient changes from 1 in 88 to 1 in 80, indicator diagrams were taken, showing 1,140 IHP was being developed (speed 23 mph, regulator 14/16th, cut-off 40 per cent, pressure 172 psi, gradient 1 in 80 up). Further diagrams, taken at MP 44, with pressure reduced to 168 psi, suggested the boiler was becoming 'winded' by the severity of the climb, i.e. the steam raising capacity was less than the steam demand, the shortfall coming from the boiler's thermal inertia, with a consequent reduction in pressure. At MP 44 the diagrams showed 1,020 IHP being developed (speed 26 mph, regulator 14/16th, cut-off 40 per cent, pressure 168 psi, gradient 1 in 80 up).

On the steepest part of the gradient, 1 in 75, the regulator was fully opened, and cut-off lengthened to 50 per cent at MP 46, where indicator diagrams showed 940 IHP being developed (speed 19 mph, regulator 16/16th, cut-off 50 per cent, pressure 165 psi and falling, gradient 1 in 75 up).

The actual IHP per individual cylinder is available for the whole of the climb from Beattock station to the summit, which took a full 28 minutes against a booked time of 22 minutes, i.e. 6 minutes were lost in the 10-mile climb. The details recorded (taken from RHP 136355/30) and illustrated as Figure A2.3 were as shown in the table (above right) (percentages added by the author).

The boiler was clearly 'winded' by this climb, pressure at the summit being 160 psi, and speed having fallen to around 18 mph at MP 47.

The taking of indicator diagrams at the front of an operational locomotive in any circumstances is a difficult exercise, prone to inaccuracies and experimental error, and the actual values recorded should be seen in that context. Looking at the actual figures, there is some evidence of an apparent consistent mismatch between the IHP output of the individual cylinders. It would seem that on average, the

MP	TIME P.M.	TOTAL POWER IHP	POWER PER CYLINDER (AS PERCENTAGE OF TOTAL)		
			RIGHT	LEFT	CENTRE
39.6	4.40	896	32.3	33.3	34.4
	4.44	1,137	34.1	31.7	34.1
	4.48	1,011	33.4	31.7	34.1
	4.52	935	32.5	32.2	35.3
	4.56	1,049	32.3	31.9	35.8
	5.00	878	31.4	33.2	35.3
	5.04	913	33.3	32.3	34.3
	5.06	940	33.7	32.9	33.9

right and left hand cylinders develop broadly similar IHPs, whereas the centre cylinder tends, on average, to produce consistently more than its proportionate share of total IHP output. The difference is around 5.0 to 7.5 per cent, at the cut-off conditions applicable, which is to be expected.

At shorter cut-offs the difference could approach 20 per cent or greater. The increase in power at 4.56 pm relates to the full opening of the regulator and the lengthening of the cut-off to 50 per cent.

Without access to the actual individual cylinder indicator diagrams, it is extremely difficult to be certain as to the reasons for IHP disparity, though some explanation of these differences is offered in the conclusions on this trial trip. However, the performance of No. 956 on Beattock Bank with a 343 ton train must be seen as more than disappointing, Demand for steam could not be sustained with a fully opened regulator and 50 per cent cut-off, pressure falling to 160 psi. Average superheat temperature at 539°F would suggest the boiler having to produce around 10 per cent more steam, for the same work output, as would have been the case with steam at 650°F.

BEATTOCK SUMMIT TO CARSTAIRS (MP 49.6 TO MP 73.6)

The summit was passed 12½ minutes behind booked time, the regulator setting being reduced thereafter to 4/16th and cut-off to 35 per cent. At Elvanfoot (MP 52.4), the regulator was fully closed and boiler pressure had recovered to 170 psi by Crawford (MP 55), where the regulator was opened to 1/16th, cut-off remaining at 35 per cent.

On the continuing downhill run through Abington and Lamington (MP 63), the regulator was opened to 2/16th at MP 64.5, cut-off remaining at 35 per cent. Indicator diagrams taken at MP 66 on the 1 in 200 climb to Symington showed 920 IHP being developed (speed 46 mph, regulator 2/16th, cut-off 35 per cent, pressure 172 psi, gradient 1 in 200 up).

On the 1 in 150 downhill (MP 71) to Carstairs, the regulator had to be opened to 2/16th to retain speed into Carstairs station, where arrival was timed at 5.35 pm, boiler pressure again being reduced, just before Carstairs, to 160 psi.

No. 956 and its train were now 15 minutes behind booked time, having lost a further three minutes on the descent from Beattock Summit, a most disappointing result. The boiler was clearly steaming very poorly in these circumstances.

CARSTAIRS TO GLASGOW (MP 73.6 TO MP 102.3)

The Carstairs departure was made 17 minutes behind booked time (total net lost time to Carstairs departure was 13 minutes) at 5.42 pm with pressure at 170 psi, the regulator set at 4/16th, cut-off remaining at 35 per cent. In climbing the 1 in 400 through Cleghorn (MP 76), followed by the 1 in 200 to the summit at MP 78.4, boiler pressure was again seriously prejudiced, the summit (MP 80) being breasted at 156 psi and falling.

The indicator diagrams taken on this section show that, at MP 75.5,

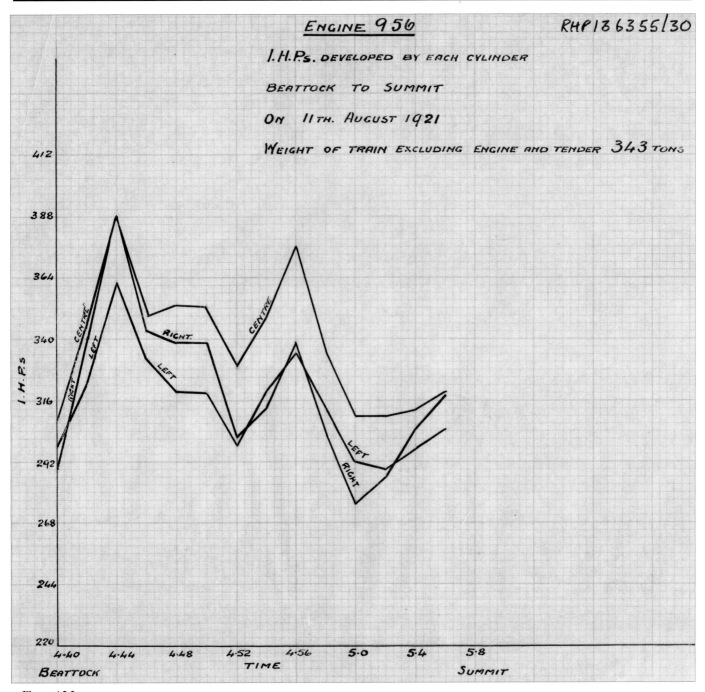

Figure A2.3
Caledonian Railway Co. 'Trials Chart' for Individual Cylinder IHPs on Engine No. 956, between Beattock station and Beattock Summit, on the 11th August 1921. Results from working the 3.35 pm Passenger Train from Carlisle to Glasgow Central. *NRS: GD456, RHP136355/30*

just south of Cleghorn, 1,020 IHP was being developed (speed 37 mph, regulator 6/16th, cut-off 35 per cent, pressure 165 psi, gradient 1 in 440 up).

The downhill running from MP 78 to Uddingston Junction (MP 93.8) was uninspiring, with a maximum speed of 48 mph passing Overton (MP 85). The short climb to Newton caused boiler pressure to again be significantly reduced to 165 psi, with continuing downhill running through Cambuslang seeing pressure drop to 156 psi. A maximum speed of 56 mph was recorded after passing Rutherglen.

On arrival at Glasgow at 6.21 pm, some four minutes had been recovered from Carstairs, though boiler pressure was only 150 psi and falling. One hesitates to use the word that No. 956 'limped' into Central station in these circumstances, but in reality that was the position.

GENERAL COMMENT ON NO. 956 PERFORMANCE

Compared to the earlier Up run to Carlisle, this return Down working seems quite uninspiring, indeed verging on the feeble. Time was consistently lost, and the six minutes alone lost in the climb from Beattock station to the summit, with boiler pressure down to 160 psi, points to steam raising problems, which seemed not to afflict No. 956 earlier in the day. A maximum speed of 62 mph was recorded on the descent from Beattock Summit to Carstairs, so, ostensibly, it would appear there were no obvious *'disturbing influences'* around the centre valve mechanism.

Coal consumption for the Down working was 58.02 lbs per mile, a much higher figure than the 38.13 lbs per mile recorded earlier in the day for the Up working, whilst a further indicator of poor steaming capability is reflected in the evaporation rate of water per lb of fired coal. An exceptionally encouraging figure in excess of 9 lbs of water was recorded earlier in the day for the Up working. For the return journey a figure of only 6.20 lbs of water per lb of coal fired applied, the normally accepted figure being around 7.5 to 8 lbs.

The fact that significantly more coal was fired for much less water evaporated is a sure sign that combustion was impaired, and as a consequence, heat transfer much reduced. There can be various reasons for this. First, primary air may have been constrained due to the ashpan becoming choked – a poor burning fire in the rear grate section would compound matters. Further, if the unburned coal accumulated in the smokebox in sufficient quantities, then the lower rows of small tubes may become blocked.

From the individual cylinder indicator diagrams, it is recorded

that the centre cylinder was providing more than its proportionate share of power. This is a known characteristic of derived motion valve gears, being lost motion and inertial load dependent, and is a complex function of locomotive cut-off, speed, valve friction and the geometry of the derived gear. Superheat conditions were marginally less than on the Up working, with smokebox vacuum conditions being the same.

No details are available as to what in the way of servicing was undertaken at Kingmoor shed during the three-hour turn-round time between workings, or if any attempt was made to empty the ashpan or clean the fire. No comment on these matters is found in the trials' schedules. It seems clear, *prima facie*, that the poorer return working by No. 956 to Glasgow was almost wholly related to adverse boiler and steam circuit performance.

TRIAL TRIP SUMMARY OF RECORDED VALUES, 11TH AUGUST 1921

MP	LOCATION	GRADIENT	SPEED MPH	REGULATOR N/16TH	CUT-OFF PER CENT	POWER IHP	BOILER PRESSURE PSI
0	Carlisle	–	–	–	–	–	175
4.0	Rockliffe	level	43	2	30	950	175
8.5	Gretna	1:200 up	45	14	30	1,140	174
12.3	–	1:200 up	45	14	30	1,120	170
19.3	–	1:200 up	51	2	30	990	170
22.5	–	1:200 down	46	2	35	1,020	175
25.8	Lockerbie	–	–	–	–	–	175
30.2	–	1:980 up	54	2	35	1,180	175
35.0	–	level	57	2	35	1,180	175
39.6	Beattock station	–	–	–	–	–	175
42.0	–	1:80 up	23	14	40	1,140	172
44.0	–	1:80 up	26	14	40	1,020	168
46.0	–	1:75 up	19	16	50	940	165
49.6	Beattock Summit	level	18	16	50	–	160
66.2	–	1:200 up	46	2	35	920	175
73.6	Carstairs	–	–	–	–	–	170
75.5	Cleghorn	1:440 up	37	6	35	1,020	165
99.0	Rutherglen	level	56	–	–	–	155
102.3	Glasgow	–	–	–	–	–	150

APPENDIX 3:
POLMADIE TO KINGMOOR RETURN WORKING, 25TH OCTOBER 1922

ENGINE: No. 956
WORKING: 08.50 AM TEST TRAIN, POLMADIE TO KINGMOOR AND 1.10 PM RETURN

COMMENTS ON INFORMATION RECORDED

This return working from Polmadie to Kingmoor, non-stop in each direction, was made by engine No. 956, hauling a 500 ton Test Train, after fitting with Stephenson's link motion in substitution for the initial form of derived motion. The instrumented working was made some four weeks after No. 956 had performed rather badly on an un-instrumented return working from Glasgow Central to Carlisle and return with Lord Monkswell on the footplate.

Recognising these workings were made between Polmadie and Kingmoor, the respective timetables for the trials were nevertheless set to accord with current express passenger train schedules. Since each working used in excess of 4,400 gallons of water, and the standard '956' Class tender held 4,600 gallons, a McIntosh 5,000 gallon bogie tender may have been provided.

Unlike the August 1921 trials data for No. 956, no indicator diagrams with steam chest pressures and MEP data has, at the time of writing, come to light for this return working.

Other comments on recorded data are as in Appendix 1.

WORKING: 8.50 AM TEST TRAIN, POLMADIE TO KINGMOOR

Specific trials information has been taken from the CR trials charts held in Montague Smith collection, the National Records of Scotland, ref. RHP136355/31 and RHP136355/34.

Weight of train, excluding engine and tender	500 tons
Water used on outward working	4,442 gallons
Coal used on outward working	6,720 lbs
Water evaporated per mile	44.64 gallons
Pounds of water evaporated per pound of coal	6.6 lbs
Coal consumed per gallon of water evaporated	1.5 lbs
Coal consumed per ton-mile	0.13 lbs
Greatest vacuum created in smokebox:	
bottom of smokebox	4.5 ins WG
top of smokebox	7.5 ins WG
Maximum temperature of superheated steam	560 °F
Average temperature of superheated steam	521 °F
Temperature of water in tank	50 °F

PASSING TIMES

	BOOKED	ACTUAL	DIFF. (MINS)*
Polmadie (MP 100.5)	08.50	08.50	-
Rutherglen (MP 98.5)	08.55	08.55	-
Motherwell (MP 88.9)	09.07	09.13	(6)
Law Junction (MP 84.2)	09.18	09.28	(10)
Carstairs (MP 73.5)	09.34	09.50	(16)
Symington (MP 66.8)	09.44	10.00	(16)
Beattock Summit (MP 49.6)	10.08	10.26	(18)
Beattock station (MP 39.5)	10.19	10.38	(19)
Lockerbie (MP 25.8)	10.34	10.54	(20)
Gretna (MP 8.5)	10.50	11.14	(24)
Kingmoor (MP 1.4)	11.00	11.23	(23)

NOTE:
*times are taken from trials chart.

COMMENTARY ON TRIALS CHARTS

The following commentary on the working uses the chart and related data shown in Figure A3.1 (ref. RHP136355/31). Comment is also made on the individual cylinder IHP data taken from chart RHP136355/34.

POLMADIE TO CARSTAIRS (MP 100.5 TO MP 73.5)

Departure from Polmadie was on time at 08.50 am and Rutherglen (MP 98.5) was passed at 28 mph, with 40 per cent cut-off, 4/16th regulator setting and a boiler pressure of 180 psi. The trials chart shows full boiler pressure being available throughout the working, with the exception of the run down into Carstairs. Indicator diagrams were taken passing Cambuslang (MP 97.5), showing that 1,001 IHP was being developed (speed 29 mph, regulator 5/16th, cut-off 40 per cent, pressure 180 psi, gradient 1 in 165 up). Speed peaked at 46 mph passing Bothwell Junction (MP 92.7).

On the climb to the summit at MP 78.4 just south of Braidwood, the regulator was progressively opened from MP 92 and further indicator diagrams taken. On the level at MP 90, diagrams showed that No. 956 was developing 1,068 IHP (speed 26 mph, regulator 8/16th, cut-off 40 per cent, pressure 180 psi, gradient level), and when passing Carluke (MP 82), diagrams showed 1,031 IHP being developed (speed 29 mph, regulator 12/16th, cut-off 40 per cent, pressure 180 psi, gradient 1 in 100 up).

The summit at MP 78.4 was passed at 24 mph with cut-off increased to 50 per cent, the regulator setting remaining at 12/16th, and boiler pressure being steady at 180 psi. The regulator was then eased to 2/16th passing Cleghorn (MP 74) and again to 1/16th on the run into Carstairs. Pressure was allowed to drop to 170 psi, though it had recovered to 180 psi on passing through the station.

A progressive delay against booked time built up over this section, the working being 16 minutes behind the booked schedule at Carstairs.

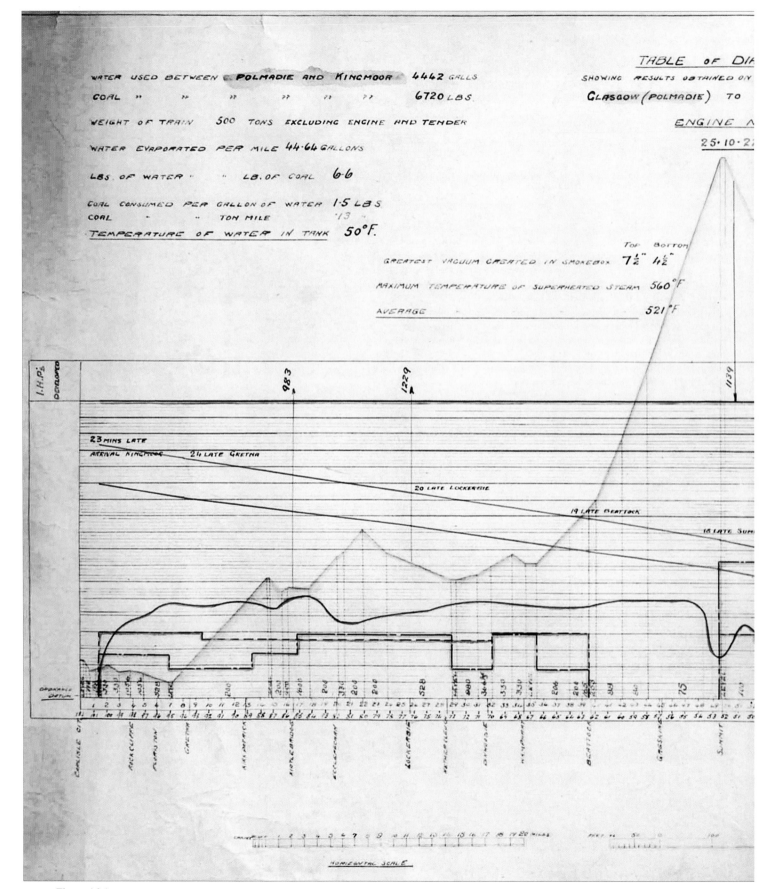

Figure A3.1
Caledonian Railway Co. 'Trials Chart' for the 8.50 am Special 500 Ton Test Train, from Polmadie Yard to Kingmoor Yard on the 25th October 1922.
Engine No. 956.
NRS: GR456, RHP136355/31

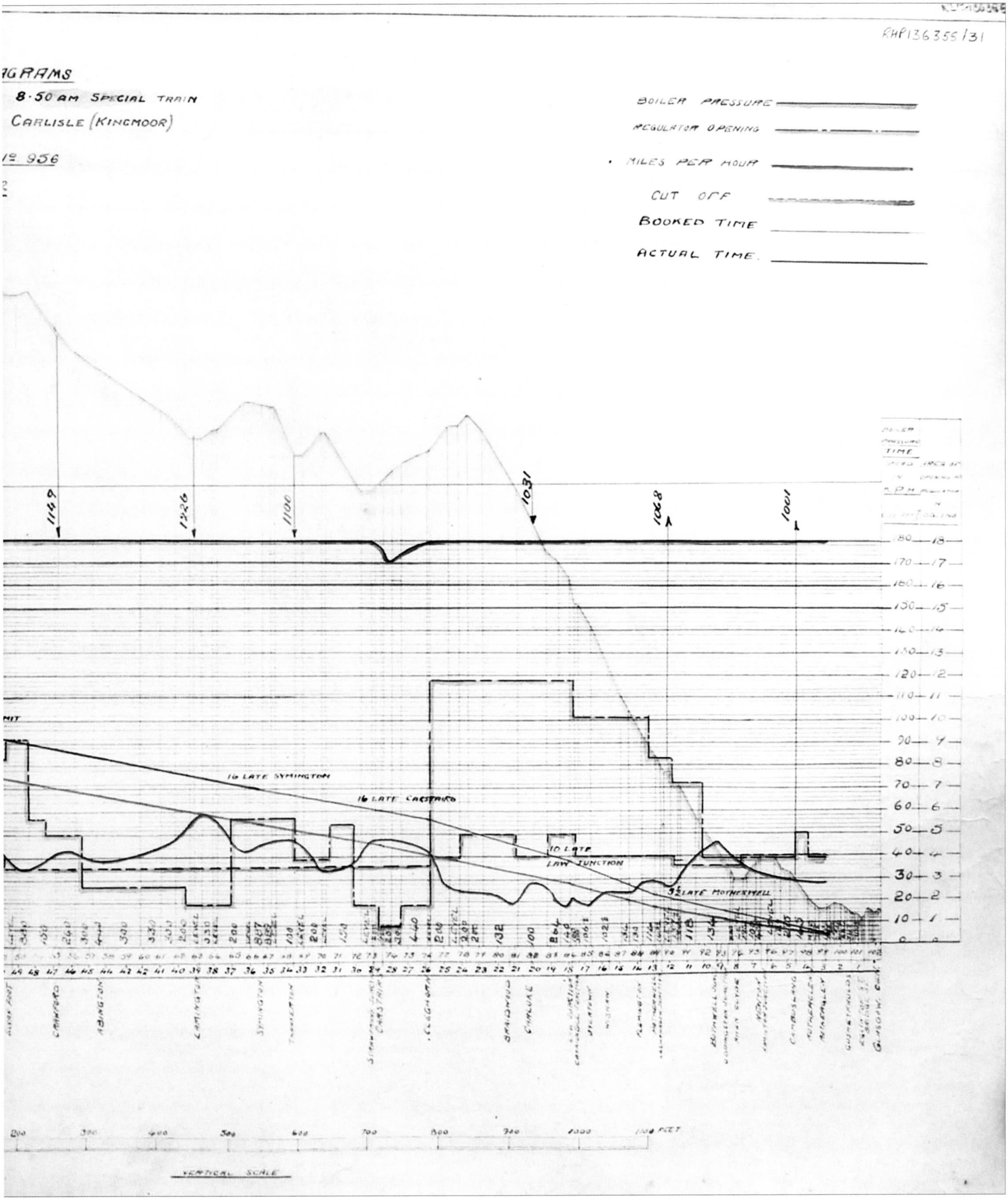

RHP136355/31
AGRAMS
8·50 AM SPECIAL TRAIN
CARLISLE (KINGMOOR)
Nº 956
BOILER PRESSURE
REGULATOR OPENING
MILES PER HOUR
CUT OFF
BOOKED TIME
ACTUAL TIME
16 LATE SYMINGTON
16 LATE CARSTAIRS
10 LATE LAW JUNCTION
3½ LATE MOTHERWELL
CRAWFORD
ABINGTON
LAMINGTON
SYMINGTON
CARSTAIRS
CLEGHORN
BRAIDWOOD
CARLUKE
WISHAW
MOTHERWELL
UDDINGSTON
CAMBUSLANG
RUTHERGLEN
GLASGOW
VERTICAL SCALE
1100 FEET

Carstairs to Beattock Summit (MP 73.5 to MP 49.6)

Passing through Carstairs (MP 73.5) recorded cut-off was 35 per cent and regulator at 1/16th, opened out to 2/16th at Strawfrank Junction (MP 73), where speed was 48 mph and boiler pressure recovered to 180 psi. At Thankerton (MP 68.5) indicator diagrams were taken showing No. 956 developing 1,100 IHP (speed 48 mph, regulator 6/16th, cut-off 35 per cent, pressure 180 psi, gradient 1 in 100 up). Further diagrams were take on the level near Lamington (MP 63), just prior to the 1 in 200 climb to Abington, where 1,226 IHP was developed (speed 58 mph, regulator 2/16th, cut-off 35 per cent, pressure 180 psi, gradient level, having just run down the 1 in 200 from Symington (MP 66.8)).

These two sets of indicator diagrams, at MP 66.8 and MP 63 respectively, are perhaps not entirely representative of locomotive capability, since they were both taken at the end of downhill runs, where gravitational assistance had resulted in higher speeds than might have been anticipated for the prevalent steaming conditions.

A more representative set of diagrams was taken at Crawford (MP 55) on the 1 in 150 up climb to Beattock Summit, where 1,149 IHP was recorded (speed 44 mph, regulator 5/16th, cut-off 35 per cent, pressure 180 psi, gradient 1 in 150 up). A further set of diagrams was taken at MP 50.5, where the gradient increased to 1 in 100 up, which showed 1,139 IHP being developed (speed 40 mph and falling, regulator 8/16th, cut-off 40 per cent, pressure 180 psi, gradient 1 in 100 up).

What is surprising and puzzling about No. 956's handling between MP 54 and MP 49.6 (Beattock summit) is that no attempt was made to open the regulator beyond 9/16th. Whilst speed increased from 35 mph (when the regulator was opened from 5/16th to 9/16th) at MP 53, to 40 mph at MP 52.2, the regulator was then eased back to 8/16th in the face of the on-going 1 in 100 climb, boiler pressure remaining at 180 psi. No chart annotation on the reasons for locomotive handling at this point are given, but the net effect was that with unchanged boiler pressure, stated regulator and cut-off conditions, speed fell progressively from 45 mph to 26 mph in the space of the two miles before Beattock Summit.

There must have been some very specific reason why, on a trials working, no attempt was made to drive No. 956 much more aggressively on the final pull to the summit. Moreover, the fact that the regulator was eased back during this climb, not ostensibly related to boiler pressure, suggests some other problem or limitation, which was not entirely speed sensitive (speeds touching 60 mph had already been recorded and were to be recorded subsequently), was at work.

Recognising that the regulator was eased back when the train was running at only 40 mph and approaching the summit, perhaps this action could also have been related to potential braking difficulties. If a 60 mph line-speed limit was imposed with a 500 ton train on the downhill section beyond the summit, then perhaps the summit could justifiably only be passed at a lower than normal speed, but that of course would not reconcile with the set timetable. Beattock Summit was passed at 26 mph, a further two minutes having been lost on the booked time since Symington.

In reality, there are a number of imponderables here, which may well remain unanswered.

Beattock Summit to Kingmoor (MP 49.6 to MP 1.4)

The regulator was fully closed on passing the summit and the train coasted for almost ten miles down the 1 in 75 followed by 1 in 80 and 1 in 88 grades to Beattock station. Speed built up down the bank to 60 mph, which was sustained for six miles, though no effort was made to make up for lost time by putting steam on. Remarkably, a further minute was lost between the summit and Beattock station, making a total loss of 19 minutes against booked time to that point. Braking may well have been applied on the descent, but the chart is silent on this.

As speed fell to 56 mph passing Beattock station (MP 39.5), the regulator was opened to 2/16th and cut-off set to 40 per cent, with speed being maintained in the mid-50 mph range for several miles. Indicator diagrams were taken passing Lockerbie (MP 25.8) on the 1 in 528 up-grade, showing No. 956 developing 1,229 IHP (speed 52 mph, regulator 4/16th, cut-off 35 per cent, pressure 180 psi, gradient 1 in 528 up). Again, surprisingly, no effort seems to have been made to further open the regulator at this point. With the same set of boiler pressure conditions, regulator and cut-off, speed dropped to 46 mph at MP 21 and rose to 62 mph at MP 18, where, following the earlier patterns, the regulator was eased to 2.5/16th, then eased further to 2/16th. Indicator diagrams taken at Kirtlebridge (MP 16.5) showed 983 IHP being developed (speed 60 mph, regulator 2.5/16th, cut-off 35 per cent, pressure 180 psi, gradient 1 in 1,600 up).

Speed was maintained in the 55 to 58 mph range for the next nine miles, though in passing Gretna (MP 8.5), the working was logged as 24 minutes behind schedule, having lost a further four minutes since Lockerbie. Again, no attempt was made to recover time, or to work the locomotive more aggressively with greater regulator openings or shorter cut-offs.

General Comment on No. 956 Performance

There are many parts of this working which are inexplicable, though if a speed restriction of 60 mph was mandated, then some rationality emerges. However, it would seem somewhat pointless to set an express passenger schedule for the working, requiring speeds in excess of 70 mph, and then mandating a speed restriction. Alternatively, rough riding above 60 mph could have been the constraining influence.

Boiler pressure, according to the trials chart, remained 'up to the mark' throughout, and the working seemed to make no call on the boiler's thermal inertia, though perhaps some front end limit had been reached. The novel exhaust passage layout, coupled to the excessive lead given to the Stephenson's motion at higher cut-offs may not have helped, but these are unlikely to have been the principal causes of this mediocre performance.

If the intention was to demonstrate that a 500 ton train could be worked non-stop from Polmadie to Kingmoor by one locomotive, with a 60 mph speed restriction imperative and no water stop, then No. 956 proved up to the task. However, it seems very clear from the method of working adopted, and the actual performance of the locomotive, the 500 ton train could not be operated to the express passenger timetable. As a matter of course, one would have assumed the operation of the newly fitted Stephenson's link motion would certainly have been examined in detail during the trial, but no related data is noted on the charts.

In terms of locomotive efficiency, coal consumption at 67.8 lbs per mile would be seen as a high figure and the evaporation rate of 6.6 lbs of water per lb of coal fired suggests boiler efficiency being not of the best. For most efficient boiler operation on a locomotive of this type, coal consumption should be around 50 lbs per mile or less, and an evaporation rate in the range 7.5 to 8.0 lbs of water per lb of coal fired would be looked for. So, one may conclude that boiler operation, in terms of combustion and heat transfer efficiencies, was some way from optimal.

The temperature of superheated steam, given as an average of 521 °F and a maximum of 560 °F must again be seen as being too low, indeed slightly lower than similar data obtained during the 1921 trials workings. These lower than normal steam temperatures arise from the free-gas area for the flues being proportionately too low, plus the use of short return loops for the superheater elements, and suggest no modifications had been made to the locomotive's boiler, or its superheater, when the valve gear changes were made. Steam consumption would have been around 10 per cent higher than would be the case with average steam temperatures of 650 deg. F., for the same work output.

Trials Trip Summary of Recorded Values, 25th October 1922

MP	Location	Gradient	Speed MPH	Regulator N/16TH	Cut-off PER CENT	Power IHP	Boiler Pressure PSI
100.5	Polmadie	–	–	–	–	–	180
98.5	Rutherglen	level	28	4	40	–	180
97.5	Cambuslang	1:165 up	29	5	40	1,001	180
90.0	–	level	26	8	40	1,068	180
82.0	Carluke	1:100 up	29	12	40	1,031	180
73.5	Carstairs	1:200 down	48	2	35	–	175
68.5	Thankerton	1:100 up	48	5.5	35	1,100	180
63.0	Lamington	level	58	2	35	1,226	180
55.0	Crawford	1:150 up	44	5	35	1,149	180
50.5	–	1:100 up	40	8	40	1,139	180
49.6	Beattock Summit	level	26	–	–	–	180
39.5	Beattock station	1:253 down	56	2	40	–	180
25.8	Lockerbie	1:528 up	52	4	35	1,229	180
16.5	Kirtlebridge	1:1,600 up	60	2.5	35	983	180
8.5	Gretna	1:200 down	56	2	40	–	180
1.4	Kingmoor	–	–	–	–	–	180

Individual Cylinder Indicator Diagrams from Chart RHP136355/34

On a separate trials chart, plots of the IHPs for the individual cylinders are given for specific points on the working. From Rutherglen (MP 98.5) to Cleghorn (MP 76), a series of twenty-three sets of diagrams were taken, at roughly one mile intervals, and the individual cylinder IHPs plotted on the trials chart. Whilst there will be experimental error in the taking of the diagrams and the transcription from indicator data to respective IHP figures, these diagrams nevertheless give evidence of No. 956's overall performance, recognising the substitution of Stephenson's gear for the centre cylinder valve motion.

From these twenty-three sets of diagrams, covering the 800 to 1,229 IHP range, the right-hand cylinder produced on average 36.1 per cent of total IHP, the left-hand cylinder 34.1 per cent of IHP and the centre cylinder 29.8 per cent. The small difference between the right and left cylinder IHPs is consistent across both the power range and the individual mile-post measurement points. Additionally, the centre cylinder consistently provides less than its proportionate share of the power output, a worst case showing the provision of only 27.2 per cent of total output IHP. At the higher power output levels, the right and left cylinder outputs tend to converge to a total of around 71 to 72 per cent of IHP, the centre cylinder providing the balance, i.e. the centre cylinder produced approximately 20 per cent less power than the outer two.

The small and consistent difference between the outside cylinders, with the right-hand always providing the higher value, is probably due to the steam distribution arrangements.

A further series of fifteen sets of individual cylinder indicator diagrams was taken between MP 71, just north of Thankerton, and MP 49.6, Beattock Summit, the maximum power developed in this section being 1,149 IHP, with the right and left cylinders providing almost equal power outputs on an averaging basis, and the centre cylinder 29.7 per cent of output on the same basis, i.e. around 15 to 20 per cent less than the outer two cylinders. In this section, the locomotive was worked for the majority of the mileage at 35 per cent cut-off, with only the last two miles to Beattock Summit being worked at 40 per cent.

The final series of six sets of individual cylinder diagrams was taken between MP 29 and MP 22, covering the climb through Lockerbie followed by the 1 in 200 to the summit at MP 22. This ascent was made at a constant 40 per cent cut-off, the outer two cylinders providing 71.3 per cent of the output power, the centre cylinder providing 28.7 per cent, i.e. the centre cylinder again provided around 20 per cent less power than the outer two. At the lower power levels on this series of diagrams, the centre cylinder provided almost 30 per cent less power than the outer two. Maximum power developed was recorded at 1,229 IHP passing MP 25.7, the centre cylinder providing 15 per cent less power than the outer two.

Recognising that with derived motion, No. 956 could, in certain circumstances, produce around 20 per cent more power in the centre cylinder, and with Stephenson's gear around 20 per cent less power in the centre cylinder, then in comparative terms, at high cut-offs (40 per cent and above) the engine fitted with Stephenson's link motion could only produce 88 per cent of the output of the one fitted with derived valve gear. This might be one reason to explain the reversion to the second form of derived motion.

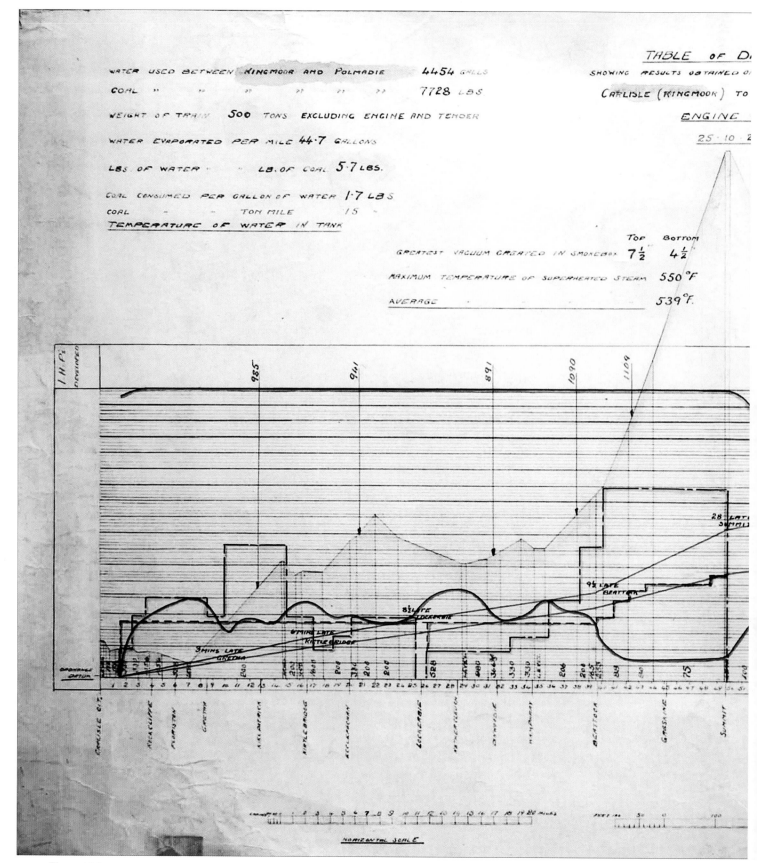

Figure A3.2
Caledonian Railway Co. 'Trials Chart' for the 1.10 pm Special 500 Ton Test Train from Kingmoor Yard to Polmadie Yard on the 25th October 1922.
Engine No. 956.
NRS: GD456, RHP136355/32

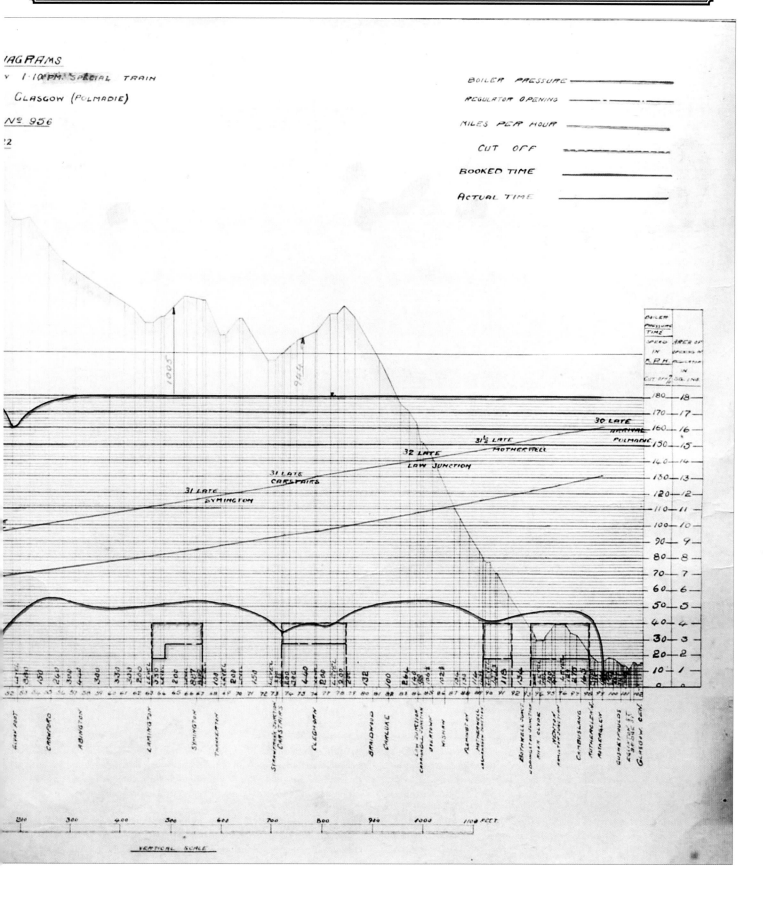

DIAGRAMS

1·10 P.M. SPECIAL TRAIN

GLASGOW (POLMADIE)

Nº 956

BOILER PRESSURE ⎯⎯⎯⎯⎯
REGULATOR OPENING ⎯⎯⎯⎯⎯
MILES PER HOUR ⎯⎯⎯⎯⎯
CUT OFF ⎯ ⎯ ⎯ ⎯
BOOKED TIME ⎯⎯⎯⎯
ACTUAL TIME ⎯⎯⎯⎯

30 LATE ARRIVAL POLMADIE
31½ LATE MOTHERWELL
32 LATE LAW JUNCTION
31 LATE CARSTAIRS
31 LATE SYMINGTON

VERTICAL SCALE

Working: 1.10 pm Test Train, Kingmoor to Polmadie

Specific trials information has been taken from the CR trials chart held in Montague Smith collection, the National Records of Scotland, ref.: RHP136355/32 and RHP136355/33.

Weight of train, excluding engine and tender	500 tons
Water used on return working	4,454 gallons
Coal used on return working	5,936 lbs
Water evaporated per mile	44.7 gallons
Pounds of water evaporated per pound of coal	5.7 lbs
Coal consumed per gallon of water evaporated	1.7 lbs
Coal consumed per ton-mile	0.15 lbs
Greatest vacuum created in smokebox:	
bottom of smokebox	4 ins WG
top of smokebox	7.5 ins WG
Maximum temperature of superheated steam	550 °F
Average temperature of superheated steam	539 °F
Temperature of water in tank	not stated

Passing Times

	BOOKED	ACTUAL	DIFF *(MINS)
Kingmoor (MP 1.4)	1.10	1.10	–
Gretna (MP 8.5)	1.19	1.22	(3)
Kirtlebridge (MP 16.5)	1.29	1.35	(6)
Lockerbie (MP 25.8)	1.39	1.48	(9)
Beattock station (MP 39.5)	1.55	2.05	(10)
Beattock Summit (MP 49.6)	2.16	2.44	(28)
Symington (MP 66.8)	2.35	3.06	(31)
Carstairs (MP 73.5)	2.44	3.15	(31)
Law Junction (MP 84.2)	2.58	3.30	(32)
Motherwell (MP 88.9)	3.05	3.37	(32)
Polmadie (MP 100.5)	3.22	3.52	(30)

NOTE:
*times are taken from trials chart.

Commentary on Trials Charts

Figure A3.2 (ref. RHP 136355/32) gives overall details of the working, whilst Figure A3.3 (ref. RHP 136355/33) gives individual cylinder IHP outputs for the climb from Beattock station to the summit.

Kingmoor to Beattock Station (MP 1.4 to MP 39.5)
Departure from Kingmoor was on time at 1.10 pm, with cut-off set at 35 per cent, this setting being maintained until Lockerbie. The initial regulator setting of 2/16th was progressively opened to 5/16th by Rockcliffe, speed rising to 50 mph at MP 7. Boiler pressure, initially 175 psi, quickly rose to 180 psi by Rockcliffe and remained at that level to Beattock station. The regulator was eased to 4/16th for about a mile from MP 8.5, then opened to 8/16th at MP 10 on the 1 in 200 climb through Kirkpatrick (MP 13). Indicator diagrams were taken at MP 13 showing 985 IHP was being developed (speed 36 mph, regulator 8/16th, cut-off 35 per cent, pressure 180 psi, gradient 1 in 200 up).

A further set of diagrams was taken at MP 20.6, showing that 941 IHP was being developed by No. 956 (speed 40 mph, regulator 4/16th, cut-off 35 per cent, pressure 180 psi, gradient 1 in 200 up). It is surprising that although the working was six minutes late passing Kirtlebridge, and boiler pressure 180 psi, unaccountably, the engine

was being worked at only 4/16th regulator output and the regulator was fully closed passing through Lockerbie (MP 25.8). The working was a further 2½ minutes late passing Lockerbie, i.e. 8½ minutes down on booked time.

This, of course, may have again been conditioned by the need to limit train speed to 60 mph on downhill sections. Indeed, on the downhill section at 1 in 528 beyond Lockerbie (MP 25.8), the speed rose to 56 mph passing Nethercleuch (MP 28.6). Further indicator diagrams were taken at Dinwoodie (MP 31.5) on the 1 in 366 climb before Wamphray, where No. 956 was developing 891 IHP (speed 40 mph, regulator 2/16th, cut-off 35 per cent, pressure 180 psi, gradient 1 in 366 up).

After passing Wamphray, the regulator was progressively opened to 8/16th when passing Beattock station, cut-off being 35 per cent. Indicator diagrams taken at MP 37.6, two miles before Beattock station, show No. 956 developing 1,090 IHP (speed 44 mph, regulator 5/16th, cut-off 35%, pressure 180 psi, gradient 1 in 200 up). However, this method of working resulted in the train being a further one minute late passing Beattock station.

Beattock Station to Beattock Summit (39.5 to MP 49.6)
This section of the working can only be described as extraordinary. Passing Beattock station, speed was reducing through 35 mph and whilst cut-off was lengthened progressively to 60 per cent and the regulator opened to 12/16th, speed continued to decline, stabilising at 14 mph at MP 42. The climb continued for a further 7.6 miles to the summit at MP 49.6 with no appreciable increase in speed, even though finally No. 956 was working in full gear (65 per cent cut-off). The regulator setting remained at 12/16th until the summit was breasted, when it was fully closed. Boiler pressure was recorded as 180 psi throughout this section, but unfortunately no data on steam chest pressure or MEP is available. The ten-mile climb took a full 40 minutes, the average speed being 15 mph.

The main trials chart, Figure A3.2, notes indicator diagrams were taken at MP 42.5, on the 1 in 80 up gradient, showing that No. 956 was developing 1,109 IHP (speed 14 mph, regulator 12/16th, cut-off 55 per cent, pressure 180 psi, gradient 1 in 80 up). In addition to the data recorded on the main trials chart Figure A3.2, Figure A3.3 records the detail of individual cylinder IHP during the climb from Beattock station to the summit.

On this climb to Beattock Summit, it is entirely possible that a quiescent point had been reach, where the locomotive's boiler limit had been reached, further opening of the regulator having no effect on output power.

The data set out in the table on the facing page, covering the climb to Beattock Summit, is taken from Figure A3.3, a time axis being used to record progress up the bank.

On average, the right and left cylinders produced 34.9 per cent and 35.1 per cent respectively of the total power developed, whilst 30 per cent was produced by the centre, i.e. the centre cylinder consistently produced around 15 to 20 per cent less power than the outer two.

Whilst one might have expected the left cylinder to exhibit a lower IHP than the right, due to the smokebox steam pipe layout, these results do not support that conclusion, though the margins of experimental error may mask the actual position. Moreover, from these results it is difficult to draw any objective conclusions on variations in centre cylinder output with changes in cut-off.

Overall, the climb to Beattock Summit resulted in a further significant delay of 18 minutes to booked time. The overall delay to the summit, which was passed at 14 mph, was 28 minutes.

Beattock Summit to Carstairs (MP 49.6 to MP 73.5)
On passing the summit the regulator was fully closed, speed rising on the 1 in 100 downhill, 56 mph being recorded passing Crawford (MP 55) before settling at 50 mph. Boiler pressure was allowed to

MP	TIME PM	TOTAL IHP	RIGHT		LEFT		CENTRE	
			IHP	PER CENT	IHP	PER CENT	IHP	PER CENT
39.6	2.06 (station)	1212	418	34.5	430	35.5	364	30.0
	2.10	904	308	34.1	316	35.0	280	30.9
	2.14	821	280	34.1	287	35.0	254	30.9
	2.18	767	268	35.0	272	35.4	227	29.6
	2.22	808	286	35.4	284	35.1	238	29.5
	2.26	760	268	35.2	266	35.0	226	29.8
	2.30	719	254	35.1	248	34.5	218	30.4
	2.34	742	262	35.3	262	35.3	218	29.4
	2.38	772	275	35.6	268	34.7	229	29.7
	2.42	747	257	34.4	266	35.6	224	30.0
49.6	2.46 (summit)	780	274	35.2	272	35.0	234	29.8

Header spanning RIGHT, LEFT, CENTRE columns: INDIVIDUAL CYLINDER IHPs AND PERCENTAGES OF TOTAL

fall after the summit was passed and declined to 160 psi at MP 52.3, before recovering to 180 psi at MP 57. Thereafter, the regulator was opened to 2/16th at Lamington (MP 63), and increased to 3/16th at MP 64.4, with cut-off set at 40 per cent. Indicator diagrams were taken at MP 65 on a short up-hill 1 in 200 section, with No. 956 developing 1,005 IHP (speed 52 mph, regulator 3/16th, cut-off 40 per cent, pressure 180 psi, gradient 1 in 200 up).

Symington (MP 66.8) was then passed at 54 mph, after which the regulator was fully closed, speed falling to 35 mph through Carstairs, where the regulator was opened to 3/16th with 40 per cent cut-off. A further three minutes was lost on the booked schedule between Beattock Summit and Carstairs, giving an overall 31 minutes lost time at this point.

CARSTAIRS TO POLMADIE (MP 73.5 TO MP 100.5)
On passing Carstairs (MP 73.3), the regulator was opened to 3/16th, with 40 per cent cut-off, and indicator diagrams taken on the 1 in 440 climb approaching Cleghorn (MP 74), where No. 956 was recorded as developing 944 IHP (speed 40 mph, regulator 3/16th, cut-off 40 per cent, pressure 180 psi, gradient 1 in 440 up). Once over the summit at MP 78, the regulator was again fully closed and the train coasted to Motherwell (MP 88.9). Speed rose to 54 mph passing Law Junction (MP 84.2), though a further minute had been lost on the booked time, giving 32 minutes lost in total.

Limited use of the regulator at 3/16th setting, with 40 per cent cut-off, was made passing through Motherwell (MP 88.9) and through Newton (MP 95.4) and Cambuslang (MP 97.3), the trial terminating at Polmadie at 3.52 pm, some 30 minutes over booked time.

GENERAL COMMENT ON NO. 956 PERFORMANCE

Whilst there may have been sound reasons to restrict downhill running speeds, the uphill performance of No. 956 was mediocre at best. Specifically, the boiler seems to have been steaming very poorly, with an evaporation rate of only 5.7 lbs of water per lb of coal fired, yet the trial's charts note boiler pressure maintained at 180 psi throughout. Further, to evaporate 5.7 lbs of water per lb of coal fired, and use 78 lbs of coal per mile in the process, suggests that heat transfer and combustion conditions were far from ideal, inferring significant amounts of unburned coal was accumulated in the smokebox.

Unfortunately, no details have survived regarding the locomotive servicing at Kingmoor, nor any similar details related to the arrival back at Polmadie. With an 11.23 am arrival at Kingmoor and a 1.10 pm departure, around 60 minutes would be available for servicing.

The incompatibilities of the Walschaert's and Stephenson's motions, in regards to lead, are unlikely to have been contributing factors to overall performance, though the fitting of Stephenson's gear would have depressed the power output by around 12 per cent, compared with a derived motion fit.

Maximum steam temperature of 550 °F was marginally lower than that recorded on the Up working and significantly lower than the 590 °F achieved by No. 956 on earlier trials. Smokebox vacuum at 4.5 ins WG in the lower and 7.5 ins WG in the upper areas would be considered to be on the low side.

Overall, this trial irrefutably demonstrated that No. 956 was

TRIALS TRIP SUMMARY OF RECORDED VALUES, 25TH OCTOBER 1922

MP	LOCATION	GRADIENT	SPEED MPH	REGULATOR N/16TH	CUT-OFF PER CENT	POWER IHP	BOILER PRESSURE PSI
1.4	Kingmoor	–	–	–	–	–	180
13.0	Kirkpatrick	1:200 up	38	8	35	985	180
20.6	Ecclefechan	1:200 up	40	4	35	941	180
31.5	Dinwoodie	1:366 up	40	2	35	891	180
37.6	–	1:200 up	44	5	35	1,090	180
42.5	–	1:80 up	14	12	55	1,109	180
49.6	Beattock Summit	1:75 up	14	12	65	–	180
65.0	–	1:200 up	52	2	40	1,005	180
74.0	–	1:440 up	39	3	40	944	180
99.0	Rutherglen	level	42	–	–	–	180
100.5	Polmadie	–	–	–	–	–	180

unable to work a 500 ton train on the main line between Glasgow and Carlisle within the express passenger timetable, indeed hauling a 400 ton train to similar timings also seemed beyond its capabilities. Handling a return trip with a 60 minute turn-round time at Kingmoor seemed out of the question.

The low superheat position may have been recognised by St Rollox from these trials results, in that tubeplate drawings were altered to allow the fitting of increased area superheater elements for new construction. One suspects these steaming problems may have been covered up at St Rollox, if indeed they were understood. Only

through the survival of the altered tubeplate drawings, plus trials data, have these difficulties come to light.

As previously noted, in September 1922, the month previous to this working, Lord Monkswell was granted a footplate trip on No. 956, taking 415 tons (gross) on a Glasgow to Carlisle working. Some uninspiring running saw the train 2½ minutes late into Carlisle. For the return leg, No. 956, with a 350 tons (gross) load, arrived at Glasgow 15 minutes late against the 2 hours and 15 minutes scheduled in the timetable, banking assistance having been taken at Beattock.

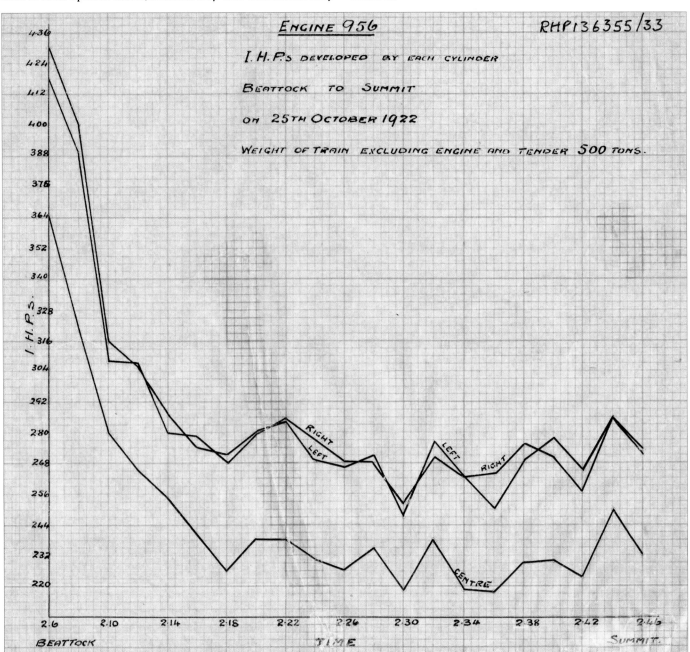

Figure A3.3
Caledonian Railway Co. 'Trials Chart' for Individual Cylinder IHPs for Engine No 956, between Beattock station and Beattock Summit, on 25th October 1922. Results from working the Kingmoor Yard to Polmadie Yard Special 500 Ton Test Train.   *NRS: GD456, RHP136355/33*

BIBLIOGRAPHY

ARCHIVAL SOURCES

Caledonian Railway Association Archive at the University of Glasgow
—— General and Photographic
—— Campbell Cornwell Collection of St Rollox Drawings
Jim MacIntosh Collection
A.E. Glen Collection, courtesy Dr Ann Glen
C.P. Atkins Collection
J.F. McEwan Papers, the William Patrick Library, Kirkintilloch, East Dumbarton Council
John G. Barr Papers, courtesy the Scottish Railway Preservation Society
National Railway Museum, York
—— A.J. Powell Papers, '956' Class, NRM
National Records of Scotland
—— Montague Smith Collection
—— Alan Dunbar Collection
—— Various BR/CAL and BR/LMS records
Graham Miller, private correspondence, 1966

BOOKS

Bridge Stress Committee Report 1928, Department of Scientific & Industrial Research, HMSO, 1928
Locomotive Engineers' Pocket Book, The Locomotive Publishing Co., London, 1929 and subsequent editions
Valve Gears, International Textbook Co., USA, 1906
E.L. Ahrons, *The British Steam Railway Locomotive, 1825-1925*, The Locomotive Publishing Co., London, 1927
C.E. Allen, *The Modern Locomotive*, Cambridge University Press, 1911
C.P. Atkins, *The Scottish 4-6-0 Classes*, Ian Allan, 1976
H.A.V. Bulleid, *Master Builders of Steam*, Ian Allan, 1963
H.J.C. Cornwell, *Forty Years of Caledonian Locomotives, 1882-1922*, David & Charles, 1974
Prof. W.E. Dalby FRS, *The Balancing of Engines*, Arnold & Co., London, 1906
Prof. W.E. Dalby FRS, *Valves and Valve Gears*, Arnold & Co., London, 1906
Prof. W.E. Dalby FRS, *Steam Power*, Arnold & Co., London, 1915
Dugald Drummond, *Lectures to L&SWR Locomotive Enginemen*, Locomotive Publishing Co., 1912
A. Dunbar and I.A. Glen, *Fifty Years with Scottish Steam*, Bradford Barton, 1982
C.H. Ellis, *The North British Railway*, Ian Allan, 1955
J.F. Gains, *Superheating on Locomotives*, The Locomotive Publishing Co., 1914
Prof. W.F.M. Goss, *Locomotive Performance*, John Wiley, 1911

F.B. Kleinhans, *Locomotive Boiler Construction*, Norman W. Henley Publishing Co., New York, 1912
A.E. Langridge, *Under 10 CMEs*, Oakwood Press, 2011
Prof. L.V. Ludy, *Locomotive Boilers and Engines*, American Technical Society, 1918
A.B. Macleod, *The McIntosh Locomotives of the Caledonian Railway*, 1948
R.H. Mann, *Steam Locomotive Design*, The Association of Engineering and Shipbuilding Draughtsmen, 1957
Lord Monkswell, *The Railways of Great Britain*, Goeffrey Bles, London, 1926
O.S. Nock, *The Caledonian Dunalastairs*, David & Charles, 1968
J.W.P. Rowledge and Brian Reed, *The Stanier 4-6-0s of the LM&SR*, David & Charles 1977
Prof. W. Schmidt, *The Use of Superheated Steam in Locomotives*, 1908
Prof. W. Schmidt, *The Application of Highly Superheated Steam to Locomotives*, 1911
G.A. Sekon, *The Evolution of the Steam Locomotive*, The Railway Publishing Co., London, 1899
D.L. Smith, *The Locomotives of the Glasgow & South Western Railway*, David & Charles, 1975
E. Talbot, *An Illustrated History of L&NWR Engines*, Oxford Publishing Co., 1985
C.E. Wolff, *Modern Locomotive Practice*, The Manchester Scientific Publishing Co., Manchester, 1907
J.H. Yoder and G.B. Wharen, *Locomotive Valves and Valve Gears*, Pennsylvania Railroad Co., 1917

PERIODICALS AND PUBLISHED PAPERS

Pennsylvania Railroad Co., Altoona Test Plant Reports on E2A, 1910; K29, 1912; E6s, 1913: K2sa 1914; L1s, 1919, etc
BackTrack, various issues
Journal of the Institution of Locomotive Engineers, various papers 1917-43
The LM&SR Magazine, various editions, 1928 onwards
The Railway Engineer, various editions, 1918 onwards
The Railway Magazine, various issues
Railway & Travel Monthly, various editions
Stephenson Locomotive Society Journal, various editions, 1948 onwards
Trains Illustrated, various issues 1953-56

UNPUBLISHED PAPERS

'Report on "2 to 1" Valve Gear, L.N.E.R. 3-Cylinder Locomotives', dated 8th June 1942, written by E.S. Cox, NRM, Cox 2/20

INDEX

Allan, Henry   45
Allen, C.J.   19, 24, 27, 29, 33, 59, 123
Atkins, C. Philip   17, 27, 59, 87

Barr, John G.   7, 9, 11, 12, 17, 26, 33, 36,
     37, 41, 49, 54, 57, 60-62, 82, 120, 132
boilers
   Belpaire firebox   26, 40, 57
   combustion   22, 51, 69
   firebox crown sheet   16, 63, 73, 76-79
   firebox temperature   51
   free-gas/grate ratio   19, 28, 29, 31, 53,
      69
   heat transfer   19, 51, 69, 72
   L/D ratio   19, 21, 22, 28, 29, 30, 31-32,
      45, 69, 78
   pressure   19, 21, 75-76, 78-79, 130
Bowen-Cooke, J.C.   44, 47, 75, 83, 90
Bullied, O.S.V.   12, 55-57

Churchward, G.J.   12, 35, 44, 47, 49, 75,
     78, 84, 90
Cliffe, Joseph   7
coal consumption   19, 22, 29, 36, 50, 59,
     69, 72-73, 78
Cornwell, H.J. Campbell   7, 13, 27, 59,
     129
Cox, E.S.   13, 27, 29, 35, 37, 41, 46, 57-58,
     63, 75, 94, 101, 110, 131-32

Dalby, Prof. W.E.   10, 12, 33, 49, 69, 83,
     108, 110, 123-24
Dean, Wm.   10, 11
Drummond, Dugald   25, 55, 57, 75, 76, 78,
     107, 132
   '66' Class   12, 19
   '80' Class   19
   '294' Class   19, 39
Dunbar, Alan   13, 17, 23, 34, 41, 51, 56,
     87, 90, 102
Duncanson, Wm.   9

Fowler, Sir Henry KBE   10, 12, 38, 55, 63

Glasgow & South Western Railway '128'
     Class   29, 33, 34, 36, 75, 132-33
Glen, A. Ernest   17, 51, 64, 65, 78-81,
     89-90, 97, 128
Glen, Dr Ann   7, 17
Goss, Prof. W.F.M.   12, 23, 83
grate and ashpan
   McIntosh engines   20-22, 68
   Pickersgill engines   30, 32, 46, 68
   '956' Class   83-88

Great Central Railway 'MM' Class   37,
     41, 45
Gresley, Sir Nigel KBE   12, 21, 32, 47,
     49, 54, 55, 56, 57, 83, 85, 89, 90, 95,
     100-101, 106, 131-32
   '2-8-0' No. 461   83-84, 121,
   'A1' Class   122-23, 130
   'K3' Class   54, 68, 73, 79, 89, 90,
      122-23, 130

Hill, Alfred J.   9, 11, 106
Holden, James   10, 11

Johnston, James   10

Kempt, Irvine (junior)   9, 12, 13, 21, 41,
     55-56
Kerr, George L.   55, 55-57, 90

Lambie, John   9, 12, 19, 55
Lancashire & Yorkshire Railway '8' Class
     4-6-0   63, 76, 87
Linn, Alexander   17, 39, 55-57
London Midland & Scottish Railway
   Class '3P' 2-6-2T   63
   Class '4P' 4-4-0   23, 124
   Class '4P5F' 2-6-0   38, 45, 63-64, 124
   Class '5' 4-6-0   24, 33, 47, 87, 124
   'Patriot' Class   63, 76
   'Royal Scot' Class   29, 59, 63, 76, 130
London & North Western Railway
   'Claughton' Class   41, 51, 56, 63, 75, 79,
      83-84, 87
   'Experiment' Class   24, 83, 124
   'G1' Class, 0-8-0   37
Ludy, Prof. L.V.   12, 30, 34-35, 83

MacIntosh, Jim D.   7, 13
Mallenby, Prof. A.L.   10, 57, 90, 102, 104,
     131
Matheson, Donald CBE   56, 57
McEwan, James F.   13, 17, 20, 22, 25-26,
     35, 37
McIntosh, John F.
   '2-6-0' proposals   21
   '4-4-2' proposals   21, 22
   '4-4-2T' proposals   22
   '4-6-0' proposals   21, 31
   '4-6-2' proposals   21-22
   '49' Class   19, 20, 24, 29, 59, 130
   '55' Class   22
   '139' Class   20, 33, 36, 61, 65, 76
   '140' Class   19, 23, 24, 34, 65,
   '179' Class   22, 79, 122-23,

'439' Class   22, 31
'721' Class   18-20, 61
'766' Class   12, 19, 40, 61
'812' Class   22, 24
'900' Class   19
'903' Class   19, 20, 21, 22, 24, 29, 47,
     59, 61, 79, 126
'908' Class   22, 79, 122-23
'918' Class   22, 23, 79
Belgian designs   22, 23, 79
CR appointments   9, 55
early years   9, 19
personality   9
retiral   9, 11, 24
staff relationships   24-26, 57, 61
mechanical design
   axle loading limits   31, 32, 49, 122-26
   balancing   121-24, 130, 131
   'bogie'   126-30
   components   32, 90, 93, 96, 111-13
   loading gauge   41, 43, 44, 49
   'nozing'   63, 128-30
   springing   126, 131
   weight balance   31, 32, 126, 130, 131
Miller, Graeme   9, 11, 17, 27, 55-57, 59-60,
     102-104, 106, 131
Monkswell, Lord   60-62, 123
Moodie, Wm. H.   20, 24, 35, 37, 41. 52,
     55-57

Newlands, David   17, 59-60, 109, 111, 116
Nock, O.S.   12, 27, 29, 30, 33, 56-57, 60,
     62, 95
North British Loco. Co.   28, 29, 30, 31, 32,
     40, 75
North British Railway   29, 57, 87
   'Atlantic' Class   73
   'C15/C16' Class   22, 31

Pendred, Vaughan   47
Pennsylvania Railroad Co.
   Altoona testing   12, 47, 50, 69, 73, 83-87
   piston valves   55, 113
Pickersgill, E.G.   10, 107
Pickersgill, John G.   9
Pickersgill, Wm. CBE
   '2-6-0' (1917) proposals   41
   '2-6-0' (1923) proposals   17, 45-46, 131
   '2-8-0' proposals   36-37, 41, 43
   '4-4-0' outside cylinder proposals   41,
      42, 75
   '4-6-0' (Oban) proposals   31
   '60' Class   21, 29, 30, 31, 36, 41, 49, 54,
      63, 75, 79, 87-88, 121, 122-23, 131

'113' Class   27, 36, 41, 54
'191' Class   31-32, 87-88, 122-23
'300' Class   23, 40
'938' Class   29, 35, 41, 57, 69, 74, 87-88,
        122-23, 126, 128, 130, 132
'944' Class   31, 36, 49, 53, 122-23
'956' Class
    boiler   49, 51, 53, 63, 69-82, 131
    grate and ashpan   63, 87-88, 131
    power requirements   44, 47, 49, 89-90
    smokebox layout   35, 81, 83-86
    superheater   51, 72-74, 79, 131
    valve gears   51, 89-121
    weight balance   49, 131
    tenders   64-68
CR appointment   9, 11
death   12, 58
early years   9
family   9, 10
GER positions   9, 10
GNSR appointment   10
ILocoE President   8, 9
IMechE application   10
LM&SR appointment   12, 45

personality   11, 56
staff relationships   27, 57-58
piston valves   20, 21, 29, 33, 113, 112
    diameter   41, 63, 75, 78
    lubrication   21, 32, 53, 55
Powell, A.J.   13, 59, 63-64, 78, 89, 123,
        126, 128-29

Reid, Sir Hugh CBE   10
Riddles R.A. CBE   29

Schmidt, Prof. Wm.   20, 21, 31, 54, 55, 57,
        69, 72, 74, 113
Smith, Montague   13, 56, 59
smokebox
    draughting   30, 34, 83-88, 131
    exhaust entrainment   34, 83
    vacuum   34, 35, 59, 62, 83-85
Stanier, Sir William KBE   110
superheater
    elements   20, 28, 29, 31, 33, 41, 59, 63,
        70-74, 79, 131
    flue/free-gas ratio   28, 29, 31, 53, 59,
        72-73, 131

pressure loss   28, 33, 36, 45, 74, 131
temperatures   20, 23, 29, 32, 33, 36, 54,
        62, 69, 131

Thompson, Edward   7, 110,

Urie, J.C.   25
Urie, Robert W.   25, 26, 55, 124, 132
Urie, Wm. M.   9, 55

valve gears
    '956' Class   89-121
    Stephenson's link motion   41, 44, 57, 59,
        62, 82, 90, 102-103, 106-10, 131
    valve setting   35-36, 101
    Walschaerts'   22, 29, 41, 42, 62, 64, 90,
        95, 131
Weir, Thomas   9, 20, 24, 26, 27, 32, 41, 54,
        55-57, 78, 132
Whitelegg, R.H.   12, 21
Wolff, C.E.   19, 128, 130
World War I influence   19, 29, 39-40

LM&SR No. 14801 at Annan in the mid-1920s.   *J.J. Cunningham, courtesy A.F. Swann*

No. 959 is seen south of Stanley in 1921.
Henry L. Salmon, courtesy Author

LM&SR No. 14803 at Kingmoor.
J.J. Cunningham, Author's collection